INVESTIGATING ECOLOGY
in the Laboratory

WILLIAM F. McCOMAS, Editor
Center to Advance Science Education
Rossier School of Education
University of Southern California
Los Angeles, California

William F. McComas, Editor
Center to Advance Science Education
Rossier School of Education
University of Southern California
Los Angeles, California 90089-0031

Published by the
National Association of Biology Teachers
12030 Sunrise Valley Drive, #110
Reston, Virginia 20191

ISBN 0-941212-31-9

Cover features School for Field Studies students investigating a Costa Rican rain forest (William F. McComas, photographer).

Printed in the United States of America by Modern Litho-Print Co., Jefferson City, Missouri.

Founded in 1938, the National Association of Biology Teachers is the oldest organization dedicated exclusively to the concerns of life science educators worldwide. NABT includes nearly 9,000 members from all levels of academia, business, industry, and others concerned with life science education issues. NABT empowers educators to provide the best possible biology and life science education for *all* students. As **The Leader in Life Science Education**, our members teach more than one million students each year!

Table of Contents

Investigating Ecology in the Laboratory

William F. McComas

Introduction

There is little doubt that ecology is one of the most important aspects of biology education. An extensive rationale for the inclusion of ecology science appears in the next chapter, but briefly it may be said that the study of organisms in their environment makes use of the variety of biological concepts encountered during the year while encouraging both inquiry and a science, technology, and society approach (S/T/S) to instruction. If the laboratory experiences are designed appropriately, perhaps by applying some of the suggestions in the next section of this chapter, students can engage in an investigation of the environment rather than simply complete laboratory activities with a predictable outcome. This shift away from verification toward investigation is at the heart of inquiry teaching. At the heart of an S/T/S curriculum orientation, students are asked to make decisions and take action. Exploration of the environment at the macroscopic level found in ecology permits students to apply what they have learned in addressing problems such as pollution in evaluating potential land use actions and in allocating natural resources.

Unfortunately, ecology is typically included as the concluding section in most biology texts, and as such is all too easily neglected when time runs out at the end of the school year. So, in spite of the utility of ecology to provide opportunities to integrate the typically discrete biology concepts and to assist students in making societal and personal decisions, ecology is frequently missing-in-action from the biology curriculum.

The effective revitalization of any science content realm depends on the quality of the curriculum resources available. One such resource relates to the nature of the hands-on opportunities provided to students. This laboratory monograph was designed to offer a range of such resources for teachers to use directly or modify in the teaching of environmental science. The laboratory strategies provided here were selected based on a number of criteria, including relevance to the basic ecology curriculum, creativity in design, ease with which the activity might be modified to support instruction at a particular grade level, and availability of equipment. Of course, not all of the activities meet each criterion nor will all activities be seen as equally useful in all classroom settings, but we hope that there will be something of use here for all of those who hope to enhance the teaching of environmental science.

Readers will note that this book is divided into sets of laboratory investigations roughly corresponding to the major ideas in ecology, along with a section on the tools and techniques that may be used to investigate the environment, simulate ecological principles, and explore the impact of humans on the environment. A glossary of ecology-related terms along with references cited in the activities is also included. It is the hope of all of those involved with this project that teachers may be encouraged to reconsider the place of ecology education in the curriculum by providing a wide set of tools by which students and teachers alike can engage in the exploration of this important field.

Enhancing the Effectiveness of Laboratory Teaching

The laboratory as a place "where students can investigate natural phenomena in an immediate or first-hand experience and apply various cognitive skills toward an interpretation of these phenomena" (Anderson, 1976, p. 7) and has long been a featured element of the school science experience. Increased use of investigative teaching has been strongly endorsed by both the American Association for the Advancement of Science (AAAS, 1993) in *Benchmarks for Science Literacy* and the National Research Council (NRC, 1996) in the *National Standards in Science Education* as well as in many new state frameworks for science instruction.

During the past century many individuals (Lowrey, 1921; Tamir, 1976; Hofstein & Lunetta, 1980; Blosser, 1981; Woolnough & Allsop, 1985) have voiced strong support for the role of laboratory instruction in science teaching. More recent research has substantiated these earlier views. When eighth graders completed laboratory work at least once a week they had significantly higher scores in a correlation study than those who did not (Stohr-Hunt, 1996). Freedman (1997) has shown that ninth grade physical science students who had laboratory experiences demonstrated increased achievement and a more positive attitude toward science than those lacking such experiences. In another study in the middle school environment, Weaver (1998) found that students report that the most enjoyable part of science class was the laboratory work.

In spite of these strong recommendations for the inclusion of laboratory experiences in school science instruction, the actual application of hands-on instruction in the classroom does not live up to its promise. The typical laboratory exercise is used simply to verify a previous classroom content lesson with students carrying out cookbook-like instructions. Such an orientation to laboratory teaching is contrary to the tenets of constructivist teaching and distinct from the way that scientists themselves use such procedures. Changes in the typical laboratory format will be necessary for this to occur. However, most educators will agree that if breaking with tradition more fully involves the students, enhances their engagement with the laboratory, and positively impacts their attitudes toward the laboratory, then some re-thinking of the role and nature of the laboratory experience is worthwhile.

Although the activities presented in this book are provided in a standard format, there is no intent that each exercise simply be copied and given directly to students. The laboratory experience itself should be orchestrated in such a way that students make as many decisions as possible regarding both the work they do and how they interpret results. What follows here is an overview of a number of research-supported suggestions for how laboratory teaching with any science content can be enhanced. It would be impractical, ill advised, and likely impossible to use all of these suggestions with every laboratory activity, but improving only a few elements of each investigation is a worthy goal.

Enhancing Teaching and Learning in the Laboratory: Considering the Level of Challenge

An initial step in enhancing the laboratory experience is to recognize that not all laboratory activities are likely to have the same impact on learners. The "cognitive burden" imposed by the exercise on the students is one of the most potent variables worth considering in predicting how the activity will be viewed by students and what learning it might help foster.

Schwab (1962) was one of the first major science educators to consider the laboratory as a potential place for enquiry. He stated that "the ... function of the enquiring laboratory is to provide occasions for and invitations to the conduct of miniature but exemplary programs of enquiry" (p. 55). He developed a taxonomy of laboratory activities based on "different levels of openness and permissiveness ..." (p. 55) expressed by the laboratory. Herron (1971) took a related approach in his proposed laboratory classification plan with his addition of the zero-level. The Schwab/Herron classification scheme is shown in Table 1.

This plan for classifying laboratory exercises is based on an appraisal of how much information the students have before beginning the activity. The central questions in the taxonomy relate to who provides the laboratory problem, who provides the methods for solving the problem, and who provides the answer to the laboratory question. In a Level Zero laboratory, the teacher gives both the problem and method. In addition, the answer is known before the laboratory work begins because of prior knowledge on the part of the students gleaned from the textbook, lecture, or laboratory manual itself. Level One activities are somewhat more challenging but do little more than give students an opportunity to follow a recipe in cookbook fashion and verify some preexisting facts. Students are given no authentic opportunities to make decisions about the nature of the procedure or choice of the problem. Only in Level Two and

Three exercises are students really acting as scientists in the choices they make about procedures and problems.

TABLE 1. Schwab/Herron Levels of Openness for Classifying Laboratory Activities

Level	Problem	Investigative Methods	Answers
0	Given	Given	Given
1	Given	Given	Open
2	Given	Open	Open
3	Open	Open	Open

No one should suggest that all laboratory work should be at the highest level. Students do need direction with respect to some procedures and techniques and they will need to gain experience in conducting high-level work. However, whenever the opportunity exists to "raise the bar" somewhat by increasing the level of challenge, teachers should do so. The first step in enhancing the laboratory experience is to determine the level of challenge that exists in the activities chosen. In reviews of laboratory manuals, researchers have consistently found that the vast majority of labs are at the Zero or One level of openness.

Enhancing Teaching and Learning in the Laboratory: What Research Says

An extensive review of the research literature with respect to laboratory teaching reveals a number of suggestions to enhance the overall student experience. The dozen suggestions associated with high-quality laboratory instruction are grouped into one of three general categories – design issues, pedagogical considerations, and teaching practices. Although these issues do not address every potential variable that may impact the laboratory experience, they are among the most important and should prove useful in visualizing and potentially enhancing laboratory instruction.

Laboratory Design Issues

1) Encourage Investigations at Sites Beyond the Classroom

The authors of Project 2061 (AAAS, 1993, p. 151) suggest that "science teachers should exploit the rich resources of the larger community ..." in the design of lessons. This implication supports an earlier call from Penick and Yager (1986) who state that students should see the world as their laboratory by moving toward what they call *real* laboratory investigation in school science. The true investigative laboratory can be "in home, in nature, in [the students'] mind and any place students can investigate ..." (p. 7). Both teachers and students should expand their definition and expectations of the laboratory experience and extend beyond the narrow confines of the traditional school laboratory. Scientists do not work exclusively in laboratory rooms, yet for many students, the classroom laboratory setting must seem like the only possible research site. Broadening the investigative arena to include parks, nature centers, the schoolyard, the students' home neighborhood, botanical gardens, zoos, and museums will help students see that investigations can take place almost anywhere.

For example, teachers could refrain from telling students about the types of rocks in the area, but instead ask them to bring in a wide assortment of samples from the community for group identification and/or classification. Rather than asking students to memorize the parts of a flower, have students examine dozens of flowers at the local nursery. These flowers may appear unique but share many similar elements in their basic construction — as students may discover. Instead of having students read in their textbooks that there is variation within the species, a field trip to the zoo or a local pet store may demonstrate this important fact without a word being read.

2) Encourage Long Term Investigations

The authors of *Criteria for Excellence in Science Teaching* (NSTA, 1987) suggest that "both long term and short term field work and laboratory studies should be both experiential and experimental" (p. 14). Hodson (1988) states that during open-ended work "children come closest to doing real science" and, therefore, "we should regard [such work] as the very pinnacle of science education" (pp. 63-64). Scientists rarely do investigations where the solution is assured within an hour or so. In contrast, students typically work in the laboratory with the expectation that an answer will be achieved quickly by simply following directions.

There are several ways to encourage long-term activities even within the tight time constraints of the school day. First, longer exercises might take place out of school. Students could make daily or weekly observations of a living thing such as a tree or a pet hamster, the pattern of moon phases, or the varying amount of daylight hours throughout the year. Allowing students to observe and discover patterns in nature is more effective than simply telling students that such patterns exist.

Another strategy for longer-term projects is to have students work on an extended activity for a few minutes each day. For instance, students could make observations of some phenomenon such as mold growth or crystal formation at the beginning of each class period. Alternately, student groups might work on part of a longer project that they will later share with each other to visualize the whole process. This suggestion could be facilitated by having students in a different part of the region or the country work together via the Internet on some project of interest such as an analysis of ground water pollution or on a census of an ecologically sensitive organism. Given the demands of time in science instruction, teachers must be somewhat clever to facilitate labs of longer duration, but such exercises are possible and rewarding. These more detailed investigations may also serve as a source of renewal for teachers who likely tire of seeing the same activity with the same results year after year.

3) Ensure that Laboratory Experiences Are Developmentally Appropriate

In all cases educators should be aware of the developmental appropriateness of both goals and methodologies applied in school science. This issue is particularly important in laboratory instruction where the student must make personal sense of the process and product. If a particular activity requires thinking skills that the students do not possess, the students may become frustrated or worse if they learn faulty lessons about the phenomenon in question. All teachers must remember that even adults do not function at the highest cognitive levels on every task.

The link between developmental readiness and laboratory task requirements has long been a feature of well-designed curricula. For instance, the hands-on project *Science – A Process Approach* (S-APA) from the 1960s and the new *Full Option Science System* (FOSS) were produced with reference to knowledge of student capabilities. In S-APA, for instance, skills such as observation, classifying, measuring, communicating, predicting, and inferring are applied for students in the primary grades. The integrated skills such as controlling variables, interpreting data, hypothesizing, and experimenting are reserved for students in the upper elementary grades. The FOSS curriculum (Lowrey, 1990) provides tasks that include observing, comparing, and communicating for primary students while upper elementary students are asked to propose relationships and organize their thoughts.

For the laboratory to be effective it must also be appropriate in terms of its cognitive demands. All those who provide laboratory experiences for learners must be aware of the learners' limitations and make suitable choices regarding the skills required by the activities involved.

4) Use Laboratory Activities and Practices That Illustrate the Authentic Nature of Science

Accurate portrayal of the nature of the scientific endeavor stands at the core of all high-quality science teaching. Although the laboratory provides a unique opportunity for teachers to help students understand how scientists gain information, it must be used with care.

Misconceptions regarding the nature of science can occur in the school science laboratory just by the teachers' choice of language. Frequently teachers indicate that the results of a laboratory experience will *prove* scientific ideas in the way that proof is used in mathematics. Scientists do not prove ideas, but only fail to disprove them at that moment. Therefore, it is most correct to talk about the role of the laboratory in verifying and substantiating ideas. Another problem results when teachers refer to any work in the laboratory as experimental. Most scientists would label something an experiment only if it involves purposeful manipulations of nature with limited variables accompanied by an appropriate control for comparison. By this definition, little classroom laboratory practice is experimental. Activities, observations, or exercises are more suitable labels for the work done in school.

Another important philosophical issue presents itself when students fail to get the *correct* answer associated with the laboratory. When only one answer is expected or valued, students may come to believe that this is also the case in science. In science, results deviating from what are expected are often among the most interesting and useful. In addition, when we ask students to accept an answer they did not see personally, what kind of message about real science are we expressing?

Pedagogical Considerations of Laboratory Instruction

5) Use the Challenge Question Approach

The best instructors usually frame the laboratory objective as a thought-provoking challenge question provided to students in the briefest fashion possible. Leonard (1991) provides a useful overview of what might be called the challenge lab approach with the following admonition. Teachers should give the students a task or goal providing only essential procedures, while refraining from telling students how to complete the investigation; students could work cooperatively using a list of resources from which they may choose to guide their investigation. By setting the goal but failing to provide step-by-step recipes that can sidetrack learning, students must think for themselves.

This technique may be used in all educational settings as long as the students and teacher are prepared for the experience. Students must know what is expected of them and realize what the teacher is prepared to provide them in terms of assistance. The teacher must avoid being too helpful in assisting students with problem solving since this can defeat the effectiveness of this innovation.

As an example of an elementary challenge question related to the properties of matter, students might be given a mixture of iron filings, salt, and sand and be asked to separate the three materials. One could provide instructions to help students meet the objective, but more learning will take place if students are challenged to suggest a solution to the problem that makes sense to each student personally.

6) Use the Laboratory To Introduce, Not Just Verify, Concepts

The majority of laboratory exercises offer no surprise to students. Typically, teachers discuss a phenomenon in a class lecture and then have students verify in the laboratory what has been said earlier in class. For years, laboratory reformers have stated that such work should have the characteristics of "experience-getting" (Powers, 1932) rather than simply being illustrative or confirmatory. Inductive methods should be used so that the laboratory work *precedes* rather than follows the classroom discussion of a topic or principle. Requiring percent error calculations – typical in many chemistry and physics classes – is just another way of telling students that there is a "right" answer they are to find. Although one could argue such calculations improve accuracy, such practices do not reflect the purpose of investigations in *real* science. The technique of performing laboratory work before extensive classroom discussions may be all that is necessary to raise the level of the laboratory on the Schwab/Herron scale.

Evidence supplied by Boghai (1978), Raghubir (1979), Bishop (1990) and Ivins (1985) reveals that the placement of the laboratory within the process of concept development is important. Ivins (1985) found that laboratory work that introduces rather than confirms discussion of ideas is most effective in helping students learn. Raghubir (1979) discovered that students exhibit higher levels of cognitive ability when they actually gained knowledge through the laboratory rather than simply using the laboratory to verify what teachers and textbooks have stated. These findings are not surprising given the constructivist view of learning that suggests students can only assimilate new information by generating personal understanding out of their own experiences. Making laboratory activities more interesting and challenging may be as simple as providing the hands-on experience before the lecture rather than with the order reversed as is frequently the case.

7) Give Students Opportunities To Make Personal Choices During the Investigation

Students rarely have much to say about the way in which an investigation is conducted despite the general acceptance of constructivism as an explanation of how learning occurs. The evidence is clear that when students are allowed a choice in the design and implementation of laboratory work they perform better and enjoy the experience more. Eggelston (1973) and Leonard (1980) found that cookbook-like laboratories frequently bore students, but "the more involved a student is in the laboratory the more productive the educational outcomes will be" (Leonard, 1980, p. 338). In empirical studies such as those by Cavana and Leonard (1985), students who were given more choices in the way they conduct investigations had higher scores on laboratory reports and quizzes and were able to work independently for longer periods than students not permitted such discretion.

8) Assess Laboratory Learning Using Authentic Means

Laboratory work would be more highly valued by teachers and more useful as a diagnostic tool by teachers if assessment were more authentic. The term authentic assessment means that progress is measured in ways that match the instructional method or are related to some real life task. The desired goal for all lab-related assessment must be that students are evaluated in ways related to the investigative methods with which they were taught.

For instance, many teachers require students to use a standard format to report the results of laboratory investigations. Although a standard format is easy for students to use and straightforward for teachers to evaluate, one might argue that this practice encourages a degree of dishonesty when students use such a report to discuss what is really the result of a creative process.

Medawar (1963) took this position when he criticized the reporting convention used by scientists in their formal journal entries. He believed that such a form hides the true nature of the experimental discovery process, with all of its inherent false starts and dead ends. The pathway appears to be straightforward and the researcher's steps unwavering, but this is rarely the case. Just as the path from problem to solution is poorly reported in professional journals, the case is the same in instructional laboratories. To avoid this problem, students could be asked to write a narrative report describing their individual process of investigation rather than a forced convention disguising their personal method.

Increasing the use of practical or hands-on exams would be another recommendation for enhanced assessment, but the inclusion of learning cycle-based activities would be even better. In the learning cycle, students first are encouraged to investigate on their own *before* moving onto the second stage during which the concepts are discussed more formally. In the final step of the cycle, the students are asked to apply what they have learned. Assessment is authentic only if students apply what they have learned by doing an additional related investigative activity that can be used to measure their progress.

Laboratory Teaching Practices

9) Engage Students in Cooperative or Collaborative Work

Cooperative learning has been widely touted as a general pedagogical tool by researchers such as Slavin (1991) who state that such learning schemes encourage "students to discover, debate, diagram and ultimately to teach one another" (p. 71). Linn and Burbules make this distinction between cooperative and collaborative learning (1993). Cooperative learning "involves dividing a task into parts and having each group member complete one of the parts"; while in collaborative learning, "two or more students join together to work out a single solution to a problem" (p. 92).

There are two principal recommendations for using cooperative and collaborative learning strategies in laboratory instruction: one practical and the other philosophical. In a practical sense, group work is valuable because students will learn how to complete a team-based task by assuming various roles in ways that will prepare students as future employees (Cohen, 1986; Schoenfeld, 1989). Also, by having students work together, limitations on equipment and supplies, as well as time constraints associated with laboratory tasks, can be addressed effectively. Breaking down a large task into smaller parts as recommended in collaborative schemes give students the opportunity to complete their assignments within the limitations imposed by time and materials.

Philosophically, group work in the laboratory is important so that students can simulate what scientists do as they solve problems. Part of the scientific process involves the negotiation and discourse that accompanies the conclusion-making phase of research. Scientists in the community of scientists decide what knowledge is important, what techniques are useful, and what the results of investigations mean. This social construction of knowledge is rarely discussed in the science classroom, but the laboratory provides an ideal opportunity to assist students in their understanding of this important dimension of the process of science.

10) Use Indirect Verbal Behaviors When Responding to Students

Although the instructor orchestrates the laboratory experience, some teacher actions are more effective than others in supporting a high-quality laboratory experience. Facilitation, not just interruption, is one such supportive laboratory teacher behavior. Students are distracted and annoyed when teachers stop their work repeatedly during the class period to add a forgotten direction, explanation, or procedural note. Once students are working, an effective technique is to guide in such a way that students know that what they are doing is valued but that they are in control.

The foundation for the suggestion that responses should be indirect is found in the work of Collins and Stevens (1983) and others who have described an inquiry approach to instruction as an alternative to more didactic methods. Inherent in an inquiry mode is the strategy that the discourse between teacher and students should be an authentic conversation rather than based on an authoritarian structure in which the students see the teacher as the ultimate source of approval and information. An indirect style of response to inquiries causes the students to look within themselves or within the group for guidance. Dillon (1979) lists indirect questions and imperatives as alternatives to traditional questioning styles. Indirect questions such as "I wonder what makes you think that?", "Have you considered ...?", or "How would you find out?" are more thought provoking than simply answering the question.

Students seem to respond well to such a technique as evidenced by McComas (1991) who observed laboratory interactions. In one classroom, the teacher would routinely answer almost every laboratory question by saying, "I don't know." This response was quickly followed by a statement from a student, "Yes he does, he just wants us to figure it out for ourselves" indicating that students understand what the teacher is trying to accomplish by being somewhat evasive.

11) Engage and Interact Briefly with Small Groups of Students

In practice, highly skilled teachers move from one group of students to another, monitoring, encouraging, and questioning, but generally avoiding long periods of contact with any single student group (McComas, 1991). While additional study of this technique must be completed to authenticate the relationship of this practice to student learning, it is still reasonable to assume that when the teacher is available to the student but not intrusive, students will appreciate the support and react in a positive way to the teacher's interest.

This technique is also valuable to the teacher in assessing student interest and concerns. Should one group of students discover something interesting or demonstrate a common problem, the instructor is in an excellent position to react appropriately and constructively. Rather than stopping the entire group of students to share a concern with the technique or an interpretation of the results — a typical response on the part of the teacher — the instructor can easily spread the word with each group she or he visits. Since this technique is based on frequent but brief visits with those in each student group, the message quickly is spread throughout the classroom.

This management mode can also be used as part of the assessment strategy. The instructor can use a formal checklist to ascertain how well each student is completing a technique or process or can make more general notes about the degree to which students are engaging in the laboratory.

12) Apply Short Prelab Discussions with Extensive Postlab Debriefing Sessions

There is evidence that laboratory instructors who spend minimal time on explanations and directions given *before* laboratory work are the most effective in encouraging their students to think for themselves. This is particularly true with the challenge-type activities advocated earlier. Of course, when serious safety or procedural issues play a role in the activity, the prelab conversation will be longer. However, generally, whole-class prelab discussion should last just a few minutes and deal mainly with procedural and safety issues or in the demonstration of apparatus, while avoiding focus on the expected results of the activity.

Emphasis instead should be placed on the postlab debriefing. The function of the postlab discussion is to establish the link between the laboratory and lecture components of the lesson by having students pool data and discuss conclusions supported by the data. Frequently, students themselves establish the underlying generalization governing the phenomenon observed with minimal help from the teacher. This approach is difficult to implement if students are accustomed to step-by-step labs, but in time, students will come to expect and enjoy the challenge-lab approach that is a part of this strategy.

Acknowledgments

Let me conclude this introduction with a few words of acknowledgment and appreciation for the contributions of many individuals who helped in the production of this new tool for laboratory teaching. First and foremost I thank the authors whose useful strategies are reprinted here. I offer special thanks to author Dr. John Cruzan of Geneva College who graciously provided extended versions of many of the activities he reported initially in *The American Biology Teacher*.

To our readers and the original authors, let me say that I alone take full responsibility for the editorial decisions that may have resulted in changes in meaning or style when the activities were modified, abridged, and molded into the final common format presented here. Although the original authors were not given the opportunity to review the changes, I am hopeful that the efforts in producing this monograph will meet with general approval from those whose interesting ideas are included here. A complete reference is provided with each activity and readers are encouraged to consult the original when quoting any of these authors.

I am also grateful to the publishers of the two journals in which these activities originally appeared. Dr. Wayne Carley, Executive Director of the National Association of Biology Teachers (Reston, VA), and Dr. David A. Phoenix, Editor of the *Journal of Biological Education* (Institute of Biology, London, England) have enthusiastically permitted these works to be included here.

There are two additional groups of individuals whose assistance with this project was vital. First, I would like to acknowledge current and former graduate students from the science education program at the USC Rossier School of Education who contributed in many ways. Brian Alters, Catherine Martin, and Susan Zweip reviewed the biology education literature and made many of the initial suggestions for the activities to be included and assisted with the editorial revisions. Gertie Cole, Tom Nowlin, Judith deNuño, Cassie Carter, and Robert DeGroot wrote the introductions for each section, and Deb Stone developed the ecology glossary. Finally, I am indebted to my colleagues at the National Association of Biology Teachers. This project would not have been possible without the leadership and untiring support of Chris Chantry with valuable assistance from Kay Acevedo, Susan Houchins, and Cheryl Merrill. I thank everyone at NABT for months of good humor while scanning, editing, and typing (and re-scanning, re-editing, and re-typing on occasion)! Finally, I want to acknowledge the work of Michelle Finney of Finney Creative. Michelle has done an amazing job in developing a clean, inviting, and visually engaging appearance for this monograph. Every time I reviewed the drafts of the document I discovered evidence of Michelle's creative skill.

So, to the original authors, my current and former USC students, our graphic designer, and the wonderful staff at NABT, I offer my sincere thanks.

We invite readers of **Investigating Ecology in the Laboratory** to subscribe to the *Journal of Biological Education* as well as *The American Biology Teacher*. *JBE* is a journal for applied educational research that covers policy and curriculum developments that apply directly to the classroom. It presents the latest results of research into the teaching, learning, and assessment of biology while providing updates of advances relevant to biology instruction and curriculum with reviews of current opinion from world-renowned experts. The *JBE* is published quarterly in December, March, June, and September. To subscribe to the journal, please log onto http://www.iob.org and click on the *JBE* icon.

WILLIAM F. MCCOMAS, EDITOR

References

Anderson, O.R. (1976). *The Experience of Science*. New York: Teachers College Press.

AAAS. (1993). *Benchmarks for Science Literacy*. New York: Oxford University Press.

Bishop, R.D. (1990). *The Effect of Laboratory Activity Ordering on Achievement and Retention*. Unpublished doctoral dissertation, Southern Illinois University, Edwardsville, IL.

Blosser, P.E. (1981). *A Critical Review of the Role of the Laboratory in Science Teaching*. Columbus, OH: ERIC Clearinghouse for Science, Mathematics, and Environmental Education.

Boghai, D. (1978). A comparison of the effects of laboratory and discussion sequences on learning college chemistry. *Dissertation Abstracts International, 39*, 6045A.

Cavana, G.R. & Leonard, W.H. (1985). Extending discretion in the high school science curricula. *Science Education, 69*(5), 593-603.

Cohen, E.G. (1986). *Designing Groupwork: Strategies for the Heterogeneous Classroom*. New York: Teachers College Press.

Collins, A. & Stevens, A. (1983). A cognitive theory of inquiry teaching. In C. Reigeluth (Ed.), *Instructional-Design Theories and Models: An Overview of Their Current Status*. Hillsdale, NJ: Erlbaum.

Dillon, J. (1979). Alternatives to questioning. *High School Journal, 62,* 217-222.

Doran, R.L. (1992). Successful laboratory assessment. *The Science Teacher, 59*(4), 22-27.

Eggelston, J.C. (1973). Inductive vs. traditional methods of teaching high school biology laboratory experiments. *Science Education, 57*(4), 467-477.

Freedman, M.P. (1997). Relationships among laboratory instruction, attitude toward science and achievement in science knowledge. *Journal of Research in Science Teaching, 34*(4), 343-357.

Herron, M.D. (1971). The nature of scientific inquiry. *School Review (American Journal of Education), 68*(1), 17-29.

Hofstein, A. & Lunetta, V.N. (1980). *The Role of the Laboratory in Science Teaching: Research Implications*. National Association for Research in Science Teaching. (ERIC Document Reproduction Service No. ED 188 912).

Hodson, D. (1988). Experiments in science and science teaching. *Educational Philosophy and Theory, 20*(2), 53-66.

Ivins, J.E. (1985). *A Comparison of the Effects of Two Instructional Sequences Involving Science Laboratory Activities*. Unpublished doctoral dissertation, University of Cincinnati, Cincinnati, OH. (ERIC Document Reproduction Service No. ED 259 953).

Leonard, W. (1991). A recipe for uncookbooking laboratory investigations. *Journal of College Science Teaching, 21*(2), 84-87.

Leonard, W.H. (1980). Using an extended discretion approach in biology laboratory investigations. *The American Biology Teacher, 42*(7), 338-348.

Linn, M.C. & Burbules, N.C. (1993). Construction of knowledge and group learning. In K. Tobin (Ed.), *The Practice of Constructivism in Science Education* (pp. 91-144). Hillsdale, NJ: Lawrence Erlbaum Associates, Publishers.

Lowrey, H. (1921). The place of practical work in science teaching. *School Science Review, 9*(1), 26-28.

Lowrey, L. (1990). *The Biological Basis for Thinking and Learning*. Monograph. Encyclopaedia Britannica Educational Corporation/Lawrence Hall of Science.

McComas, W.F. (1991). *The Nature of Exemplary Practice in Secondary School Science Laboratory Instruction: A Case Study Method*. Unpublished doctoral dissertation, The University of Iowa, Iowa City, IA.

Medawar, P.B. (1963). Is the scientific paper a fraud? In P.B. Medawar (Ed.), (1990), *The Threat and the Glory* (pp. 228-233). New York: Harper/Collins.

National Research Council. (1996). *National Science Education Standards*. Washington, DC: National Academy Press.

NSTA. (1987). *Criteria for Excellence*. Washington, DC: National Science Teachers Association.

Penick, J.E. & Yager, R.E. (1986). Trends in science education: some observations of exemplary programs in the United States. *European Journal of Science Education, 8*(1), 1-8.

Powers, S.R. (1932). A program for teaching science. *The Thirty-First Yearbook of the National Society for the Study of Education, Part I*. Bloomington, IL: Public School Publishing Company.

Raghubir, K.P. (1979). The laboratory investigative approach to science instruction. *Journal of Research in Science Teaching, 16*(1), 13-18.

Schoenfeld, A.H. (1989). Ideas in the air: Speculations on small group learning. Environmental and cultural influences on cognition and epistemology. *International Journal of Educational Research, 13*(1), 17-88.

Schwab, J.J. (1962). The teaching of science as inquiry. In J.J. Schwab & P.F. Brandwein (Eds.), *The Teaching of Science* (pp. 3-103). Cambridge, MA: Harvard University Press.

Slavin, R.E. (1991). Synthesis of research on cooperative learning. *Educational Leadership, 48*(5), 71-82.

Stohr-Hunt, P.M. (1996). An analysis of frequency of hands-on experience and science achievement. *Journal of Research in Science Teaching, 33*(1), 101-109.

Tamir, P. (1976). *The Role of the Laboratory in Science Teaching.* (Technical Report 10). Iowa City, IA: The University of Iowa, Science Education Center.

Weaver, G.C. (1998). Strategies in K-12 science instruction to promote conceptual change. *Science Education, 82*(4), 455-472.

Woolnough, B. & Allsop, T. (1985). *Practical Work in Science.* New York: Cambridge University Press.

Section Images

I - Lily pond at the Brooklyn Botanical Gardens, New York City

II - Beach at Cape May, New Jersey

III - Stream in upstate New York

IV - True bugs in Costa Rican rain forest

V - Millipede in Madagascar rain forest

VI - Stream survey in the Adirondack Mountains of New York

References - Forest scene in upstate New York

Appendices - Sea turtle near Hilo, Hawaii

About the Editor - Serengeti plain during the migration, Tanzania, Africa

(All images courtesy of William F. McComas, photographer)

ENVIRONMENTAL SCIENCE EDUCATION:
The Nature of the Ideal Ecology Curriculum as Suggested by a Review of Texts, Misconceptions, and Standards

Introduction

April 22, 1970 will be remembered by many as the date of the first nationwide celebration of Earth Day. This event, according to Gordon (1993, p. 32) in his thoughtful appraisal of the American environmental movement, was "one of the more remarkable happenings in the history of democracy ... 20 million people demonstrated their support [and] ... American politics and public policy would never be the same again." From a science and science education perspective, this national opportunity to express concern for the environment was unique. Never in history had there been such an outpouring of emotion focused on the contributions of a particular scientific discipline. Only the launch of Sputnik and the aftermath of the Scopes evolution trial have impacted science teaching as dramatically as the rise in interest in environmental issues. The legacy of Earth Day was clear and immediate. Environmental science quickly found a home in both the public consciousness and the school science curriculum.

Now it is a rare day when the news media fail to include a story with an environmental message. From the Rio Earth summit in 1992 to the 2002 Johannesburg World Summit on Sustainable Development, much attention during this past decade has focused on the environment. Science educators have the responsibility to ensure that citizens gain the intellectual tools to engage fully in the ensuing debates and decisions.

The recent renewed interest in environmental education may have had its origins in Earth Day, but the roots and founders of ecology are many; Aristotle, Buffon, Wallace, Darwin, and the nameless agriculturalists worldwide who for millennia have noted and nurtured the relationships between the living and non-living worlds have helped to establish the science of ecology. It was German biologist Ernst Haeckel who is generally credited with developing the modern conception of ecological science at the end of the 19th century. He defined the study of the interactions of organisms with each other and with their environment (*oikos* = Greek for "household") in the following fashion:

> By ecology we mean the body of knowledge concerning the economy of nature – the investigation of the total relations of the animal both to its inorganic and to its organic environment: including above all, its friendly and inimical relations with those animals and plants with which it comes directly or indirectly into contact – in a word, ecology is the study of all those complex interrelations referred to by Darwin as the conditions of the struggle for existence (Haeckel, 1866).

Since Haeckel, many scientists have added to our understanding of relationships between organisms and their link to the environment in which they live. We now have a much more robust appreciation for the concept of the web of life and the fabric formed between and within the biotic and abiotic realms. This scientific appreciation has even extended into philosophical thought with the proposal of the Gaia hypothesis, a conception that the Earth itself acts as if it too is a living entity.

As the modern conception of ecology was being formed in Germany, the foundation for environmental education was being laid in the United States. Natural history is at the base of both the science of ecology and environmental education but the two would not come together until the latter half of the 20th century. At the end of the 1800s, the nature study movement – a partial proxy for present-day biology instruction – was widely found in schools sometimes coupled with conservation education. In 1891 Wilbur S. Jackman published *Nature Study for the Common Schools,* and through this book established the rationale for the inclusion of many ecology-related concepts in the science curriculum. Other groups and individuals such as Harvard's Committee of Ten and Cornell's Anna Botsford Comstock (1939) and Liberty Hyde Bailey further enhanced the rationale and source materials available to support the study of nature in the schools. As ecology evolved as a science and public awareness was heightened with books such as *Silent Spring* (Carson, 1962) and *The Population Bomb* (Ehrlich, 1968) that warned of pending disaster, environmental education also matured. Now it would be unthinkable to exclude some study of ecology from the school science learning experience. The *National Science Education Standards* (NRC, 1996) and many of the state science content frameworks recommend or require elements associated with the domain of environmental science.

Ecology Education: Rationales and Pedagogical Perspectives

As nature study grew into environmental education, it became obvious to members of the science education community that a formal position on the teaching of environmental science should be developed. William Stapp and colleagues (1969) of the University of Michigan are credited with producing the first such definition. He stated that, "Environment education is aimed at producing a citizenry that is knowledgeable concerning the biophysical environment and its associated problems, aware of how to help solve these problems, and motivated to work toward their solution" (Stapp et al., 1969, 30-31).

In the years leading up to Earth Day, President Richard Nixon publicly advocated "environmental literacy" as a goal of science instruction and in October 1970 signed the Environmental Education Act. This law defined the focus of such education as " ... the educational process dealing with man's relationship with his natural and manmade surroundings, and included the relation of population, conservation, transportation, technology, and urban and regional planning to the total human environment" (United States Public Law 91-516).

Through UNESCO, the international community found its voice with respect to environmental education during the 1972 Conference on the Environment in Stockholm and the 1975 International Environmental Workshop in Belgrade, Yugoslavia, both of which featured the drafting of position papers about the teaching of ecological topics. The Yugoslavia conference (UNESCO-UNEP, 1976) resulted in the Belgrade charter titled a *Global Framework for Environmental Education* that was enhanced by those attending the Intergovernmental Conference on Environmental Education in Tbilisi, capital of the Republic of Georgia, two years later. In part, the Tbilisi declaration stated that:

> Environmental education, properly understood, should constitute a comprehensive lifelong education, one responsive to changes in a rapidly changing world. It should prepare the individual for life through an understanding of the major problems of the contemporary world, and the provision of skills and attributes needed to play a productive role towards improving life and protecting the environment with due regard given to ethical values. (UNESCO, 1977, pp. 26-27).

The Tbilisi delegates recommended a series of 10 criteria to help guide the development of environmental education programs worldwide. These criteria included the ethical, social, cultural, and economic dimensions of environmental awareness, the roles played by different sciences in the study of the environment, and the interdependence of different nations and peoples. The Tblilisi working group further recommended that environmental education should provide necessary background knowledge while developing links between problems faced by real people and the possible solutions to those problems, at the same time catering to as wide a variety of people as possible in the educational process. The Tbilisi declaration further refined the goals for environmental education by suggesting an increase in awareness and concern, advocating increased opportunities for every person to acquire knowledge, skills, and commitment while creating new patterns of behavior on the part of individuals and society.

In 1980, Hungerford, Peyton, and Wilke suggested a curriculum development framework based on the Tbilisi declaration. Their model recommended the inclusion of ecological foundations, awareness, investigative abilities, and taking environmental action.

More recently, the U.S federal government has again heightened interest in and funding for ecology instruction with the National Environmental Education Act of 1990 (United States P. L. 101-619). This law renews the role of the federal government in environmental education and establishes an office of environmental education with the Environmental Protection Agency. The act provides funding for environmental education and training programs, establishing education grants, career fellowships, and other related activities. Unlike other sciences, ecology has always had a "grassroots" consistency and advocacy component. Presently, a wide range of groups – many operating locally – help to spread the word about the importance of including an environmental component and message in science instruction. These groups do much of the work in providing educator workshops and public awareness campaigns, and in promoting environment-specific instructional standards. One such important set of guidelines developed by the North American Association for Environmental Education (NAAEE) will be reviewed here.

Rationales for Ecology Education

The study of the interactions of organisms with each other and with their environment is worthy content for a number of reasons. From a pedagogical perspective, ecology is easy to defend as school science content because of what it contributes to and demands from learners. Ecology education provides students the opportunity to apply and synthesize much of what they have learned throughout a typical year of biology instruction. Many of the basic biological concepts that students encounter assist them in understanding the environment; ecology is a more sophisticated, higher-level, and synthetic pursuit that involves almost all other domains in the life sciences. In this regard, ecology is equal only to evolution as a concept that is both informed by, and provides a foundation for, much of the rest of biology. In the integrated domain of environmental science, students acquire a richer and wider view of the life sciences and come to recognize biology as a web of interrelated and interconnected ideas.

Ecology is inherently interesting because it represents the modern day successor to the popular nature study of previous generations of students. This realm of study encompasses a variety of interesting laboratory techniques, encourages students to work both in the field and with living organisms in the laboratory, permits discussion of fascinating interspecies relationships and the exploration of energy flow in nature, and provides the practical and intellectual tools so that students might effectively gauge the impact of humans on the environment and suggests solutions to problems.

It is this last dimension of environmental science that impacts students in ways that few other areas of science content can. Even the most basic study of ecology has the potential to affect students' understanding of the interaction of science and society. The larger view that study of the environment demands permits and encourages students to apply what they have learned in addressing problems, in allocating resources, and in gaining a rich view of the interplay of science and society.

The Ideal Environmental Science Curriculum

In the past four decades, ecology has found its place in the life science curriculum alongside other newer science fields such as molecular biology. However, even though the environmental science movement has more than reached its majority, little has been described about the ideal environmental science curriculum – although many clues are available to form a synthesis. Even less has been written about the nature of ecology instruction in U.S. schools.

The conceptual foundation guiding this review is one of curriculum orientation. Here the intended or ideal curriculum is the focus. This term defined by Cuban (1992) and others refers to the recommended content and process elements that should comprise the ideal instructional goals for a particular area of inquiry. A full taxonomy of curriculum types would include what is actually provided in class (the taught or enacted curriculum) and what is learned and remembered by those students (the received curriculum).

Four sources of information have been amassed to help describe the ideal ecology curriculum. Research studies of student misconceptions regarding environmental topics provided the first data source. Next, this article reports on the environmental science content included in virtually all current secondary school biology textbooks. Finally, the ecology content recommendations of the *National Science Education Standards* (NSES) and those of one of the principal advocacy groups, the North American Environmental Education Association (NAAEE), are reviewed. Together, these sources of information will help to define the most complete or ideal version of the ecological science content designed for a K-12 audience.

What Students Think They Know About Ecology: The Challenge of Misconceptions

Most educators accept the notion that one of the most important predictors of a student's future understanding is the level of current understanding. This constructivist view has resulted in a wide variety of research studies designed to determine what students know about aspects of nature. These views are generally called alternative or naïve conceptions if they are at odds with current scientific perspectives. Knowledge of these non-standard views of nature could be quite useful to educators who could then base instructional plans on what students already know rather than starting instruction at some random point.

Given the prominence of environmental education initiatives and the interests held by students in nature study topics, one might expect that there would be a range of studies of students' alternative conceptions in this domain. Unfortunately, that is not case. Furthermore, the few studies of misconceptions in ecology that do exist are widely scattered in terms of their target population and include investigations of young children, pre-service teachers, secondary school learners, and foreign students (Adeniyi, 1985). Although there is an expectation that environmental misconceptions known in one group might be generalized across similar populations, care must be taken in making such an assertion because the data are so sparse. Furthermore, many investigations, such as the one conducted by Brody and Koch (1989), were designed with reference to a specific environment, such as the marine ecosystem. It is not known if the findings in such cases could be extended to students' views with respect to other environments, but care should be taken until more data are available.

Two sources of information regarding ecology misconceptions appear in the literature – those based on general perceptions of environmental opinions and those based on research studies of such views. In the first case, Krebs (1999) discusses a number of errant views related to ecology that he believes are widely held by members of the general public. He suggests that people generally misunderstand a number of fundamental ecology issues. First, he cites the inaccurate notion that "each plant or animal is independent and therefore has no effect on . . ." or "relationship to other organisms" (p. 220). He further states that people believe the "idea that a community (population) consists of a group of similar living things" (p. 220). The entire structure of ecology as a science negates these views. The faulty conclusion that an "imbalance of species within its local environment or community is always bad" (p. 221) and that " ... once a biological community is destroyed by either natural disaster or mankind, it will be damaged forever" (p. 221) are also suggested by Krebs as incorrect but common views.

He devotes considerable attention to what he sees as the false link between the science of ecology and the political agenda of environmentalism; many believe that they are same. In other words, Krebs is concerned that members of the public base their environmental views and action on too little science and technology but consider it ecology nonetheless. For instance, he questions the current conceptions and prediction with respect to energy depletion, overpopulation, toxic substances, global warming, and similar issues. If these alternative conceptions are as widespread as Krebs suggests, they should help to inform the development of an ideal environmental science curriculum.

Munson (1994) has provided one of the most compressive syntheses of the results of actual empirical research studies of student knowledge of ecological concepts. His work forms the basis of the following section accompanied by the few newer studies not available earlier. Clearly, the domain of students' alternative ecological conceptions is an area that requires much additional research attention.

Food Chains and Webs

With respect to food chains, studies have shown that students have several fundamental misconceptions (Brumby, 1982; Griffiths & Grant, 1985; Munson, 1991). Students generally believe that food webs are more simple than they really are, that organisms higher in the food web always eat things lower in the web, and that organisms at the top of food chain have the most energy and increase in number at the expense of those below (Leach et al., 1996). Hogan (2000) has added to the data with the finding that students generally fail to see the two-way or cyclic nature of energy flow. Her work supports Munson's finding that students believe that energy flows from the bottom to the top of the food pyramid. Hogan used students' knowledge of pollution as an indicator of their ability to apply what they know about food webs. She found that students did not realize that chemical pollutants are changed in form as they move through food chains. Also, students tended to overstate the importance of the initial contact with pollutants while failing to appreciate cumulative or concentration effect of pollution. Eutrophication as a consequence of pollution was also poorly understood.

Population Size and Carrying Capacity

Munson (1991) has shown that many students fail to see the link between the fluctuations in population size and related constraining and supporting environmental issues such as food supply. Instead, some students believe that populations will increase indefinitely due to limitless resources (Brody & Koch, 1989) or will increase until the limits are reached at which point the population will crash and the organisms become extinct. In nature, neither view is accurate in the majority of instances.

Ecosystems and Populations

Griffiths and Grant (1985) and Munson (1991) have shown that many students fail to understand the web-like link between organisms in an ecosystem. They found that students tend to believe that certain organisms in a population are important *only* to those other organisms on which they prey for food sources. The concept that each organism is a thread in the fabric of an ecosystem seems missing for many students in much the same way that they lacked such understanding with respect to the food chain generally.

Biology Textbooks and Ecology Education

In an attempt to elucidate the nature of the intended or ideal curriculum, every major current secondary school biology text was reviewed. The number of pages of ecology content, the nature and extent of ecology readings, and laboratory activities included in each text were noted. The specific content analysis itself consisted of a grounded strategy in which the books were reviewed individually without any prediction about what they would contain. A list of ecology content included in each book was made. This list was further developed into a general checklist that was used to review all of the books. Following this second review, the books were examined again in a qualitative fashion to gauge the extent of the content inclusion. The label *minimum* is used if the content appeared at a level less than in other texts with *extensive* used if the content appears at a greater level than is typical in the overall set of books reviewed. The results of this review appear in Appendices A and B.

It should be noted that this review focused solely on degree of inclusion of particular content elements; there was no check on whether the content is appropriate for any particular audience or is scientifically accurate. With respect to this last point, it is useful to note that in a comprehensive study of the ecological concept of succession, Gibson (1996) found that many current biology texts feature both incomplete and outdated treatment. His conclusion was that even though a textbook contained information about succession, there was no guarantee of its accuracy. Content accuracy is important not just from the perspective of the textbook itself, but also from the standpoint of what is discussed in classrooms and internalized by students.

This content review of texts is both current and comprehensive, but is not unique. Wilson (2000) analyzed biology textbooks to determine the extent of the inclusion of ecology topics through time. However, she used a different kind of content unit in her work. As an example, in the analysis reported here, ecology topics such as *succession* and *habitat* were noted, but Wilson was primarily interested in suggestions made by the text regarding the role that students ought to take toward environmental issues and in content such as *forest* and *wildlife conservation, insects, birds,* and *energy.* Using her rubric, she found that, "By the 1990s, the EE [environmental education] content [had] leveled off at approximately 10% of the text" (Wilson, 2000, p. 102). Here, using a different unit of analysis for those books that included a discrete section for ecology, this examination revealed that the current biology text devotes 9.7% of its pages on average to environmental science. So, two different researchers using two different sets of ecology-related content found that the level of environmental science included in the average high school biology texts was approximately 10%.

An examination of Table 1 reveals much about what current textbooks contain and present as the ideal ecology curriculum. The most striking conclusion is that the majority of the secondary biology texts contain very similar sets of environmental science content B, although not all to the same degree of comprehensiveness. Ten of 13 books reviewed have a discrete chapter or section addressing ecology while the rest of the texts integrate such content. Not surprisingly, the texts designed specifically with an ecology focus (*BSCS: An Ecological Approach* and *Biology: A Community Context*) take this integrative approach. Many have argued that major topics such as ecology as a synthetic domain and evolution in its role as the foundation of modern biology should be woven throughout the text. Almost half of the books include ecology in a discrete chapter or two at the end of the text, almost guaranteeing that this important content will be relegated to coverage at the conclusion of the school year — if time remains. One inescapable conclusion is that integrating environmental science content or including it earlier in the text could encourage its inclusion in the biology curriculum.

As a broad generalization it is possible to conclude that all of the books examined include a fair measure of environmental science. It was not a goal of this study to rank one book against another, but it is clear that some books present a richer and more comprehensive view of this scientific discipline than do others.

Laboratory Instruction and Ecology Education

There is no doubt that the most robust and complete environmental science curriculum would include laboratory inquiry of ecological principles. Not surprisingly, most of the texts reviewed supplied such opportunities by including a variety of ecology-related laboratory activities. In fairness, only the texts themselves were analyzed and it is likely that additional exercises were provided in the supporting materials including laboratory manuals that frequently accompany the texts. However, it was revealing to see what the texts offered in the way of environmental science laboratory activities. First the theme of each included laboratory activity was listed and then grouped into categories similar to those developed for the content analysis. Appendix C shows the results of this examination.

The most common activities provided address population size, population interactions such as competition and predation, biodiversity, and aspects of environmental harm caused by human action such as pollution. For reasons that are not entirely clear, a surprising number of exercises targeted aspects of composting. Several of the texts included activities related to decision making with titles such as "Is everyone pleased with conservation efforts?," "A study of local human impact," and "Making decisions about land use." No book contained a full range of hands-on explorations linked to each of the major environmental topics, but some texts were more inclusive than others.

It is important to conclude this section with the same kinds of warning that were shared with respect to the textbook content reviews. The inclusion of labs in the science classroom is very much at the discretion of the teachers. Just because an activity appears in the text is no promise that it will be used in class. Laboratory work can be designed in many ways — from the "cookbook" to the "true exploration" — depending on the nature of the activity itself and when it is used with respect to the discussion of the content material. Most experts recommend that laboratory activity introduce, rather than simply reiterate, content discussions.

The Ideal Ecology Curriculum: The Views of Scientists and Standards

Scientists and the Ideal Ecology Curriculum

The quest for the ideal ecology curriculum continues with the views of expert scientists and educators. Cherrett (1989) surveyed members of the British Ecological Society resulting in a list of the top 20 most important concepts (Table 1). As will be noted by examining the other data sources, this list contains many of the same concepts. It should be noted that Cherrett did not have as his goal the development of a K-12 environmental science curriculum per se, nor would the scientists surveyed understand the dynamic nature of the school science curriculum, so it is likely that some of these concepts would not figure prominently in a final version of the ideal definition of environmental science for pre-college students.

Science Educators and the Ideal Ecology Curriculum

Rank	Concept	Rank	Concept
1	The ecosystem	11	Food webs
2	Succession	12	Ecological adaptation
3	Energy flow	13	Environmental heterogeneity
4	Conservation of resources	14	Species diversity
5	Competition	15	Density dependent regulation
6	Niche	16	Limiting factors
7	Materials cycling	17	Carrying capacity
8	The community	18	Maximum sustainable yield
9	Life-history strategies	19	Population cycles
10	Ecosystem fragility	20	Predator-prey interactions

TABLE 1. The 20 most important ecology concepts in rank order from a survey of members of the British Ecological Society. (Cherrett, 1989)

The well-respected *National Science Education Standards* (NRC, 1996) were consulted to determine the extent of environmental science coverage. Content in the *Standards* is found in narrative form (rather than listed) throughout the document and grouped into thematic areas within a particular science discipline keyed to grade level. As an example, one finds the theme "populations and ecosystems" for grades 5-8 within the Life Science domain and the theme "natural resources" for grades 9-12 in the domain of Science in Personal and Social Perspectives. Because the NSES are not laid out as a checklist, the review of the *Standards* was both difficult and somewhat subjective. Some might lump several ecology-related issues together while others would split a single paragraph from the NSES into a number of discrete content recommendations. Using a reductionistic qualitative view, 40 ecology-related items in the NSES were discovered after careful reading of the entire document. The grade level, theme, and page number in the document were recorded. Next, the ecology content issues were grouped into categories similar to those used in the review of textbooks and provided in Appendix D. An example from the NSES narrative is " ... humans modify the ecosystem ..." (p. 186) through population, pollution, etc. and "All organisms cause changes in the environment in which they live" (NRC, 1996, p. 129).

Comparing the NSES environmental science content to the list of such content from current textbooks proved interesting. Of the 17 ecology content issues found in the texts (see Appendix A), all but five such as biosphere, biodiversity, succession, and biomes are specifically contained within the *Standards*.

The ecology content specified in the *Standards* is highly comprehensive. First, as can be seen in Appendix D, the authors of the *Standards* were primarily interested in issues of population, limits on growth, and the impact of humans (and other organisms) on the environment and each other. The *Standards* further point out that science and technology should guide decision-making about environmental issues. This point would undoubtedly please Krebs (1999) who, as stated earlier, believes that many individuals confuse environmentalism with environmental science. Second, the ecology content is spread evenly through the grade levels and, although it is primarily included as a Life Science topic, it is also featured in Earth and Space Science and in Personal and Social Perspectives. This spiral instruction approach is in evidence throughout the *Standards*. For instance, the notions of population ecology, food chains, energy flow, and human impact (the dominant ecology themes in the *Standards*) appear in all the grade levels. If this plan were followed, students would encounter these key concepts at increasingly higher levels of sophistication as they progress through school. Third, if teachers accept the recommendation of the *Standards* that science be taught in an inquiry fashion supported by hands-on activities, environmental science instruction could be enriched immeasurably.

Instructional Goal-Setting by Advocates of Environmental Education

It has been useful to examine the guidelines for ecology education developed by the North American Association for Environmental Education – one of the major advocates for environmental education. The NAAEE guidelines for excellence (NAAEE, 2002) in environmental education (K-12) are framed around several strands (Questioning and Analysis Skills, Knowledge of Environmental Process and Systems, Skills for Understanding and Addressing Environmental Issues, and Personal and Civic Responsibility). Each strand is further subdivided with specific objectives and examples for students at grades 4, 8, and 12 with an appendix targeting such learning at the local level.

All of the NAAEE guidelines were reviewed without regard to grade level and the recommendation for each specific content inclusion was noted in the table in Appendix A. Scientific terms such as community and food chain/web, and others are not typically used in the guidelines, but the concepts they represent are implied. For instance, learners are asked to understand that the living environment is comprised of interrelated dynamic systems. This term contains many elements of the concept of community.

The NAAEE standards are most comprehensive when it comes to action taking. Standards include the recommendation that learners understand the influence of group action on the environment, the role of political and economic systems, global impacts and links, and the role of technology on the environment. There is also an extensive set of standards focusing on the skills necessary to take action. Such skills include the application of information and analysis to investigate environmental issues, skills in decision-making and citizenship, and issues related to the rights and responsibilities of citizens toward the environment. It is clear that the NAAEE guidelines emphasize the social responsibilities and action elements associated with the study of the environment. Therefore, perhaps they have consciously decided not to concentrate on the underlying scientific aspects of ecology since those aspects are well-described in traditional texts.

Another important role played by ecology-advocacy groups is that of curriculum development. There are few other examples in science instruction where one would be well-advised to look beyond the traditional textbooks and laboratory manuals for sources of curriculum support. Environmental advocates have developed a wide range of supplemental curricula, from local models developed at nature centers to the well-respected *Project Wild,* available nationally. In addition, these advocacy groups actively promote the teaching of ecology by providing teacher-training opportunities.

Conclusions and Recommendations

This review has revealed much about the ideal nature of the ecology education for K-12 learners. As stated previously, knowledge of ecology makes use of many diverse scientific principles and helps to tie them together synthetically while providing explanations and the foundation for accurate predictions. In this fashion, ecology plays a role in the curriculum and in science in providing a thread linking together the various sub-domains of biology. The only other domain that does this as well is the study of evolution.

In addition to its potential to unite the life science curriculum, environmental science also shares another attribute with evolution and that is one of misunderstanding, whereby environmental science is frequently seen as environmentalism. A recent investigation of teachers' attitudes toward environmental education by Holsman (2002) demonstrates that point strongly:

> There was almost no immediate recognition by the study group of the value of environmental education (EE) for achieving general learning goals. The most apparent implication of the results suggests that the best way to talk about EE is to not call it EE. While this suggestion may strike some ... as unacceptable, we should at least not lead with references to the phrase and instead stress the specific outcomes with education professionals. (p. 22)

The positive conclusion of this review is that when the various data sources are taken as a whole there seem to be generally agreed upon goals for the study of ecology. The survey of environmental scientists conducted by Cherrett (1989) (Table 1), the ecology domains defined as important by the *National Science Education Standards* (Appendix D), and the review of current biology textbooks (Appendix A) show a high degree of content uniformity with respect to the science of ecology and by inference what ought to be included in the K-12 instructional setting.

In brief, the ideal ecology curriculum for the K-12 learner would be driven by the rationales provided by the Tbilisi conference delegates, defined by the content issues cited in Appendix A, tempered by the emphases on population ecology and human impact from the *National Standards* and informed by the action-taking goals of the NAAEE guidelines. Furthermore, the ideal curriculum should be guided by the recommendations of the *National Science Education Standards* with respect to the application of authentic inquiry; science content should be delivered through the spiral curriculum approach in which important concepts are revisited at several points in the learner's school career. Strong decision-making strategies and role-playing activities should be included to provide guidance and experience in making environmental decisions.

However, there is certainly a difference between any ideal and the one actually provided to students. What science educators and environmental science experts recommend with respect to ecology education and what students actually learn in real world classrooms are frequently quite distinct. For instance, with few exceptions, ecology is typically included in the final section of the texts reviewed. As such, ecology may be ignored if time is short at the end of the school year. The potential misalignment between the ideal and enacted curricula lies at the heart of the problem and challenge for those interested in high quality ecology instruction. The ideal curriculum with its robust content, spiral curriculum, and laboratory investigations provides a rich potential to guide science education. However, only through an investigation of actual teachers in real world classroom settings will we know how closely allied are the ideal and actual environmental science curricula.

Textbooks Reviewed

A. Biggs, A., Gregg, K., Hagins, W.C., Kapicka, C., Lundgren, L., Rillero, P. & National Geographic Society. (2002). *Biology: The Dynamics of Life.* Ohio: Glencoe/McGraw Hill.

B. BSCS. (1998). *BSCS: An Ecological Approach,* 8th edition. Iowa: Kendall Hunt.

C. BSCS. (1997). *BSCS: A Human Approach.* Iowa: Kendall Hunt.

D. BSCS. (2001). *BSCS: A Molecular Approach,* 8th edition. Illinois: Everyday Learning.

E. Johnson, G. & Raven, P. (2001). *Biology: Principles and Explorations.* Florida: Holt, Rinehart and Winston.

F. Kaskel, A., Hummer, P. J. & Daniel, L. (2003). *Biology: An Everyday Experience.* Ohio: Glencoe/McGraw Hill.

G. Leonard, W.H. & Penick, J.E. (1998). *Biology: A Community Context.* New York: South-Western Educational Publishing.

H. Miller, K. & Levine, J. (2002). *Biology.* Upper Saddle River, New Jersey: Prentice Hall.

I. Oram, R.F. & Hummer, P. J. (2003). *Biology: Living Systems.* Ohio: Glencoe/McGraw-Hill.

J. Pruitt, N.L., Underwood, L.S. & William, S. (2000). *BioInquiry: Making Connections in Biology.* New York: John Wiley & Sons, Inc.

K. Schraer, W.D. & Stoltze, H. J. (1999). *Biology: The Study of Life,* 7th edition. New Jersey: Prentice Hall.

L. Strauss, E. & Lisowski, M. (2000). *Biology: The Web of Life.* California: Scott Foresman/ Addison Wesley.

M. Towle, A. (1999). *Modern Biology.* Texas: Holt, Rinehart and Winston.

	A	B	C	D	E	F	G	H	I	J	K	L	M	NSES	NAAEE
Physical Environment (abiotic vs biotic)	√	√		√	√	√	√	√	√	√	√	√	√	√	√
Ecosystems (habitat, community, etc.)	√	√	√	√	√	√	√	√	√	√	√	√	√	√	√
Biosphere Defined (lithosphere, atmosphere, etc.)	√	√				Min	√	√	Min	√	√		Ext		Min
Populations (general info, density, shape)	√	√	√	√	√	√	√	√	√	√	√	√	√	√	
Population Growth & Dynamics	√	√	√	√	√	√	√	√	√	√	√	√	√	√	
Population/Species Relationships (competition, parasitism, predation, etc.)	√	√	√	√	√	Min	√	√	√	√	√	√	√	√	Min
Energy: Flow & Tranformations (food webs, chains, pyramids)	√	√	Min	√	√	√	√	√	√	√	√	√	√	√	√
Energy: Autotrophs vs. Heterotrophs	√	√	Min	√	√	Min	√	√	√	√	√	√	√	√	√
Cycles (O_2, N_2, CO_2, H_2O, etc.)	√	√		√	√	√	√	√	√	√	√	√	√	√	
Biodiversity (biodiversity index)	√		√	√	√		Ext	√	√	√		√			
Succession (primary, secondary, climax)	√	√		√	√	√	√	√			√	√			
Biomes Defined & Examples (tundra, tropical, etc.)	√	√	Min	√	√	√	√	√	√	√	√	√	Min		
Environmental Harm (non-pollution such as overpopulation, urbanization)	√	√	√	√	√	√	√		√	√	√	√	Min	√	Min
Environmental Harm (impact on land, water, air, through acid rain, ozone, thermal pollution, etc.)	√	√	√	√	√	√	√		√	√	√	√	Min	√	
Conservation Issues (natural resources)	√	√	√	√	√	√	√			√	√	√	√	√	Ext
Relationship of Evolution and Ecology				√								√			
Environmental Ethics, Decision-making & Action-taking	√	√	√	√	√		Min		√	√		√	Ext	√	Ext

APPENDIX A. Ecology Content in Current Biology Textbooks, the *National Science Education Standards (NSES)* and the Guidelines from the North American Environmental Education Association (NAAEE). Min = Minimum, P = Average, Max = Maximum Inclusion

	A	B	C	D	E	F	G	H	I	J	K	L	M
Ecology Content/ Integrated (I) or Discrete (D)	D	I	D	D	D	D	I	D	D	D	D	D	D
If Discrete Is the Content in the Beginning (B), Middle (M) or End (E) of the Text?	E	N/A	Note 1	E	E	E	N/A	B	E	E	E	E	M
Are Readings About Ecology Included in the Textbook?	No	Yes	Yes	Yes	Yes	Yes	Yes	Yes	Yes	No	Yes	No	Yes
Approximate Number of Pages Devoted to Ecology	107	Note 2	63	46	91	63	Note 2	105	117	67	67	91	107
Total Pages in Book	1089	674	662	681	1025	691	527	1053	873	512	885	941	1081
Percent of Book Dedicated to Ecology	9.8	N/A	12.5	6	8.9	9.1	N/A	10.0	13	13	7.6	9.7	9.9

Note 1: *Biology: A Human Approach* is unique in its delivery of content. The book is organized around an instructional philosophy designed to Engage, Explore, Explain, Elaborate, and Evaluate. The first part of the book contains the Engage, Explore, and Explain sections. This section also contains many activities. The second part of the text contains a series of essays to Elaborate the content. Environmental science content was found in discrete sections in several parts of the book. The total number of pages dedicated to ecology is the sum of all such pages no matter where the content was found.

Note 2: Two books, *An Ecological Approach* (BSCS, 1998) and *Biology: A Community Context* (Leonard & Penick, 1998), are written with environmental science as the central theme. Not unexpectedly, these books weave the ecology content throughout, making a determination of total pages dedicated to such content difficult to determine.

APPENDIX B. Presentation of Ecology Content in Current Biology Textbooks

	A	B	C	D	E	F	G	H	I	J	K	L	M
Number of Ecology-Related Activities Included	18	22	12	4	11	6	10	12	4		6	19	5
Physical Environment/Abiotic Issues		√		√				√					√
Niche & Habitat	√	√			√								
Water Quality	√		√	√					√				
Limiting Factors (including land area)	√												
Population Interactions (competition & predation)	√	√	√		√		√	√				√	
Population Growth and Size	√	√	√		√		√	√				√	√
Energy: Flow (food webs, chains, pyramids)	√	√		√			√	√			√		
Cycles (O_2, N_2, CO_2, H_2O, etc.)	√	√		√	√	√	√	√			√	√	√
Biodiversity/Ecodiversity	√	√			√		√					√	
Succession (primary, secondary, climax)	√				√		√	√			√	√	
Soil & Composting	√		√						√		√	√	√
Environmental Harm		√	√		√	√						√	√
Environmental Techniques (i.e., population size)	√	√											
Natural Selection & Ecology					√								
Conservation, Human Impact & Decision Making	√	√					√					√	√

Note: Some texts have several activities addressing the same content theme, therefore the checkmarks do not necessarily equal the total number of laboratory activities included. Also, text "J" does not contain activities in the book itself.

APPENDIX C. Types of Ecology Laboratory Activities Included Current Secondary Biology Textbooks

	Grade Level			Life Science	Earth & Space Science	Personal and Social Perspectives	NSES Page Reference(s)
	K-4	5-8	9-12				
Biotic & Abiotic Factors/Issues	✓	✓		✓			129, 140, 157-8
Food Chain Issues	✓			✓			129
Environment Defined	✓					✓	140
Organisms Impact the Environment & Each Other for Good & Bad	✓		✓	✓		✓	129, 149, 186, 198, 199
Ecosystem Defined		✓		✓			157-8
Population Defined		✓		✓			157-8
Overpopulation, Population Density & Consequences	✓	✓				✓	140, 168
Population Change, Growth (reasons & types)	✓		✓			✓	140, 198
Predator, Producer, Consumer, etc.	✓	✓	✓	✓			129, 157-8
Energy Flow (sun)		✓	✓	✓			157-8, 186
Cycles (water, geochemical, nitrogen, etc.)		✓	✓	✓	✓		186, 160, 189
Organisms Interact			✓	✓			186
Limits on Growth & Carrying Capacity		✓	✓	✓			157-8, 186, 198
Pollution - Causes, Risks & Consequences	✓	✓	✓	✓		✓	140, 169, 186
Resources Are Limited	✓					✓	140, 198
Humans Impact the Environment, Its Cycles & Other Species			✓			✓	168, 198
Humans Use Natural Resources			✓			✓	198
Environmental Decisions Should Be Based on Science & Technology		✓	✓			✓	198, 199

APPENDIX D. Environmental Science Content in the *National Science Education Standards*

Acknowledgments

I would like to sincerely thank Dr. Paul Narguizian of California State University, Los Angeles for his assistance with this project. Without his extensive collection of science textbooks and his willingness to double check references, this project would not have been possible. Cassie Carter, Director of Education of the Outdoor Science School of Bozeman, Montana, was extremely helpful in reviewing a draft of the manuscript and in making a number of very useful suggestions.

References

Adeniyi, E.O. (1985). Misconceptions of selected ecological concepts held by some Nigerian students. *Journal of Biological Education, 19*(4), 311-316.

Brody, M.J. & Koch, H. (1989). An assessment of 4th, 8th, and 11th grade students' knowledge related to marine science and natural recourse issues. *The Journal of Environmental Education, 21*(2), 16-26.

Brumby, M.N. (1982). Students' perceptions of the concept of life. *Science Education, 66*(4), 613-22.

Carson, R. (1962). *Silent Spring.* Boston: Houghton-Mifflin.

Cherrett, J.M. (1989). Key concepts: The results of a survey of our members' opinions. In J.M. Cherrett (Ed.), *Ecological Concepts* (pp. 1-16). Oxford: Blackwell Scientific Publications.

Comstock, A.B. (1939). *Handbook of Nature Study.* Ithaca, NY: Comstock Publishing Company.

Cuban, L. (1992). Curriculum stability and change. In P.W. Jackson (Ed.), *Handbook of Research on Curriculum.* The Free Press: American Education Research Association.

Ehrlich, P.R. (1968). *The Population Bomb.* New York: Ballantine Books.

Gibson, D.J. (1996). Textbook misconceptions: The climax concept of succession. *The American Biology Teacher, 58*(3), 135-140.

Gordon, J.S. (October, 1993). The American environment. *American Heritage Magazine, 44*(5), 31-51.

Griffiths, A.K. & Grant, B.A.C. (1985). High school students' understanding of food webs: Identification of learning hierarchy and related misconceptions. *Journal of Research in Science Teaching, 22*(5), 421-36.

Haeckel, E. (1866). *Generelle Morphologie der Organismen (General Morphology of Organisms)* Berlin: G. Reimer.

Hogan, K. (2000). Assessing students' system reasoning in ecology. *Journal of Biological Education, 35*(1), 22-28.

Holsman, R.H. (August, 2002). *Non-science Teacher Perceptions of Environmental Education: Results from Environmental Education and Training Partnership (EETAP) Focus Groups* (Unpublished manuscript). Stevens Point, WI: University of Wisconsin, College of Natural Resources.

Hungerford, H., Peyton, P. & Wilke, R. J. (1980). Goals for curriculum development in environmental education. *Journal of Environmental Education, 11*(2), 42-47.

Jackman, W.S. (1891). *Nature Study for the Common Schools.* New York: Henry Holt.

Krebs, R. E. (1999). *Scientific Development and Misconceptions through the Ages.* Westport, CT: Greenwood Press.

Leach, J., Driver, R., Scott, P. & Wood-Robinson, C. (1996). Children's ideas about ecology 3: Ideas found in children aged 5-16 about interdependency of organisms. *International Journal of Science Education, 18,* 129-141.

Munson, B.H. (1991). *Relationships Between an Individual's Conceptual Ecology and the Individual's Conceptions of Ecology* (Unpublished doctoral dissertation). University of Minnesota, Minneapolis.

Munson, B.H. (1994). Ecological misconceptions. *Journal of Environmental Education, 24*(4), 30-34.

NRC (National Research Council). (1996). *National Science Education Standards.* Washington, DC: National Academy Press.

NAAEE (North American Association for Environmental Education). *Excellence in Environmental Education: Guidelines for Learning (K-12).* www.naaee.org/npeee/learner-guidelines (Retrieved on September 19, 2002).

Stapp, W.B. et al. (1969). The concept of environmental education. *Journal of Environmental Education, 1*(1), 30-31.

UNESCO-UNEP (1976). The Belgrade Charter. *Connect: UNESCO-UNEP Environmental Education Newsletter, 1*(1), 1-2.

UNESCO (1977, 14-26 October). *Final Report B Tbilisi.* Paper presented at the Intergovernmental Conference on Environmental Education, Tbilisi, Republic of Georgia. Paris: UNESCO.

United States Public Law 91-516. *The Environmental Quality Education Act.* Enacted October 30, 1970.

United States Public Law 101-619. *The National Environmental Education Act.* Enacted November 16, 1990.

Wilson, A.H. (2000). *A Content Analysis of Environmental Education as Presented in Selected High School Biology Textbooks: 1910-1994.* (Unpublished dissertation). University of Maryland, College Park, MD.

Wratten, S.D. & Hodge, S. (1999). The use and value of prior knowledge assessments in ecology curriculum design. *Journal of Biological Education, 22*(4) 201-203.

I

THE ENVIRONMENT

Investigating & Simulating Nature

THE ENVIRONMENT:
Investigating & Simulating Nature

This short section contains only three activities, but even so provides a fitting introduction to the rich set of laboratory activities to come. Although the first entry does contain a few worthy suggestions for ecological activities — such as an exploration of the relationship of temperature to hatching rate in brine shrimp — the major reason for the inclusion of this strategy relates to the philosophy of laboratory instruction included in the introduction. Among other suggestions, instructors are encouraged to give students as many opportunities as possible to make decisions about the questions to be asked, the methods followed, and the meaning of the data collected. This can only be accomplished if a suitable organism is available to support such open-ended investigations. As stated in the title of the first entry, the brine shrimp *Artemia salina* is an ideal organism to support studies of many ecology questions. These crustaceans are easy to raise, multiply rapidly, and respond to a number of interesting environmental stimuli.

The next two activities are both designed to bring nature into the classroom with sophisticated but relatively easy-to-develop simulations. The first simulation uses a Winogradsky column to produce a working model of many of the bacterial associations found in the muck at the bottom of a pond. Students will be able to see the fascinating metabolic factors demonstrated by microbes living in an anaerobic environment.

In the third and final activity, students can make a "pond in a jar" to study predator-prey relationships and population dynamics that occur in such an environment. This simulation will serve well as a demonstration or, as in the case of the other exercises in this section, can be used by students in their own investigations. It would be easy to imagine an entire range of activities targeting many ecology principles that could be designed by instructors and students using a simulation such as this one.

The study of ecology would be greatly enhanced if appropriate living organisms were available for investigation, but it is not easy to find animals suitable for use in academic settings. The brine shrimp *Artemia salina* is suggested here as an ideal experimental animal. It has a short life cycle (a few weeks to several months, depending on temperature), allows the importance of a wide range of environmental variables to be investigated, and is straightforward to culture. The adults are large enough (5 to 10 mm in length) to be easily visible with the naked eye. This chapter provides details of how to maintain brine shrimp in laboratory culture and gives suggestions for a number of ecological investigations that may be done with these interesting animals.

Artemia salina: An Ideal Invertebrate for Ecological Studies

Based on an original activity by Kirsty Ward-Booth and Michael Reiss

Ecological Principles Illustrated

The brine shrimp can be used for a wide variety of ecological and behavioral studies such as:

- The impact of temperature on the life cycle

- Predator prey relationships

- Population dynamics

- The relationship of growth rate and population density

- Hatching rates as a function of temperature or salinity

- A variety of instructor or student-designed demonstrations or investigations

Materials

- *Artemia* eggs

- food source such as *Liquifry*

- synthetic seawater

- suitable container(s)

Culture Procedures

Artemia eggs can be purchased from many aquarists or from specialist biological suppliers. Ideally they should be cultured at a density of approximately 250 eggs per cubic decimeter in synthetic seawater (35 g artificial sea salt per dm³) at 25° C. However, as shown below, *Artemia* is extremely tolerant of variations in density, temperature, and salinity. Hatching and early growth are virtually guaranteed. The eggs may be kept for months without loss of viability.

If *Artemia* is to be cultured throughout its life cycle, an appropriate source of food is obviously necessary. Natural seawater is likely to be adequate, as is salt water, whether artificial or natural in origin, if taken from an established marine aquarium. Commercial food is available from biological supply houses and aquarium suppliers. Once a culture is set up, it is self-perpetuating, provided access to sunlight or a strong light is allowed, so as to permit marine algae to photosynthesize. If the water is allowed to evaporate, eggs will be deposited at the bottom of the aquarium where they will then be ready to hatch once more water is added. A layer of sand or gravel on the bottom of the tank, jar, or aquarium is desirable, allowing a large surface area for the growth of the microorganisms on which the brine shrimps feed. The chlorine in tap water does not appear harmful, nor is the hardness of the water crucial.

General Biology of *Artemia* sp.

Artemia salina belongs to the order Anostraca within the subclass Branchiopoda of the Crustacea. The Branchiopoda are characterized by the possession of a flattened leaflike structure. The exopodite and endopodite each consist of a single flattened lobe, bearing dense setae along the margin. The coxa is provided with a flattened epipodite that serves as a gill; hence the name Branchiopoda — "gill feet." In addition to gas exchange, the trunk appendages are usually adapted for filter feeding, and often for locomotion. The Anostraca, known as the fairy shrimps, are characterized by an elongated trunk containing 20 or more segments. There is no carapace: hence the name Anostraca — "without carapace"; the compound eyes are stalked. All members of the genus *Artemia* are usually classified in the one species, *A. salina.*

The eggs of *Artemia* hatch into free-living nauplii larvae which reach the adult stage by a very gradual series of changes in which new somites and appendages are added until the full number is reached (Figures 1 and 2).

Artemia swims on its back, producing water currents by the beating of the thoracic limbs. The same movements serve to propel the creature through the water and to gather its food. The limbs do not all move in unison: one limb is usually about one-sixth of a complete beat ahead of the one in front of it. The beating of the limbs alternately enlarges and reduces the space between two successive limbs, sucking water in and blowing it out again. Small particles are swept into the median space between the two rows of limbs and are prevented from leaving by the fine setae projecting backwards from the inner edges of the limbs to form a strainer. Food is moved forwards in the midline until it reaches the level of the second maxilla, where it becomes entangled in a secretion from the large glands in the labrum. The maxillules push the sticky mass into the mouth.

Few Crustacea can survive in places that contain more salt than the sea. *Artemia salina* is by far the most successful of the ones that can. Indeed, it can survive in water so saturated with salts that crystals form around the edge of the pool. It can also survive in water that is only one tenth the strength of seawater (see Experimental Investigations). In the south of Europe it is found, as it formerly was in England, in the shallow ponds in which seawater is exposed to evaporation for the manufacture of salt. It is also found in salt lakes, like the Great Salt Lake of Utah, in the United States, and in many other parts of the world. Clearly such an animal must have an efficient means of regulating the composition of its blood (see Figure 3).

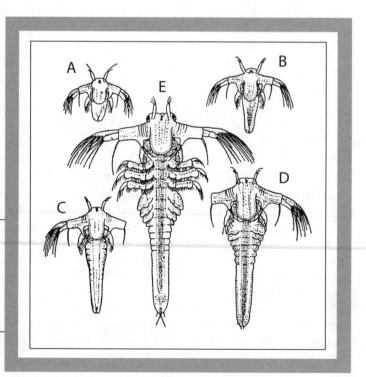

FIGURE 1. Larval stages of the brine shrimp, *Artemia salina.* A: *Nauplius,* just hatched; B-E: later stages, showing progressive increase in number of somites and appendages. From Calman (1911). (Approx. 15x)

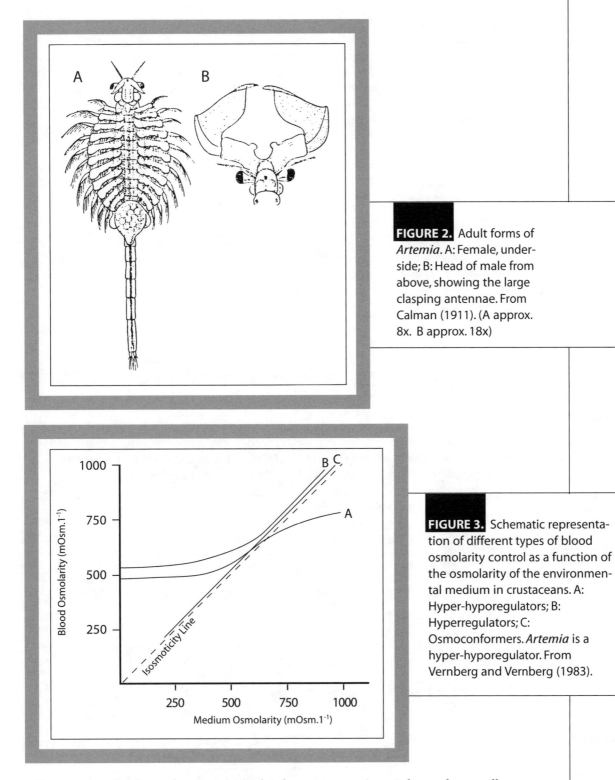

FIGURE 2. Adult forms of *Artemia*. A: Female, underside; B: Head of male from above, showing the large clasping antennae. From Calman (1911). (A approx. 8x. B approx. 18x)

FIGURE 3. Schematic representation of different types of blood osmolarity control as a function of the osmolarity of the environmental medium in crustaceans. A: Hyper-hyporegulators; B: Hyperregulators; C: Osmoconformers. *Artemia* is a hyper-hyporegulator. From Vernberg and Vernberg (1983).

When in water that has eight times as much salt as seawater, *Artemia* keeps the overall concentration of the solutes in its blood only slightly more concentrated than those of normal seawater. The gills play an important part in this process by excreting salt, while the gut is also important, taking in water to compensate for that which naturally tends to be lost by osmosis.

Artemia is also interesting in that it has hemoglobin in its blood. As might be expected, the scarcer the oxygen, the more hemoglobin the brine shrimps have. As *Artemia* normally lives in exceptionally salty conditions, the possession of hemoglobin is a considerable evolutionary advantage. (As a solution increases in salinity, it is able to hold less oxygen.)

Artemia shows considerable sexual dimorphism (Figures 4 and 5). As a prelude to reproduction, the adult males and females swim tightly together — one on top of the other, for several days — at the end of which they separate and the female begins to develop two egg sacs (Figure 4). Under favorable conditions females liberate active young from their brood pouches. In other circumstances eggs are laid that may hatch within hours, but can also lie quiescent for months or years. These eggs are remarkably resistant to adverse conditions, as suggested by the sample experimental investigations provided below.

Suggested Experimental Investigations with Brine Shrimp

Temperature and Hatching Rates

Eggs may be set up in artificial seawater at three different temperatures: 33° C (± 3° C) (heated tank), 19° C (± 3° C) (room temperature), 4°C (± 3°C) (refrigerated). The eggs at 33° C will hatch between 18 and 24 hours later; the eggs at 19° C will hatch between 54 and 58 hours later; and the eggs at 3° C will likely not hatch even after 105 hours. However, these eggs are still viable. This may be demonstrated by gradually raising the temperatures to 16° C, at which point hatching occurs.

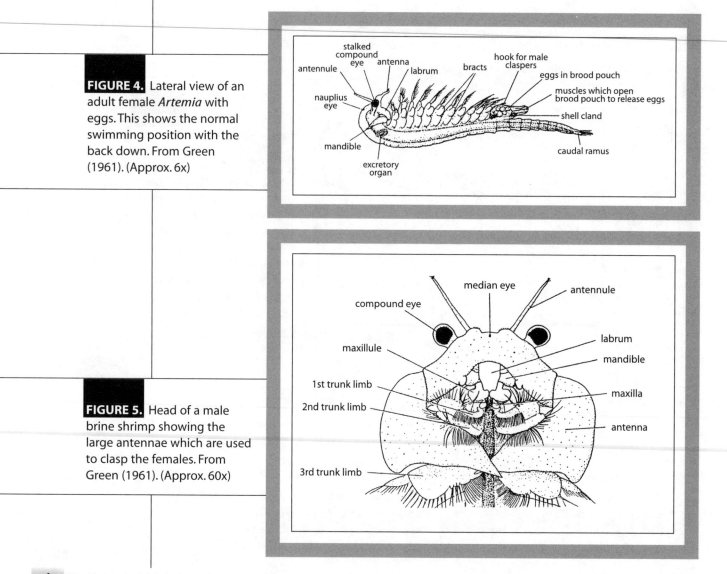

FIGURE 4. Lateral view of an adult female *Artemia* with eggs. This shows the normal swimming position with the back down. From Green (1961). (Approx. 6x)

FIGURE 5. Head of a male brine shrimp showing the large antennae which are used to clasp the females. From Green (1961). (Approx. 60x)

Egg Survival at Different Temperatures

Subject batches of eggs to temperatures ranging from -36° C to 100° C for 10 minutes. Place these eggs in artificial seawater at room temperature to see whether normal hatching occurred within a week. The results are summarized in Table 1.

Hatching Speed at Different Salinities

Fill 11 jam jars (each approximately 10 cm tall and 6 cm in diameter) each with 100 cm³ tap water. In the first jar, place tap water. To the second jar, add 1 gram of artificial sea salt, to the third 2 grams, to the fourth 3 grams, etc. The final jar will therefore contain 10 grams of salt and be saturated. (Seawater contains approximately 3.5 grams of salt per 100 cm³.) Add a pinch of eggs to each jar; cover the jars with plastic film to prevent evaporation, and place them along a windowsill so that all gain equal amounts of light. Students should make observations several

Temperature to which eggs lowered or raised (° C)	Subsequent hatching at room temperature
-36 (frozen solid)	Yes
-22	Yes
-17	Yes
-12	Yes
-7	Yes
+38	Yes
+49	Yes
+52	Yes
+66	No
+79	No
+100	No

TABLE 1. Survival of *Artemia* eggs after 10 minutes at various temperatures.

Salinity (g dm⁻³)	Eggs unhatched (%)	Eggs hatching (%)	Eggs hatched (%)	No. of *Artemia* mobile
0 (pure H₂O)	12	Hatched and died		0
10	10	30	60	6
20	16	20	64	10
30	11	16	73	>100
40	14	28	58	>50
50	15	35	50	>50
60	16	63	21	>25
70	14	61	25	12
80	75	25	0	3
90	87	13	0	1
100	84	16	0	2

TABLE 2. Hatching and subsequent development in *Artemia* subjected to different concentrations of salt. Results 72 hours after the experiment was set up.

times a day for several days and record the proportion of *Artemia* eggs in each jar reaching the following stages of development: unhatched egg, hatching, hatched but not mobile individuals, mobile individuals.

A representative set of results obtained 72 hours after the eggs were introduced into the jars is presented in Table 2. The results show how maximal hatching and development occur at about the concentration of salt in natural seawater. In tap water the eggs either hatch and die or fail to hatch. Even in the jar that contained water saturated with salt, the eggs all eventually hatched and developed into mobile *Artemia*.

Effect of Density on Growth Rate

Set up 16 jars (each 10 cm tall and 6 cm in diameter) each with approximately 100 cm³ of artificial seawater and a pinch of sand containing marine algae taken from a tank in which *Artemia* have been kept over several generations. Keep the jars at room temperature, and after two days add a single *Artemia* egg to 10 of them, and different numbers of eggs to each of the other six. Calculate the number of *Artemia* per dm³ after 13 days for each density by finding the average number in ten 5 cm³ samples and multiplying by 200. The average length of the *Artemia* at each density is determined by measuring 10 individuals randomly selected from each jar. Sample results are shown in Figure 6. The anomalous result at a density of 680 *Artemia* per dm³ is not easily explained, but otherwise lower densities correlate with larger individuals, as might be expected from density-dependent competition. It would be interesting for students to see if the apparently anomalous result occurs in other trials.

Other Possible Investigations

1. Swimming speeds mostly vary with temperature, so that, as might be expected, *Artemia* kept under warmer conditions swim faster. The precise form of this relationship could be investigated.

2. Since saltwater solutions hold little oxygen, it might be that the introduction of a pump for aeration allows *Artemia* to grow larger.

3. We are not aware of any studies that investigate brine shrimp courtship. It might be expected that larger (and stronger) males would pair with larger (and more fecund) females.

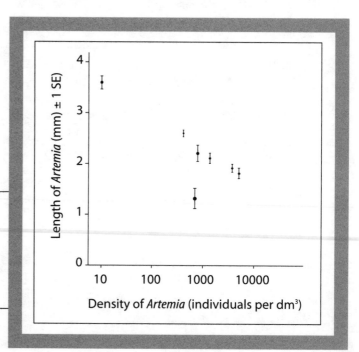

FIGURE 6. The effect of density on the size of *Artemia* after 13 days culture. Mean lengths are given ± one standard error of the mean.

4. If just a few eggs are introduced into a large tank, a population growth curve can be obtained.

5. *Artemia* are an ideal food source and can be used for a wide range of experiments investigating feeding in fish and invertebrates.

Acknowledgments

Stephen Tompkins supplied the *Artemia* and suggested topics for investigation. Mrs. R. Ward-Booth generously allowed her kitchen to have jar upon jar of swimming *Artemia*. We are grateful to Cambridge Research Biochemicals for funding biology projects at Hills Road Sixth Form College.

Original Source

This activity has been adapted from an original by Kirsty Ward-Booth and Michael Reiss (1988) titled "*Artemia salina*: An Easily Cultured Invertebrate Ideally Suited for Ecological Studies" and appeared in *The Journal of Biological Education*, 22(4), 247-251. It has been reprinted and modified with permission of the publisher.

Simulating a Pond Bottom Environment with a Winogradsky Column

Based on an original activity by Helen K. Pigage

An excellent but frequently overlooked tool for the study of microbial activity in the soil, nutrient cycling, microbial succession, and ecology is the Winogradsky column. Devised by Sergei N. Winogradsky in the 1880s to study soil microorganisms, it is simple and inexpensive to set up and can be used by high school or college students. Another advantage is that, once assembled, the column may be maintained with minimal effort for several months. If students wish to study the bacteria within the column, it may be systematically emptied and the microorganisms observed or subcultured.

Ecological Principles Illustrated

- Nutrient cycling
- Succession
- Microbial interdependence

Materials

- clear cylinder (4.0 to 7.5 cm in diameter and 10 to 25 cm tall)
- soil tamper (a sturdy rod or pipet with a rubber stopper at one end will work)
- a colander or screen
- soil from any source (best if from a garden, woodland, or field)
- water from a pond, stream, puddle, birdbath, or aquarium
- a carbonate source, such as 2.5 to 3.0 g of calcium carbonate, ground egg shells, or sea shells
- organic carbon source, such as a piece of newspaper (20 x 25 cm) finely shredded, fine sawdust, shredded leaves or roots.
- a sulfate source, such as 2.5 to 3.0 g of calcium sulfate, magnesium sulfate, a piece of shredded cooked meat or hard-boiled egg yolk
- red, green, blue, amber, and clear sheets of cellophane

Procedure

To assemble a Winogradsky column, follow these steps:

1. Prepare the soil by sifting it to remove any stones, twigs, or lumps. If the soil is very wet, allow it to settle and remove any extraneous material.

2. Shred the newspaper (or other organic carbon source), add the carbonate and sulfate and mix these together with a handful of soil. Additional substances, such as acids, pollutants, or insecticides may be added to test the tolerance of soil microorganisms to these agents (Aaronson, 1970).

3. Pack the soil mixture into the bottom of the container with the tamper to eliminate trapped air. The soil should be about 2.5 to 3.0 cm deep at the bottom of the column (Steckmayer, 1978; Aaronson, 1970).

4. Add more soil to the column; then add water and tamp to remove air bubbles. Continue until the column is packed to within 4 to 5 cm of the top of the cylinder.

5. Cover the surface of the soil with water about 2.5 cm deep.

6. Seal the top of the container tightly with plastic wrap and a rubber band or a suitably sized rubber stopper.

7. Place the column in a window that receives indirect sunlight.

Experiments with the Winogradsky Column

Various conditions may be imposed on the column to test the responses of the microorganisms in the soil. Here are some possibilities:

1. Vary the soil and water samples. Combine pond sediment with water from a puddle, birdbath, pond, or other source. Many combinations are possible, but if soil or sand from brackish or saltwater is used, the water should also be brackish or saltwater.

2. Use different carbonate, sulfate, or organic carbon sources; for example, use ground-rolled oats in place of shredded leaves or newspaper.

3. Add varying amounts of pesticide, acid, fertilizer, or specific pollutants in the first step to several otherwise identical columns.

4. Change the wavelength of light reaching the column. This may be done by wrapping several identical columns each with a different colored sheet of cellophane. Try red, green, blue, and amber, as well as clear.

5. A more complicated experiment would involve the use of environmental chambers. Set up identical columns in the same light intensity in two or more chambers at temperatures above or below normal room temperature.

In each experiment, set up one Winogradsky column to serve as a control. This column will be the standard, and each of the other columns should vary in only one aspect, such as the concentration of a given pesticide, from the control column. The results in the columns may be obtained by observing the color changes within the columns. Each change represents the activity of a different group of soil microorganisms.

Discussion

Chemical Reactions in the Winogradsky Column

The sequence of events in the Winogradsky column may take as little as 6 weeks to 2 months under warm conditions. Under cooler conditions, the reactions will occur more slowly. The succession observed by Kobyashi and Okuda (Hattori, 1973) in a column containing soil and water from a rice paddy required 2 1/2 months and occurred in this order: (1) green algae (green) appeared in about 1 week; (2) sulfate-reducing bacteria (black) were evident at 4 weeks; (3) photosynthetic purple-sulfur bacteria (red) appeared 5 to 6 weeks later; and (4) the purple-nonsulfur bacteria (green) were seen within the next few weeks.

Personal experience shows that Winogradsky columns made from soil and water from a small pond produce the following results: (1) green algae appear in 2 to 3 days and disappear by about 10 days after the column is set up; (2) sulfate-reducing bacteria produce black spots of hydrogen sulfide that appear within 5 to 6 days and increase in size for the next 2 to 3 weeks, until the entire column appears black; (3) photosynthetic purple-sulfur spots approximately 5 to 7 centimeters from the base of the column appear at 3 to 4 weeks; the area of the spot gradually increases but then disappears at about 6 weeks; and 4 purple-nonsulfur bacteria form a rust-colored zone that first appears in the upper third of the column at 2 1/2 weeks and proliferates with time. These results were obtained by placing the column in a northfacing window (Figure 1).

Once the microorganisms begin to flourish within the column, students may observe the actions of different organisms that are aerobes, anaerobes, and microaerophiles. These microorganisms may be heterotrophic, chemosynthetic, or photosynthetic, depending on their location and time of appearance within the column. Several chemical reactions occur as sulfur and carbon cycle within the closed system; each of the reactions is carried out by different genera of bacteria.

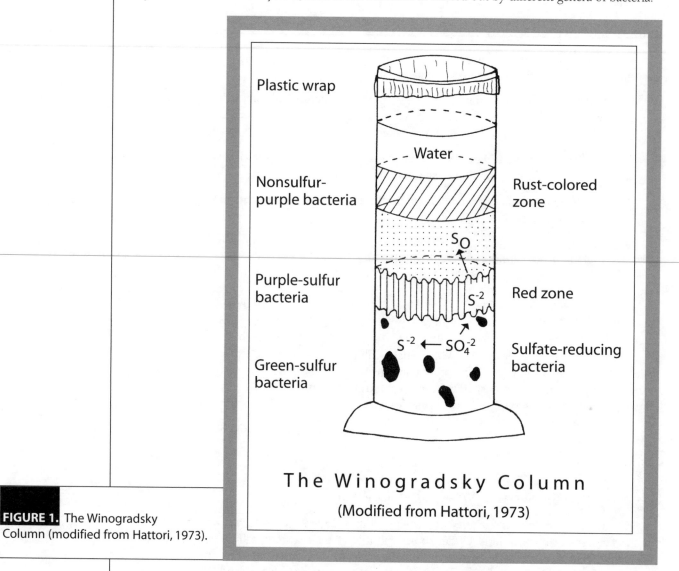

The Winogradsky Column
(Modified from Hattori, 1973)

FIGURE 1. The Winogradsky Column (modified from Hattori, 1973).

Shortly after the column is assembled, aerobic microorganisms exhaust the oxygen supply within the column, producing anaerobic conditions. Then sulfates are reduced by anaerobic microorganisms (*Desulfotomaculum* and *Desulfovibrio*) resulting in the production of sulfides that cause the column to become black. Other anaerobes ferment organic material in the mud. The sulfides are converted to molecular sulfur during anaerobic photosynthetic reactions performed by the purple-sulfur bacteria (*Chromatium* and *Chlorobium*). In the upper third of the column where concentrations of sulfides are lower and some oxygen is present, microaerophillic bacteria (*Rhodopseudomonas, Rhodospirillum* and *Rhomicrobium*) will flourish, producing a characteristic rust-colored zone that replaces sulfides below the surface of the water. These organisms are facultatively phototrophic and carry out photosynthesis under anaerobic conditions when light is available. Under aerobic conditions, they carry out respiration.

If soil samples do not contain green algae or purple-sulfur bacteria, the column will gradually become black because of the activity of the sulfate-reducing bacteria. The rust-colored zone will appear 5 to 10 centimeters below the soilwater interface as the purple-nonsulfur bacteria grow. These results may occur if garden soil is used because the purple-sulfur and related green-sulfur bacteria are usually found in the mud of pond and stream bottoms.

Further explanations of the chemical reactions briefly discussed here may be found in several sources: Pelczar, Reid, and Chan (1977); Hattori (1973); Atlas and Bartha (1981); and Steckmayer (1978). Aaronson (1970) also discusses more sophisticated flow-through columns that may be used by advanced students in ecological and microbiological studies. More ideas for experimentation may be found in the works of Winogradsky (1949), which describe his studies, and in Veldkamp (1970). Further information about the microorganisms may be obtained from Buchanan and Gibbons (1974).

Conclusion

The Winogradsky column can be a useful tool to demonstrate succession and microbial interdependence, with relative ease and simplicity for a wide variety of students in biology classes. Students may also follow the chemical reactions and recycling of material within the column to gain an understanding of how they occur in nature.

Original Source

This activity has been adapted from an original exercise by Helen K. Pigage (1985) titled "The Winogradsky Column: A Miniature Pond Bottom" in *The American Biology Teacher*, 47(4), 239-240, and has been modified and reprinted with permission of the publisher.

Simulating a Pond Environment in the Laboratory

Based on an original activity by David W. Allard

Creating a "pond in a jar" is an easy and versatile way to set up a self-sustaining ecosystem. This simple and inexpensive exercise works for students at almost any level, elementary school to graduate school. It can be used as a simple observation activity or as a means to perform a variety of experiments. Field trips can be combined with a long-term indoor activity, or the "pond in a jar" can be a substitute when field trips are impractical.

Ecological Principles Illustrated

- Succession
- Predator-prey relationships
- Population dynamics

Introduction

Initially described by Taub (1969) as a means for observing and manipulating single natural phenomena, simulations allow students to investigate in a laboratory situation important principles of ecology, such as succession, predator-prey relationships, population dynamics, and the effects of manipulating various environmental factors. Investigations with microcosms are also becoming an important area of sophisticated research in modern ecology (Odum & Deyers, 1992). There is a growing body of research literature using microcosm techniques (e.g., Larsen et al., 1986 & Taylor et al., 1990). Ecologists are using very elaborate microcosms to simulate natural environments (Adey, 1992). The studies are limited in that whole ecosystem responses cannot be observed, but they still provide valuable insights into ecological processes. These techniques are also being used in the classroom (Comer, 1992; Jones, 1992; & Murphy et al., 1992) to give students hands-on experiences.

Materials

The following materials are needed to assemble the microcosm:

- glass or plastic wide-mouthed quart jar (Jars with plastic lids work best as they do not rust; bigger jars are okay, but smaller sizes do not work very well.)

- plankton nets (Often, commercial plankton nets are used, but handmade nets of stocking or other materials may be substituted.)

- water samplers (A Van Dorn Sampler works well, but homemade equipment may be substituted.)

- small hand trowel

- bottom sampler (A Petersen Dredge is excellent, but a shovel will suffice if that is all that is available.)

- a light setup or a well-lighted window

Procedure

A good way to begin this exercise is to take the class on a field trip to a local park that has a pond in it. However, if field trips are impossible, teachers can do the collecting and bring the materials gathered to school. The students will then assemble their microcosms in the lab. Ask the students to bring their own jars and provide sampling equipment to the class. Teach the students how to use the various samplers, so they can prepare their own "ponds in a jar."

Preparing the Microcosm

To prepare the microcosm, students working individually or in groups should perform the following steps:

1. Take a sample of bottom mud with the dredge.

2. Place an inch or two of mud in the bottom of the jar. (There should be some benthic organisms in this mud).

3. Take plankton samples and add them to the jar (such samples include cladocerans, copepods, etc. and algae).

4. Place some sticks, rooted aquatic plants, filamentous algae, duckweed, etc. in the jar.

5. Fill the jar up with pond water and cap it.

6. Return the jars to the lab for further observations and experimentation.

It is not a good idea to place larger organisms, such as fish and insects, in the jar. Students who have ignored this direction and placed minnows in their jars have found that it is possible for minnows to survive an entire semester, but the use of minnows or larger organisms should be discouraged.

The jar should be kept closed. The ecosystem will remain functioning for a very long period of time if given adequate light. A good way to insure adequate light is to use a light setup and keep the jars under fluorescent lights. The lights should be on a timer and stay on 14 hours per day. Nevertheless, these ecosystems can also be stored in the dark and brought out at a later time. They rejuvenate when placed in light.

Investigations

Students may pursue a variety of investigations using their microcosms. The following is a list of some of the possibilities:

- Measurement of pH and other physiochemical parameters over time.

- Successional studies done by keeping records on the organisms found in the jars over time. Students have found leeches, hydra, amphipods, copepods, cladocerans, ostracods, midge larvae, various types of algae, snails, etc.

- Controlled investigations using paired jars (experimental and control) to determine the effects of: 1. Different lighting conditions. 2. Fertilization with inorganic nutrients. 3. Organic enrichment, such as adding sucrose. 4. Inorganic and organic pollution.

Original Source

This activity has been adapted from an original exercise by David W. Allard (1994) titled "Pond in a Jar" in *The American Biology Teacher*, 56(6), 372-373, and has been modified and reprinted with permission of the publisher.

II

EXPLORING ECOLOGY
Basic Principles

EXPLORING ECOLOGY:
Basic Principles

This section includes a variety of laboratory investigations, some of which are conducted in the field and some in the classroom. What they have in common is their ability to demonstrate one or more important ecological principles. Some of these studies are directed to specific environmental regions, but most educators can adapt them to the local environment and illustrate the underlying ecological principles, intended. All are intended for general biology classes and half may be used in advanced biology settings as well. Many of the lessons are designed for students working in teams so the labor in the activity is distributed, the level of collaboration increased, and the authentic work of scientists demonstrated.

The ecological principles illustrated include the following: immigration, succession, extinction, island biogeography, predator-prey relationships, organism interaction, organism-environment interaction, adaptation, optimality, microbial interdependence, population dynamics, population growth, dispersal of offspring, nutrient cycling, watershed ecology, materials transport, abiotic factors, and fire ecology. These principles are illustrated in a number of environments including the ocean shoreline, ponds, streams, forests, and the microbial world.

The following overview of this section is designed to demonstrate the dual nature of many of these activities in which study of the foundation principle is intertwined with investigation of a specific environment. For instance, Kuserk gives students an opportunity to explore stream ecology while learning about materials transport, and the important concept of biological zonation is demonstrated on the beach. Both of these concepts could, just as easily, be developed as student activities in other environments, but the important lesson is that they *apply* to other environments. As an example, there are biological zones in forests, and materials are transported by wind as well as water. This approach also encourages transfer; students may learn about a given principle in one environment and transfer that knowledge to a new one.

Island biogeography, a very important concept not just on islands but in the management of reserves such as national parks, may be experienced in the microbial setting in an activity provided by Cruzan. The notion that environments change through a predictable process of success is exemplified in forests with a lesson by Stronck, and in milk in a strategy provided by Gillen and Williams. Wind dispersal of tree seeds by Thomson and Neal, the role of fire in seed germination by Steele and Keeley, and Westmoreland's activity on thermal acclimation round out the set of interesting and useful laboratory lessons in this section on basic principles.

The following study is divided into four parts. Since the first two are accomplished in the field, it is advisable to check local tide tables and plan to conduct these parts at low tide when shore regions are exposed. In the first study part, students draw a profile of the beach scene as they see it. This provides a visual description of the habitat and how it changes across the shore. Secondly, students collect plants and animals from the various zones of the shore. This portion introduces students to the diversity of the community and its distribution. The last two study components, then, are accomplished in the laboratory where, in the third step, the students identify their collections with the aid of reference books. Lastly, students are asked to relate the scene drawn in Part 1 with the distribution of plants and animals collected and identified in Parts 2 and 3. If all goes well, students will be able to determine that this scene, which varies from continuously wet to continuously dry over a short distance, is inhabited by a diversity of organisms, each adapted for and occurring in their own particular place on the shore.

A Study of Sandy Beach Zonation

Based on an original activity by Steve K. Alexander

Ecological Principles Illustrated

- Organism interaction
- Organism-environment interaction

Materials

- clipboards
- 20' x 4' beach seine (0.5 cm)
- plastic bags
- marker for plastic bags
- ice
- refrigerator
- shovel
- sieve (easily made by nailing a 2' x 1' piece of wire screen onto a wooden frame)
- 5% formalin
- jars with screw-on caps

Procedures

1. Beach Profile

After arrival at the beach, direct students to draw a profile (side view) of what they see. Since students will probably seek direction as to what to include, a few suggestions follow. They should take notice of the upward slope of the beach and the obvious difference in elevation between the water's edge and the dunes. Areas of wet, packed sand versus areas of dry, piled sand are also important to note. The former indicates regions occasionally covered by water at high tide, while the latter indicates shoreline areas not covered by water where windblown sand collects. Additionally, the zones of the shore should be included: subtidal, intertidal, and supratidal.

The *subtidal* is the zone of the shore continuously submerged by seawater, even during low tide. This zone may be subdivided into near-shore (shallow water) and offshore (deep water). Near-shore organisms either burrow into the sand or swim offshore to avoid the force of breaking waves.

The next zone, moving up the shore, is the *intertidal*. This region of the shore is alternately covered by seawater at high tide and left dry at low tide. This alternating cycle of wet and dry is repeated once or twice per day, depending on location. Intertidal organisms burrow into the sand to escape the fluctuating nature of this shore region. Two visible lines of litter should be noted in the intertidal. These are referred to as "drift lines" and represent trash and subtidal animals cast up on the beach by the tide. The line nearest the water represents drift most recently washed ashore, while the line further up the shore represents an accumulation of drift previously washed ashore and concentrated by high tides.

The last zone to note still further up the shore is the *supratidal*. This zone begins at the edge of dry, piled sand and extends upward to the back of the sand dunes. This region is dry, being constantly exposed to air and wind and only rarely covered by seawater during extreme weather (like hurricanes). Sea breezes blow sand up on the beach, where it is trapped by front row vegetation. In this way, dunes tend to build up seaward. Therefore, vegetated areas nearest the water represent young dunes characterized by relatively low relief and sparse vegetation. This region of the supratidal is termed "active dunes." On the other hand, vegetated areas furthest from water represent old dunes characterized by high relief and dense vegetation. This region of the supratidal is termed "stable dunes." Lastly, students should be directed to mark on the profile the location of each sample (see Figure 1).

FIGURE 1. Profile of a Texas Gulf Coast sandy beach. Numbers correspond to location of sample collection.
1 = nearshore subtidal nekton; 2 = nearshore subtidal benthos;
3 = intertidal benthos;
4 = driftlines;
5 = supratidal plants;
6 = supratidal animals.

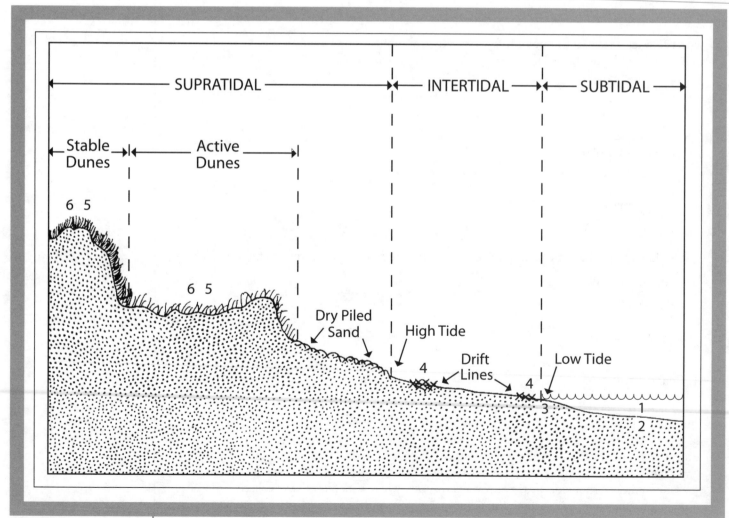

The profile step is critical as it directs students to focus on the beach as a natural setting with obvious differences in conditions over a short distance. For this reason, it is important that students spend the time necessary to translate the details of what they see onto paper. The profile of a typical sandy beach for the Texas Gulf Coast is presented in Figure 1.

2. Collection of Organisms

After completion of the profile, students should begin sample collection. Although quantitative sample collection is too involved in most cases, the relative abundance of an organism in a sample can easily be noted; i.e., *abundant, occasional,* or *rare.* The following is a listing and description of the samples to be collected: 1) nearshore subtidal nekton; 2) nearshore subtidal benthos; 3) intertidal benthos; 4) drift lines; 5) supratidal plants; and 6) supratidal animals. These sample numbers and descriptions should correspond with those marked on the profile (see Figure 1).

Nearshore subtidal nekton is collected by pulling through the water a 20' x 4' beach seine (0.5 cm netting). Two students should take the net out into the surf, one ahead of the other, until four feet of water is encountered at the deep end. At this point, the deep end is turned back toward the shore and then both ends of the net are moved simultaneously to the shore. This shoreward movement should be done as quickly as possible to avoid losing the catch. Once ashore, a representative of each animal is placed into a plastic bag and sealed. This bag should be clearly marked as to sample number and student(s) initials. The contents of the bag (and all perishable items not placed in formalin) should be kept on ice in the field and in the refrigerator in the laboratory until analysis.

Nearshore subtidal benthos is sampled by having two students wade out in the water to about waist deep. There they will use a shovel (one with a long, thin blade is best) to dig into the sand. The sand obtained is placed into a sieve, which is then moved up and down in seawater to wash the sand through the wire screen. Any animals larger than the 1 mm opening of the screen will be retained. These can be picked out by hand and placed in a jar containing 5% formalin. Again, make sure jars are labeled properly.

Intertidal benthos is taken from the shore region where the waves are washing up and then down the beach. Students should use a shovel to collect sand at the lowest end of this washed area. The sand should be sieved through the wire screen and the animals placed in a jar with formalin as before. One animal of the intertidal, the hermit crab (*Isocheles wurdemanni*), resides on top of the sand and can be collected by hand.

Up the shore from the water's edge are the two drift lines. Both lines contain a mixture of trash, seaweed, and subtidal animals. The trash can be ignored or included in the study (if included, compare results with those from the Texas Gulf Coast; various plastic items are the primary form of trash both by volume and number of items). Seaweed (*Sargassum* spp.) may or may not be present, since it drifts ashore in large amounts only on occasion. The most important part of the beach litter is the remains of subtidal animals. These remains are routinely a part of drift lines, but they are especially abundant after heavy weather (like a winter norther or hurricane). The remains of a representative of each animal should be put in a labeled plastic bag and placed on ice.

Students should now move up into the dunes of the supratidal. They can begin by collecting plants in the active dunes. Plants should be cut at the base and placed in a labeled plastic bag. Collect only a representative of each of the most common plants (likely to be 10 to 12 species). This should be repeated in the stable dune area. Students should be directed to avoid disturbing the roots of dune plants, since these are vital to dune stability. The extensive underground root system serves not only to anchor the plant and stabilize sand but also to retrieve valuable rainwater as it moves quickly through the sand.

The supratidal animals are the last collection. Start in the active dune area by lifting (carefully) large debris (tree trunks, plywood, rope, etc.) cast up by extreme weather. A variety of life can be noted under debris, including ants, lizards, and spiders. Certain snakes, such as the western diamondback rattlesnake (*Crotalus atrox*), occasionally seek refuge here and under vegetation.

Also note tiger beetles that move swiftly across the sand when approached. The most common resident of the dunes, the ghost crab, may not be seen, but evidence of its presence readily occurs in the form of holes in the sand. These burrows, which range from 1 to 10 cm in diameter, house the crabs during periods of inactivity. The crabs may exit burrows and be active during the day in undisturbed areas, but they may quickly retreat to burrows when approached. They can be more easily approached and observed at night when they typically exit their burrows and are active on the beach. These animals periodically visit the water's edge to feed and replenish the seawater in their gill chambers. Thick hairs around the openings to the gill chambers help reduce the loss of water until the next visit.

3. Laboratory Analysis

Within several days after returning from the beach, have students retrieve all their samples. Each sample should be examined and a list prepared of the plants and/or animals present. Both common and scientific names should be listed for each organism identified, as well as its relative abundance. Identification is aided by the use of references that illustrate and describe the plants and animals of the shore where the collections were made. This approach to identification is far easier and faster than the use of taxonomic keys. Descriptive references are available for every shoreline area of the United States. The author has used the following reference to identify plants and animals from sandy beaches of the Texas Gulf Coast: Fotheringham & Brunenmeister (1989) for benthic and pelagic invertebrates, Hoese & Moore (1977) for fish, and both Cannatella & Arnold (1985) and U.S. Army Corps of Engineers (no date) for dune plants. Descriptive references are also available for the Atlantic Coast. For example, both Ricciuti (1982) and Amos & Amos (1985) describe the plants and animals occurring along Atlantic Coast sandy beaches. With a little searching through the appropriate descriptive references, students should find the identity of most plants and animals in their collection. After the identification of organisms is complete, the six example lists are compiled into a simple table. A listing of organisms found on a typical sandy beach along the Texas Gulf Coast is presented in Table 1.

If taxonomic keys are introduced, the laboratory analysis of samples described previously can be slightly modified for that purpose. Choose a group of shoreline organisms that are both abundant and diverse. For this group of organisms, students would not be allowed to use the descriptive references. Instead, they would use a simple key for this group that you have prepared. Along the Texas Gulf Coast, crabs are abundant and comprise a diverse group. Table 1 lists seven species of crab commonly encountered along Texas sandy beaches. A simple key to these species is presented in Table 2.

4. Putting It All Together

Students now have completed the first three parts of the study. In these steps, they have gained an appreciation of the beach habitat and have identified organisms collected from various regions of the shore. The final part of the study is to ask students to relate organism distribution to the changing habitat of the shore. For example, the brittle star, lettered olive, disk clam, and giant cockle inhabit continuously submerged subtidal sand (see Figure 1 and Table 1). The Atlantic needlefish and blue crab are nekton found in nearshore subtidal waters. The coquina clam, hermit crab, and mole crab live in association with alternately submerged and dry intertidal sand. Pennywort and sunflower are plants growing in dry, supratidal sand, and so on. If the students are successful at this stage, a similar examination of their results should lead to a clear statement regarding sandy beach zonation; i.e., that a plant or animal along the shore occurs only in a certain area of the shore under a certain set of environmental conditions.

The exercise presented here can be expanded for more advanced, college-level classes to include: (1) a quantitative sample collection with subsequent statistical analysis of data and/or (2) an analysis of diversity using a simple diversity index.

Sample No. (see Fig. 1)	Sample Type	Common Name	Scientific Name
1	nearshore subtidal nekton*	Atlantic needlefish (0)	*Strongylura marina*
		blue crab (A)	*Callinectes sapidus*
		gulf whiting (A)	*Menticirrhus littoralis*
		hardhead catfish (A)	*Arius felis*
		rough silverside (A)	*Membras martinica*
		speckled crab (0)	*Arenaeus cribrarius*
		striped mullet (A)	*Mugil cephalus*
2	nearshore subtidal benthos	brittle star (R)	*Ophiophragmus moorei*
		coquina clam (A)	*Donax texasiana*
		lettered olive (0)	*Oliva sayana*
		moon snail (0)	*Polinices duplicatus*
		polychaete (A)	*Lumbrineris tenuis*
		sand dollar (0)	*Mellita quinquiesperforata*
		sea pansy (R)	*Renilla mulleri*
3	intertidal benthos	coquina clam (A)	*Donax variablis*
		hermit crab (A)	*Isocheles wurdemanni*
		mole crab (A)	*Emerita portoricensis*
		mole crab (A)	*Lepidopa websteri*
		tube worm (0)	*Diopatra cupraea*
4	drift lines**	disk clam (0)	*Dosinia discus*
		giant cockle (A)	*Laevicardium robustum*
		incongruous ark (A)	*Anadara brasiliana*
		pen shell (0)	*Atrina seminuda*
		spider crab (0)	*Libinia dubia*
5	supratidal plants	beach evening primrose (0)	*Oenothera drummondii*
		beach morning glory (0)	*Ipomoea stolonifera*
		beach tea (A)	*Croton punctatus*
		coastal dropseed (A)	*Sporobolus virginicus*
		fiddleleaf morning glory (0)	*Ipomoea pes-caprae*
		marshhay cordgrass (A)	*Spartina patens*
		pennywort (A)	*Hydrocotyle bonariensis*
		sea ox eye daisy (0)	*Borrichia frutescens*
		sea purslane (0)	*Sesuvium portulacastrium*
		sea rocket (0)	*Cakile* spp.
		sunflower (A)	*Helianthus* spp.
6	supratidal animals	ants (0)	unidentified
		ghost crabs (A)	*Ocypode quadrata*
		grasshoppers (0)	unidentified
		lizards (0)	unidentified
		mushrooms (0)	unidentified
		spiders (0)	unidentified
		tiger beetles (A)	*Cincindela* spp.

TABLE 1.
Representative plants and animals of a Texas Gulf Coast sandy beach. Relative abundance designation next to common name:
A = abundant;
0 = occasional;
R = rare.

*Several species of floating jellyfish may be taken with nekton, such as cabbagehead (*Stomolophus meleagris*), moon jellyfish (*Aurelia aurita*), and Portuguese man-of-war (*Physalia physalia*). During certain times of the year, floating brown algae (*Sargassum* spp.) may be encountered as it drifts shoreward. Inhabitants of this algae include sargassum shrimp (*Latreutes fucorum*), sargassum crab (*Portunus sayi*), sargassum fish (*Histrio histrio*), and sargassum nudibranch (*Scyllaea pelagica*).

**Listed are benthic animals that live in offshore subtidal. Remains of nektonic and benthic animals that live in a nearshore subtidal are also found here, including blue crab, hardhead catfish, speckled crab, striped mullet, coquina clam, lettered olive, moon snail, and sand dollar. Other items typically present, but not listed, include jellyfish, *Sargassum* spp., and trash (bottles, aluminum cans, wood, rope, and a variety of plastic items). Residents of driftwood include gooseneck barnacles (*Lepas* spp.) and boring clams (*Bankia gouldi* and *Teredo bartschi*).

Original Source

This activity is based on an original exercise by Steve K. Alexander (1991) titled "A study of Sandy Beach Zonation" in *The American Biology Teacher, 53*(l), 37-41, and has been modified and reprinted with permission of the publisher.

Key to the Adult Stage of Crabs

1	Lives inside a snail shell	hermit crab (*Isocheles wurdemanni*)
	Does not live inside a snail shell	2
2	Animal size of I inch or less	3
	Animal size much greater than 1 inch	4
3	Long, blade-like tail held beneath body	mole crab (*Emerita portoricensis*)
	Tail not blade-like and not held beneath body	mole crab (*Lepidopa websteri*)
4	Last pair of legs (different from the first three) flattened into paddles	5
	Last pair of legs (similar to the first three) not flattened into paddles	6
5	Top of carapace and claws with white spotted pattern	speckled crab (*Araneus cribrarius*)
	Top of carapace and claws without white spotted pattern	blue crab (*Callinectes sapidus*)
6	Long, nose-like projection between eyes	spider crab (*Libinia dubia*)
	No long, nose-like projection between eyes	ghost crab (*Ocypode quadrata*)

TABLE 2. Key to the adult stage of crabs listed in Table 1.

Demonstrating
Island Biogeography
with
Microorganisms

*Based on an original activity by
John Cruzan*

Ecologists have long been interested in populations and communities on islands because they are relatively self-contained and isolated from other populations and communities. The number of species on a particular island is the result of an equilibrium between two processes: immigration and extinction. In general, the more isolated an island, the lower the probability of immigration. So more remote islands tend to have fewer species.

Ecological Principles Illustrated

- Immigration
- Extinction
- Island biogeography

Introduction

Extinction on islands seems to be a function of island size. In the first place, larger islands may contain more potential niches. Therefore, immigrants are more likely to find an unoccupied niche rather than becoming extinct (locally). Secondly, and perhaps of greater importance, is extinction due to random fluctuations in populations. All populations fluctuate due to changing environmental conditions and species interactions as well as random changes in natality and mortality. This is especially true of small populations, such as those on islands. These fluctuations occasionally result in a population decline to zero (local extinction). In a continental area, recolonization from adjacent populations may occur quickly, but on an island there may be no adjacent population to provide recolonizers. The smaller the island is, the more likely this is to be true.

These two hypotheses — that small islands have fewer species, and that more remote islands (those with fewer potential immigrants) have fewer species — can be somewhat evaluated using aquatic microcosms. The microcosm can be either autotrophic or heterotrophic. If autotrophic, it is just filtered spring water (or its equivalent) to which a measured sample of pond or lake water has been added. A heterotrophic microcosm has some form of organic detritus that promotes bacterial growth, the bacteria serving as the food source for the "primary consumers." One way to produce one is to boil hay in spring water in a proportion of 7 grams to 1000 ml. It is important that the hay be qualitatively equivalent as well as quantitatively equivalent. Leaf, stem, and seed head pieces will break down at different rates and provide different levels of nutrition to the bacteria.

The inoculum (pond water) should contain as many species of potential colonizers (mostly protozoa, rotifers, and algae) as possible. Collect it from the bottom (including detritus) from 2 or 3 different ponds or shallow areas of lakes. Agitate it thoroughly, but gently, immediately before removing an "averaged" sample with a calibrated pipet.

Materials

- 4 various-sized glass containers (10 ml to 1000 ml)
- pond water inoculum
- microscope
- microscope slides and coverslips
- calibrated pipet
- algae and protozoa identification manuals
- pond biology references

Procedure

To examine the effect of island size, create several islands (microcosms) in glass containers ranging in size from 10 ml to 1000 ml. As much as possible maintain the same ratio of surface area to volume since oxygen absorption from the air can be a limiting factor. Inoculate each with 1 ml of the pond water inoculum. Examine them weekly by withdrawing a measured volume (0.05 ml) drop from the agitated culture and placing it on a microscope slide with a coverslip. Scan the sample in a regular pattern, using the IOX objective where possible. Organisms can be identified by reference to algae and protozoa identification manuals and pond biology references. Some of the organisms will defy identification. They still need to be included in the species listing even if they are just identified as species A, B, C, etc. The number of species (richness) is what we are primarily concerned with; however, we can also calculate a diversity index by counting the number of each identifiable type and plugging the numbers into the formula for an index such as the Shannon-Weiner index.

To examine the effect of immigration, establish four microcosms as above, each 200 ml in a culture dish. Inoculate each with 1 ml of the pond water inoculum. Maintain the pond water stock culture in a well-lit area for future use or create a new one weekly from the same sources. After a week, and at weekly intervals thereafter, add another ml of inoculum to two dishes, the experimental ones, and leave the other two as controls. After five weeks, take several measured samples from each dish, after agitating them, and examine each under the microscope, as above. Identify the species present and count each to calculate a diversity index. Compare the experimental cultures (with weekly immigrants) with the control cultures.

Original Source

This activity is based on an original exercise by John Cruzan (1988) titled "Teaching Ecology with Microcosms" in *The American Biology Teacher, 50*(4), 226-228, and has been modified by the author specifically for this monograph.

Physiological ecology has contributed much to our understanding of adaptation to the physical environment, both among humans (Ingram, 1975) and other organisms (e.g., Kavaler, 1981; Alsher, 1990). Yet it receives relatively little attention in high school or college-level introductory biology laboratories, probably because most experiments in this area of biology require sophisticated and expensive equipment. The following is a laboratory exercise on acclimation that is simple, reliable, and inexpensive.

Thermal Acclimation in Ectotherms

Based on an original activity by David Westmoreland

Ecological Principles Illustrated

- Adaptation
- Optimality

Introduction

Acclimation is the process by which organisms adjust their cellular and physiological systems to cope with changes in the physical environment. Most organisms have an inherent range of conditions (a range of temperatures, for example) that are optimal for them (i.e., they will stay within this range as long as food and other requirements are met). In nature, however, environmental conditions change frequently. Acclimation is the process by which an organism adjusts its metabolism to cope with a changing environment.

This exercise examines the response of an aquatic ectotherm to changes in water temperature. In such organisms, body temperature is nearly the same as water temperature. If an animal that is acclimated to 20° C water is transferred to 30° C water, then the short-term response is a rise in metabolic rate as its body temperature increases. In most cases, a 10° C increase in environmental temperature will produce a two- to three-fold increase in metabolic rate over a span of hours; the exact magnitude of change is called the organism's Q_{10} (Schmidt Nielsen, 1979). Left in the 30° C environment for a few days, the animal's metabolic rate will decrease gradually until it returns to the previous level. At that point, it has fully acclimated.

Materials

- approximately 60 ramhorn snails (*Helisoma* spp.). These are available at pet stores and biological supply houses. (Other snails will probably work as well, but they have not been tried in this experiment.)
- access to a refrigerator
- 1 tropical fish aquarium heater
- three 5-20 gallon fish aquaria
- 10 vials, lOX the volume of the snails
- equipment necessary to perform a Winkler dissolved O_2 test (Hatch Chemical sells a Micro Winkler unit.)
- 5 rubber bands
- 3 thermometers

Procedure

Step 1: Preparing for the Experiment

In this exercise, ramhorn snails (*Helisoma* spp.) are placed in 10° C, 20° C, and 30° C aquaria and given time to acclimate. Then, the snails are moved between aquaria to contrast the short term and longer term (acclimation) responses to temperature change.

About a week before the experiment is to be done, three aquaria are set up with differing water temperatures; 20° C is near room temperature, and the other temperatures can be reached by refrigerating one aquarium and using tropical fish heaters in the other. About 20 snails are placed in each tank.

Step 2: Practicing the Winkler Test

The metabolic rate of a snail is measured by enclosing the animal in a water-filled vial; an identical vial without the snail is used as a control. The depletion of dissolved oxygen in the treatment vial as compared to the oxygen content of the control vial is a direct measure of metabolic rate in milliliters (ml) of O_2 consumed per hour. Vials with volumes that are about 10 times greater than the volume of a typical snail work well in this test. Within an hour, the snail will deplete the oxygen of the treatment vial to a measurable extent. If snails must be left in the vials overnight, larger vials (about 100 times the volume of the snail) can be used.

To measure dissolved oxygen, a version of the Winkler test with 10 ml water samples that have been drawn into plastic syringes can be used. Details of the method are available in Dolphin (1992) or Drew & Robertson (1974). The Winkler test requires precise technique to be accurate. Thus, students working in groups of two should practice the procedure four or five times before actually performing the test. Each group practices with water samples taken from the same aquarium; usually, their precision improves. In addition, groups may compare their results and note that cold water has a higher dissolved oxygen content than warm water.

Step 3: Setting Up the Experiment

The experimental design is illustrated in Figure 1. There are five treatments; in each, two equal-sized vials are tied together with a rubber band. One vial contains a snail and water from the aquarium where it was housed, and the other contains water only. In Treatments 1 to 3, metabolic rates are measured for snails that are kept in their original conditions. In Treatment 4, snails from the 10° C tank are placed in the 20° C tank; and in Treatment 5, snails are transferred from 30° C to 20° C. In larger classes, transfers from the 20° C tank to the other tanks can also be done.

Students work in teams, with each team carrying out all five treatments. Vials are left in place for one hour, after which the oxygen consumption for each snail is determined. Because it takes about 10 minutes to complete a single run of the Winkler test, some snails are kept in the vials longer than others. To compensate for this bias, students calculate metabolic rates on a per-hour basis. During the hour between setting up the experiment and doing the first Winkler test, the students propose hypotheses and identify the appropriate comparisons for testing them. For example, if the animals have acclimated as expected, the metabolic rates should be about the same for Treatments 1 to 3. Snails that have been transferred to a warmer temperature (Treatment 4) should have higher metabolic rates than those that remained in their original aquaria (Treatment 1). Similarly, snails that were moved to a cooler temperature (Treatment 5) should have lower metabolic rates than those that remained at 30° C (Treatment 3). Teachers may also want to occasionally set up an experiment so that at least one finding is unexpected. Thus, students will be challenged to explain the unexpected result without using the familiar appeal to shoddy laboratory techniques. In this experiment, snails have consistently been found to be unable to acclimate to the 10° C environment. This challenges students to think about their findings and their assumptions in designing the experiment.

Typical Results

Figure 2 shows the results from one run of the experiment in which eight pairs of students participated. The median values show that the snails acclimated in Treatments 2 and 3,

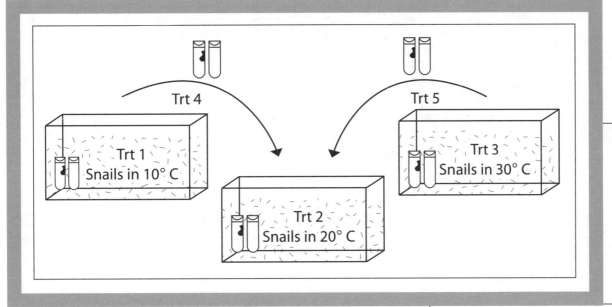

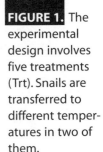

FIGURE 1. The experimental design involves five treatments (Trt). Snails are transferred to different temperatures in two of them.

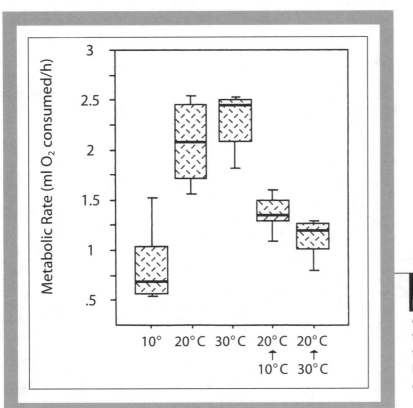

FIGURE 2. Boxplots of the results found by one class. The thick horizontal lines are the medians for each treatment. The shaded boxes enclose the 25th to 75th percentiles, and the vertical lines extend from the 5th to the 95th percentiles.

but not in Treatment 1. Statistical analyses confirm one's visual interpretation of the data: Mann-Whitney U-tests show that Treatments 2 and 3 are not significantly different, while Treatment 1 differs from both of them ($P < 0.05$). To explain this, students usually suggest that the 10° C water temperature is beyond the lower limit for acclimation in this species. Another possibility is that acclimation takes longer when the snails are moved to a cooler temperature than when they are moved to a warmer one, which Schmidt-Nielsen (1979) suggests is a general phenomenon.

The short-term responses to temperature changes are as predicted. Snails moved from the 10° C tank to 20° C experienced a two-time increase in metabolic rate, while those transferred from 30° C to 20° C had a two-fold drop in metabolic rate. Both of these differences are statistically significant ($P < 0.05$).

Discussion

After examining the results of the experiment and attempting to explain anomalous results, the class is asked to speculate on how acclimation is achieved. What changes occur in cells to enable the organism as a whole to cope with the temperature change? The scientific literature indicates that acclimation may be achieved at the cellular level by:

1. Production of a host of enzymes that are more efficient at the new temperature.

2. Keeping the same enzymes but changing their abundances.

Cells in colder climates require a greater number of enzymes if the rate of metabolism is to be constant. Among ectotherms, the second mechanism is most common (Hazel, 1989).

Original Source

This activity has been adapted from an original exercise by David Westmoreland (1994) titled "Thermal Acclimation in Ectotherms" in *The American Biology Teacher, 56*(4), 244-246, and has been modified and reprinted with permission of the publisher.

The following are two exercises designed to help students understand the process of the dispersal of tree seeds by the wind.

Ecological Principles Illustrated

- Dispersal of offspring

Wind Dispersal of Tree Seeds and Fruits

Based on an original activity by James D. Thomson and Paul R. Neal

Introduction

Dispersal of offspring can be an important aspect of the biology of an organism at many levels: colonization of new habitats (MacArthur, 1972), escape from predators and pathogens (Janzen, 1969), and reduction of competition with relatives, to name a few (Howe & Smallwood, 1982). Dispersal seems especially advantageous in temporary habitats, but extremely general evolutionary models suggest that organisms with some capacity for dispersal can always displace nondispersers (Hamilton & May, 1977). For stationary organisms, such as plants and many marine invertebrates, dispersal may be a particularly important determinant of gene flow (Levin, 1981; Levin & Kerster, 1974).

Trees have a variety of dispersal mechanisms; many produce diaspores (the general term for dispersal units, which may technically be fruits, seeds, or other structures) that are adapted for dispersal by the wind. Several studies have shown the importance of these adaptations in the dispersal process (Augspurger, 1986; Augspurger & Franson, 1987; Augspurger & Hogan, 1983; Green, 1980; Guries & Nordheim, 1984). Generally speaking, diaspore characteristics are likely to represent an evolutionary compromise. Seeds that contain more resources for the seedling are more likely to become successfully established but, due to their heavier weight, will not disperse as far. Green (1980), for example, proposes that the seeds of the sugar maple (which grows well in the shade) have a morphology with less dispersal potential than that of the red maple, a more opportunistic, light-requiring species that must "find" forest gaps or clearings to survive.

Diaspore Morphology

Wind-dispersed diaspores fall into several morphological groups (Burrows, 1975; Harper et al., 1970; Ridley, 1930). Each group has a characteristic aerodynamic behavior (rolling, autogyration, undulation, tumbling, etc.) and set of equations that can be used to describe this behavior (Green, 1980; Guries & Nordheim, 1984; McCutchen, 1977; Sheldon & Burrows, 1973). Although many factors may affect the dispersal characteristics of these fruits and seeds (Burrows, 1973; Sharpe & Fields, 1982), most of the apparent adaptations of wind-dispersed diaspores reduce the rate of descent, thereby increasing time aloft. Since the distance a dispersal unit can be carried horizontally is dependent on the time aloft, adaptations reducing the rate of descent will serve to increase dispersal.

Two aerodynamic characteristics of seeds that affect the rate of descent are the mass of the unit and its surface area. The weight of a flattened, wing-like diaspore divided by its area is called "wing-loading." The square root of wingloading has been shown to be highly correlated with the rate of descent (Augspurger, 1986; Green, 1980). A low wing-loading value indicates a slow rate of descent relative to a diaspore with a higher value within a morphological group.

The exercises described here are designed to investigate the properties of winged seeds and fruits. Several types of comparisons are possible. One can use variation occurring naturally among individuals within a species or among different species, or one can manipulate the weight or area of natural or artificial diaspores. Since each morphological group is aerodynamically unique, it is difficult to make interspecific comparisons using only wing-loading measures.

However, diaspores with similar morphologies can be directly compared. For instance, intra-generic comparisons of natural or introduced species of ash (*Fraxinus*), maple (*Acer*), or pine (*Pinus*) would be interesting (and would be feasible in many parts of the temperate zone).

Manipulations

In some species [e.g., *Ailanthus altissima,* the tree-of-heaven (personal observation)], trees may vary in fruit size. Where such variation is not naturally present, or when particular contrasts are desired, diaspores of a single species can be manipulated to change their aerodynamic properties (Figure 1). Some diaspores have asymmetrical wings; for example, the tree-of-heaven has a centrally placed seed in an elongated wing. The two ends of the wing are similarly shaped, but one is flat, while the other is twisted. This twist gives the unit its characteristic roll. Manipulation by removing the twisted end gives a different dispersal behavior than removing the flattened end.

Wing-loading can be manipulated by changing either the weight or the surface area of the dispersal unit. Weight can be added to the diaspore by applying pieces of tape to the area that contains the seed. Additional pieces of tape would simulate even larger seeds. In some diaspores (e.g., tree-of-heaven), all or part of the seed can be removed without significantly changing the exposed surface of the dispersal unit. A change in the surface might change the air flow around the unit, confounding the effect of the weight change. The diaspore's surface area can be manipulated by removing a portion of the wing. Reducing the area will increase the wing-loading, subsequently increasing the rate of descent, and ultimately reducing the dispersal distance.

Diaspores with identical wing-loading properties can have different aerodynamic behaviors (Augspurger & Franson, 1987). The distribution of weight on the wing and the shape of the wing will determine the type of motion during the descent. For example, changing the center of mass from the middle of the diaspore to the edge may change the motion during descent from rolling to spinning.

Artificial Diaspores

Artificial diaspores can also be constructed to examine the effects of the changes in the dispersal unit's mass, area, shape, and symmetry. Stiff paper can be formed into wings of various sizes and shapes and will maintain its shape during the descent. The weight of the diaspore seed can be simulated by affixing weights to this wing.

FIGURE 1. *Ailanthus altissima* diaspores. The group on the left displays intertree variation in size and shape. In the center group, treatments are shown that could be used to examine the effect of wing area and asymmetry. Tape has been added to the group on the right, changing the weight and the distribution of the weight of the diaspore.

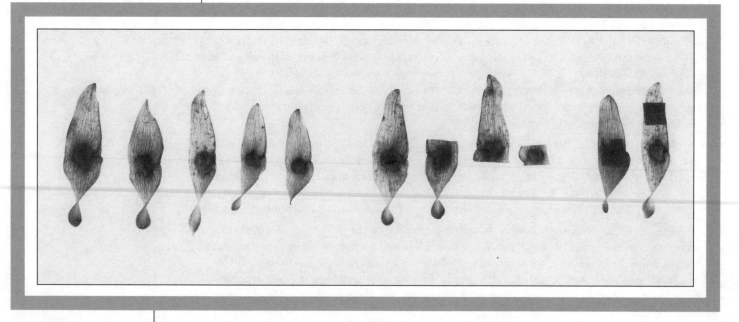

Augspurger and Franson (1987) used thin sheets of paraffin ("Parafilm") folded into small rectangles. The advantage of this method is that sheets of a given size will all have approximately the same weight, and each individual seed need not be weighed.

Marking Diaspore Treatments

Data collection is facilitated by color coding each species or treatment of the dispersal units to be tested. Choose colors that are easily distinguishable from each other and from the landing zone background color. Color coding is accomplished by shaking diaspores in a bag that contains a small amount of powdered fluorescent pigment. Diaspores with these pigments are highly visible in a grass landing zone. Alternatively, quick-drying spray paint could be used to color code the diaspores. Artificial diaspores of each treatment can be constructed of different colored paper.

Laboratory Exercises

The mass and area of seeds or fruits are easily measured and manipulated by students. Additionally, students can construct artificial dispersal units that vary in these properties. From simple calculations of wing-loading, predictions of the rates of descent for each category of dispersal unit can be formulated. After the dispersal units have been collected and prepared, students can release the seeds or fruits in either a natural or laboratory setting, thereby observing the dispersal process. The differences in dispersal distance or time aloft are readily related to the aerodynamic characteristics of the diaspore.

Two types of exercises are (1) determining rates of fall in still air and (2) measuring displacement distances from a release point. The still air exercise is designed to be conducted indoors, while the horizontal wind exercise is conducted outdoors. Each may be used independently to investigate the influence of morphological differences of various dispersal units, or they may be combined for a more complete understanding of the dispersal process.

1. Still Air Exercise: Rate of Descent of Dispersal Units

Rationale

The purpose of this exercise is to determine the rates of descent for diaspores without the influence of horizontal winds and to relate this information to measured differences in their aerodynamic properties. Since diaspores with slower rates of descent will spend more time aloft, they will have the potential to achieve greater dispersal distances (Augspurger, 1986).

Questions or hypotheses can be formulated and tested by students who investigate the role of diaspore morphology in the dispersal process. It is important to keep these questions rather simple. Although both mass and diaspore area are taken into account by wing-loading, it is best to examine one variable at a time (i.e., examine the effect of diaspore weight or area separately, but not both together.). If the question is too complicated, it is difficult to intuitively understand the cause of the differences in rates of descent.

Equipment and Mechanics

The most difficult aspect of this exercise is finding a suitable place to release the diaspores. Ideally, the drop site should allow the diaspores to fall a distance approximately equal to the height of the tree from which they were obtained. Since some diaspores will drift laterally even in draft-free areas, the release point should be above the center of a large landing zone. A large building, such as a school gymnasium, theatrical stage, or auditorium is ideal. The easiest system is to manually release the diaspores from a balcony or catwalk. An alternative release mechanism can be fashioned and attached to a pulley system that can be raised above the landing zone. The area required for the landing zone will depend on the lateral movement of the particular dispersal units being tested.

The area of the diaspores can be determined by tracing the outline of the dispersal unit onto millimeter graph paper and counting the number of intersecting lines within this area. The area of the diaspore will be given in square millimeters. Alternatively, a transparent millimeter grid can be laid over a seed or fruit and the number of intersections can be tallied. Thirdly, the area of an irregularly shaped diaspore can be determined indirectly by tracing the outline of the diaspore on a piece of paper and weighing on a sensitive balance the paper contained inside this outline.

The weight can be converted to an estimate of the area by multiplying this weight by a conversion factor composed of the measured area of a regularly shaped piece of paper divided by its weight.

A balance for weighing the dispersal units, a meter tape to measure the release height, and stopwatches for recording descent time are the only other equipment required to perform this exercise.

Analysis and Discussion

The rate of descent can be calculated as height divided by time. Although the terminal velocity of the diaspore is technically the best descriptor of descent (Green, 1980), this calculated rate provides a reasonable means of comparing various diaspores. The time to reach terminal velocity is a minor portion of the total descent time, if the dispersal units are released from a sufficient height (Augspurger, 1986; Guries & Nordheim, 1984). Since dispersal characteristics of trees are being considered, the time should be an insignificant portion of the seed or fruit's descent period.

Rate of descent can be plotted against the square root of wing-loading for each morphological type of diaspore. For more sophisticated students, morphological types can be compared using a regression analysis. Discussion of the results might center around tradeoffs between the size and number of the seeds and the benefits of achieving greater dispersal distances.

2. Horizontal Wind Exercise: Dispersal Distance

Rationale

Like the exercise described previously, this activity examines the influence of the aerodynamic properties of the diaspore on dispersal potential. The property of interest here is the distance the dispersal unit is laterally displaced from the release point. Of course, the actual distance each seed or fruit travels is subject to the additional variables of the wind's direction, strength, and variability during the period the diaspore is aloft after release from the parent tree. No absolute conclusions can be drawn about the distance a given diaspore will travel. However, comparisons of distances obtained by diaspores of different aerodynamic properties that were released at the same moment will yield relevant information about the dispersal process. The questions and hypotheses are similar to those of the "Still Air Exercise."

Equipment and Mechanics

The optimal site is one where the diaspores are exposed to a wind that blows steadily and where there are no nearby obstructions to cause eddies that might obscure differences in aerodynamic performance. It is also important that the seeds or fruits are free to fall to the ground without striking any objects, such as shrubs or fences, that might obscure differences in dispersal potential. A landing zone of mowed grass, as opposed to pavement, causes the diaspores to stay where they land, rather than blowing along the ground.

A flag-raising mechanism is easily adapted for raising a container of diaspores to any desired height. A line could also be suspended between buildings, trees, or stadium bleachers, and a rope thrown over the line. The container is a plastic bucket with a friction fitting lid. Eyebolts are placed in the lid and the bottom of the bucket. The line of the flagpole is attached to the eyebolt on the bottom of the bucket for hoisting. A second line allows the lid to be pulled off and out of the way (don't let anyone get hit by the falling lid!), allowing the diaspores in the bucket to simultaneously begin their descent. Trial drops of a few dispersal units will help establish the best release height for the actual test. Diaspores should be neither extremely aggregated nor diffused in distribution.

Mapping the exact coordinates of every dispersed diaspore in relation to the release point would provide the most accurate description of the results of the dispersal process. However, since there may be a large variance in the distance traveled by diaspores of a particular morphology and wing-loading, large numbers of each diaspore type may be needed. The mapping process would be extremely tedious, and data analysis would require a computer. A somewhat less demanding variant would be to measure only the radial distance traveled by each diaspore, swinging a measuring tape anchored at the release point.

A more practical method of characterizing dispersal distances is to divide the landing area into zones or quadrats and count the number of each type of diaspore. The sophistication of the students and the type of questions to be answered will influence the type of quadrat design used. To simply compare dispersal distances of diaspores, the landing area can be divided into consecutive circles using meter tapes. Boundaries can be marked with powdered chalk, or one can simply swing the tape to decide on borderline diaspores. Choosing the radii after the release ensures that each zone contains a manageable number of diaspores. Four to six distance categories, chosen to contain roughly equal numbers, should allow good discrimination of different diaspore types.

For more sophisticated analyses of the data, it is better to establish a grid system of smaller square quadrats of equal area. Collecting each diaspore type into separate bags labeled with the quadrat identification and diaspore type is strongly recommended since having a lot of students carrying collections around invites confusion. Diaspores can then be counted immediately or later in the lab.

This exercise can be completed in one long laboratory session or broken into shorter periods. Preparation and manipulation of four treatments of 700 to 1000 *Ailanthus* diaspores required about a half hour for a class of 25. Seventy to 80 percent of the diaspores were recovered from mowed grass, and this yielded more than adequate sample sizes. A trial drop, grid construction, and collection of diaspores from two release exercises required less than two hours.

Analysis and Discussion

The type of statistical analysis depends on the sophistication of the students, the information desired, and the type of quadrat design used. A comparison of the relative dispersal distances for various types or treatments of dispersal units can be analyzed using a chi-square test of independence for data organized into a contingency table. The chi-square test of independence is explained in most elementary statistics texts, such as Walpole (1983), and can be taught in conjunction with this exercise. The null hypothesis is that there will be no difference between the different types of dispersal units in their frequency of distribution in each quadrat. Significant deviation from this expectation will yield a chi-square value greater than the critical value and will indicate which unit has the greater dispersal potential. One advantage of this method of analysis is that it allows the use of the sector quadrat sampling technique that requires much less effort to set up and fewer quadrats.

Though more time-consuming, a grid of equal-area quadrats will allow a better characterization of some additional biologically important parameters. Once diaspores of each type or treatment have been counted for each quadrat, the means and standard errors for three biologically important measures of dispersal — the distance from the drop point, the distance from the centroid of the distribution, and the crowding (a measure of dispersion) — can be calculated. These analyses require knowledge of more advanced statistical procedures not explained here (see Augspurger & Franson, 1987).

Additional Questions for Discussion

1. Many plant species have seeds that germinate best in certain microhabitats. Can you imagine any ways in which the morphology of wind-dispersed diaspores might promote selective dispersal to particular microhabitats?

2. Contrast wind dispersal with dispersal by birds or bats. Fleshy fruits that attract vertebrates would seem to be more expensive to make than winged seeds — are there compensating advantages?

3. We have discussed only primary dispersal, or dispersal from the parent to the landing point. Consider situations in which secondary dispersal may be important as well — think of the city tree *Ailanthus,* for example, that often germinates in pavement cracks or storm sewers.

4. Consider seasonal timing of dispersal. Are some seasons more favorable than others? Consider winter release in terms of Question 3. During what seasons do wind-dispersed species in your area release their seeds?

5. How much force is required to separate a diaspore for its point of attachment? What are the consequences for dispersal?

Acknowledgment

These exercises were inspired by the research work of Carol Augspurger and, to a lesser extent, by an exercise designed by R.C. Plowright on the aerodynamics of maple samaras. The authors especially appreciate Augspurger's encouragement. An anonymous reviewer provided useful comments.

Original Source

This activity is based on an exercise by J.D. Thomson and P.R. Neal (1989) titled "Wind Dispersal of Tree Seeds & Fruits" in *The American Biology Teacher, 51*(8), 482-486, and is modified and reprinted with permission of the publisher.

Forests or even small woodlots can provide an excellent site for demonstrating succession. The great advantage of using trees is the easy determination of their ages. The most accurate way to recognize the age of a tree is to use an increment borer that removes a small sample from the outside to the center of the tree. By counting the rings of this sample and estimating additional years of development before the tree grew to the height from which the sample was taken, the age of the tree is determined. Companies that supply specialized equipment to foresters and some scientific supply companies sell increment borers. Students can sometimes also estimate the age of a tree without using any equipment. They may assume that each major node of branches on the stems of young pine trees represents one year. By counting these nodes and adding two or three years for the development of the seedling, the age of the tree is reasonably determined.

Teaching Succession in a Forest Ecosystem

Based on an original activity by David R. Stronck

Ecological Principles Illustrated

- Succession

Materials

- increment borer (optional)
- tape measure
- protractor
- soda straw
- string
- metal washer

Procedure

1. In order to understand the dynamics of a forest, it is not necessary to determine the age of more than a few samples. Trees of similar diameters in approximately the same circumstances of available light and water may be assumed to have the same ages. Phillips (1959) explained that the diameter of a tree may be used as a rough indication of its age. He notes that one may tentatively conclude that species "B" is replacing species "A" if the following conditions exist in a forest: species "A" is represented by 100 trees of an average diameter of 24 inches and by 20 trees of an average diameter of 12 inches, while species "B" is represented by 20 trees of a diameter of 24 inches and by 100 trees of 12 inches. These data imply that species "B" has rather recently invaded the area and now has the many young trees that will gradually dominate the forest.

2. For additional evidence of succession, students should also count seedlings. Another reasonable assumption is the following: if the seedlings are the same as the dominant trees, the forest has reached climax (i.e., the populations of each species are relatively stabilized). If the seedlings are mostly from a species that has few mature individuals in the area, then the process of succession is continuing.

3. A very inexpensive tape measure allows students to measure the circumference of trees. The diameters are recognized when these circumferences are divided by π (3.14). Although professional timber cruisers use sophisticated sighting instruments to measure quickly the diameters of trees, such techniques seem unnecessary for beginning students. Students can probably reach many correct conclusions about the dynamics of forests by using tape measures as their only type of equipment.

Sample Field Studies

The following tables represent data gathered and interpretations made previously by students in five areas local to their school. Each study plot was one-fifth of an acre and had a radius of 52.7 feet. The five plots were selected to provide different stages in the succession by which Douglas fir tends to replace Oregon white oak. The counts of the trees and the diameters of the trees at their bases are given in Tables 1 through 5. The five plots have suffered little from human disturbance in recent years.

Table 1 describes the trees found in the first plot. All of these trees are relatively young. Oak seedlings and young trees are numerous. The Douglas fir is present but is relatively far from a source of seeds. The students interpreted the plot as a prairie recently released to forestation. Clear cutting of an earlier forest or the end of grazing on the plot are hypotheses to explain why trees did not make an earlier invasion of this area.

Table 2 presents data for the second plot that is dominated by Oregon white oak. Nevertheless, there is a dense understory of young Douglas fir trees that have a good seed source from large mature trees on the crest of a nearby ridge. The largest Douglas fir is only 25 years old. Because oak seedlings are few, the plot was interpreted as an example of Douglas fir succeeding Oregon white oak.

Table 3 for the third plot shows almost equal numbers of Douglas fir and Oregon white oak. In this rather dense, mature stand, many of the large oaks are dead. The living oaks are unusually tall poles with relatively few leaves compared to oaks in the first two plots. The living oaks of Plot 3 often have many conks (the shelf-shaped bracket fungus or basidiocarp of *Fomes applanatus*); conks indicate decay and poor health in the trees. In this third plot, an oak of 10 inches in diameter is 70 feet high. The tallest tree in the plot is a Douglas fir of 96 feet in height, with a diameter of 20 inches and an age of 52 years. Throughout this third plot, the Douglas fir trees are usually much taller than the oaks and more successful in reaching for the sunlight. Given the same conditions, the Douglas fir tends to grow taller more quickly than the oak and, therefore, dominates a mixed stand of the two species.

Another indication of the dominance of the Douglas fir in the third plot is the fact that oak seedlings are absent, while Douglas fir seedlings are numerous. The Douglas fir is well represented in many age classes. Especially because the oaks are dying in the shade of the Douglas fir trees, this plot is interpreted as one where the Douglas fir will soon totally replace the oaks.

A student can measure the height of a tree by using these inexpensive materials: a protractor, a soda straw, a metal washer tied to a string, and a tape measure. The soda straw is taped to the straight edge of the protractor. By looking through the soda straw, the student sees the

TABLE 1. Diameters of bases of trees in Plot One.

| | **Number of Trees** | | | |
Diameter in inches	Douglas fir living	Douglas fir dead	White oak living	White oak dead
1-2.9	3	2	4	7
3-4.9	2		9	3
5-6.9	3		9	1
7-8.9			14	
9-10.9			15	
11-14.9			2	
15-18.9			2	
Totals	8	2	55	11

	Number of Trees			
Diameter in inches	Douglas fir living	Douglas fir dead	White oak living	White oak dead
1-2.9	63		4	11
3-4.9	12		27	4
5-6.9	3		31	11
7-8.9			19	
9-10.9			5	
11-14.9			5	
Totals	78	0	91	26

TABLE 2. Diameters of bases of trees in Plot Two.

	Number of Trees			
Diameter in inches	Douglas fir living	Douglas fir dead	White oak living	White oak dead
1-2.9	19	6		2
3-4.9	5	2		6
5-6.9	3		5	8
7-8.9	5		6	8
9-10.9	3		7	3
11-14.9	2		5	
15-18.9	4			
19-22.9	3			
Totals	44	8	23	27

TABLE 3. Diameters of bases of trees in Plot Three.

top of the tree. Attached to the middle of the straight edge of the protractor is a string with a metal washer. The student walks to the distance from the tree where the string hangs over the 45° mark of the protractor. This place is one corner of a right triangle; the distance from this place to the base of the tree equals the height of the tree. By using a tape measure, the student observes the distance from the place he/she is standing to the base of the tree.

Table 4 demonstrates that the fourth plot is dominated by a few large, mature trees. One Douglas fir has a diameter of 42 inches, a height of 130 feet, and an age of 70 years. Some of the living oaks in this same plot are 90 years old. The mature Douglas fir trees shade most of this plot, which contains the fallen trunks of many dead oaks, mostly from 3 to 7 inches in diameter. These fallen oaks are not counted or recorded in the table, but they are included as evidence for interpretation that the plot is a more advanced stage of Douglas fir replacing Oregon white oak.

Table 5 is for the fifth and final plot. This is the only plot lacking any living oak trees.

Seedlings of both species are absent in this dense stand of crowded Douglas fir trees. Most of these trees have a diameter of approximately 17 inches and an age of 52 years. The plot was interpreted as a place released from grazing or fire at least 53 years ago. The area was then well seeded by both oak and Douglas fir. The Douglas fir has been more successful in competing for sunlight and now has totally eliminated the rival species. This plot seems to show the end of a growth race between two species of trees.

TABLE 4. Diameters of bases of trees in Plot Four.

Diameter in inches	Number of Trees			
	Douglas fir living	Douglas fir dead	White oak living	White oak dead
1-2.9	2	2		1
3-4.9	3		1	2
5-6.9			2	2
7-8.9	2		2	3
9-10.9	1		1	
11-14.9	2			
15-18.9	3			
19-22.9	4			
26	1			
42	2			
Totals	20	2	6	8

TABLE 5. Diameters of bases of trees in Plot Five.

Diameter in inches	Number of Trees			
	Douglas fir living	Douglas fir dead	White oak living	White oak dead
1-2.9				4
3-4.9		1		3
5-6.9	2	1		6
7-8.9	2			5
9-10.9	1			5
11-14.9	4			
15-18.9	12			
19-22.9	2			
24	1			
Totals	24	2	0	23

Conclusion

The plot studies have been described in some detail to suggest possible conclusions that students can make from considering forests of mixed species. Wherever stands of trees are available, students may be challenged to make similar interpretations. Some students may wish to search historical records to show the validity of their interpretations. The ability to interpret the appearance of a forest as it looked many years ago is a very satisfying experience to most students. Such interpretations also suggest predicting the future composition of the undisturbed forest within the next 50 years. This study should persuade students never again to view a forest as a static, ageless thing. A forest is a dynamic, complex, and challenging ecosystem that often illustrates well the patterns of succession.

Original Source

This activity has been adapted from an original exercise by David R. Stronck (1982) titled "Teaching Succession with Forests" in *The American Biology Teacher,* 44(1), 44-47 & 65, and has been modified and reprinted with permission of the publisher.

This exercise is designed to tie together two subjects usually taught separately — plant structure and function and ecology — by using a California fire-evolved ecosystem. The laboratory exercise simulates natural conditions of the California chaparral where fires may be relatively frequent, summers are hot and dry, and winters are mild and wet.

This activity requires 8 to 10 weeks. Students will test several hypotheses to seek to explain why some California chaparral seeds only germinate (or germinate best) after a fire has burned through the surrounding chaparral.

Ecological Principles Illustrated

- Abiotic factors
- Fire ecology

Introduction

Plant species have evolved different life histories and germination behaviors as their environments dictate. Dormancy and germination patterns have been correlated with seed structural parameters, such as seed size, thickness of seed coat, and type of seed coat (Atwater, 1980; Taylorson & Hendricks, 1977). In general, germination is blocked by seed morphology and triggered by the environment (Amen, 1968).

While some plants appear to require little more to germinate than oxygen, water, and the right temperature (e.g., radish), others have more rigid requirements dictated by their environments. This lab focuses on fire annuals and shrubs of California chaparral but can be adapted to any hard-to-germinate plants for which the ecological conditions are known or surmised.

Mature California chaparral consists mainly of small to large shrubs, such as sage, chamiso, California lilac, and sumac. Few herbaceous wildflowers bloom in the spring. By contrast, in the first growing season after a fire, burned areas exhibit a riot of colors from up to 200 recorded species of wildflowers (Keeley & Keeley, 1987). The variety and amount of flowers, however, taper off gradually each succeeding year, and eventually wildflowers seemingly disappear, not to bloom again for many years until the next fire. These annuals are termed "fire annuals" because of this behavior (Keeley & Keeley, 1987). Other chaparral plants also have seeds that germinate only after a fire has burned the canopy (Keeley et al., 1985).

The seeds of these chaparral plants lie dormant in the soil and do not germinate except under conditions usually present after a fire. Variables created by a fire include:

1. The heat from a fire.

2. The charred wood left on the ground after a fire.

3. Greater light intensity that would reach seeds once the canopy has burned.

(Keeley et al., 1985; Keeley, 1987; Keeley & Keeley, 1987)

Germination is marked by rapid uptake of water, but in these plants, the presence of soil moisture is not enough to trigger germination. Two hypotheses have been presented to explain the mechanisms that produce seed germination after fires:

1. Seeds are chemically inhibited by substances produced in mature chaparral shrubs, and these chemicals are removed by fire.

2. Seeds receive some stimulus from the fire itself (Keeley et al., 1985).

Both of these hypotheses can be tested in the laboratory. Since better evidence exists for the second hypothesis, this exercise concentrates on the various effects of the fire itself.

Each group will test two or three species. As a control for the germination technique, one group will test an easy-to-germinate species, such as radish, for each of the germination conditions. At the completion of the laboratory, each group will share its results with the class and will write up the lab for all species tested by the class.

Materials

- 150 to 250 seeds of each species (see Table 1) to be tested

- petri dishes - 1 per tested variable for each species

- potting soil (Gro-lite™ recommended) sifted through 1/16" (2 mm) wire mesh

- oven (accurate up to 200° C)

- wooden dowels (balsa or birch) or small branches of chamiso (*Adenostema fasciculatum*) that have been charred (do not burn to ash) and then finely ground to a powder. (Activated charcoal will not work. If a mill is not available to grind the wood, soak the charred wood in water for 24 to 48 hours and use this extract to water the soil.)

- plastic bags large enough to hold a petri dish

- tape to cover petri dishes

- refrigerator

TABLE 1.
Germination requirements for common California plants.

SCIENTIFIC NAME	COMMON NAME	GERMINATION REQUIREMENTS
Antirrhinum coulterianum	white snapdragon	charate, light
Camissonia californica	camas	charate
Ceanothus integerrimus	deer brush	heat, darkness
Ceanothus megacarpus	buckthorn	heat, charate
Emmenanthe penduliflora	whispering bells	charate
Penstemon spectabilis	penstemon	charate
Phacelia grandiflora	phacelia	charate, no heat
Romneya trichocalyx	matilija poppy	heat and charate; germinate on filter paper, not soil

Sample Procedure

Tell students they will be testing the following treatments of seeds — heat (80° C for 30 minutes or 120° C for five minutes), light, and charred wood (hereafter called *charate*). By testing charate against a commercial fertilizer or ashed wood, charate's effects can be further explored to demonstrate that it is not an inorganic fertilizer.

Seeds are finicky in other ways. Some will require a period of cold treatment, and one to two months in a refrigerator will be necessary. Also, all seeds from a species are not alike. One subpopulation will germinate easily without heat or charate; whereas, another will germinate until at least a year after seed fall. The students' job is to try to determine the particular germination requirements for a particular species and relate what happens in the lab to what happens in nature.

Depending on the seed size and quantity available, there will be 10 to 20 seeds per dish for each species.

1. Treat batches of half of the seeds as instructed: heat (80° C for 30 minutes or 120° C for 5 minutes). Do not heat the other half (control for the effect of heat).

2. Fill 8 dishes about half full with moist potting soil (or use dry soil and add a wetting agent to the water in Step 5). Label each dish with species, number of seeds, and treatment. See Table 2 for treatments.

3. Counting the number of seeds sown, sow heat-treated and nonheat-treated seeds each into 4 dishes.

4. Add 0.25 to 0.50 g charate to half the heat-treated and nonheat-treated dishes (dishes without control for the effect of charate).

5. Add water to each dish, adding about 5 to 10 ml (add about 20 ml water if soil was dry at the start).

6. Seal dishes with tape and place in plastic bags to prevent drying out. Place dishes in refrigerator (about 4° C) for 4 to 6 weeks.

7. Every 2 weeks, remove and count any seedlings. Add water if necessary to prevent drying out.

8. After cold incubation, remove dishes and incubate them at room temperature an additional 4 weeks. Place 1 dish with each treatment in the dark and count in darkness (control for the effects of light). To count in darkness, illuminate seeds with green light only. Incubate the rest in light. Count and remove seedlings every week. Add water as necessary.

9. Show results for each species in a table like the one shown in Table 1.

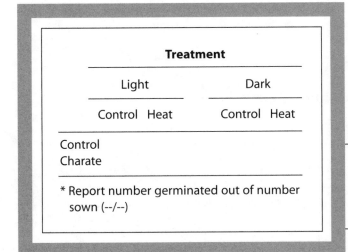

	Treatment			
	Light		Dark	
	Control	Heat	Control	Heat
Control				
Charate				

* Report number germinated out of number sown (--/--)

TABLE 2.
Germination of
(species tested*).

Discussion and Analysis

1. Write one paragraph identifying which species showed the greatest germination under each condition (heat vs. no heat, light vs. dark, charate vs. no charate, and combinations of these). Discuss the conditions that significantly increase or decrease germination rate over another related condition.

(Note: Judge the level of statistical analysis appropriate to your students. This may be a good opportunity to introduce some statistical analysis.)

2. Explain how heat treatment differs from charate treatment in its effects on the seed.

(Heat is a mechanical treatment. Heat may crack the seed coat allowing germination. Charate represents a chemical treatment. Some chemical produced by burned cell walls cues the seed to germinate.)

3. Describe what real life conditions would be necessary for plants whose seeds germinate under the following lab conditions:

(a) Seeds incubated in a refrigerator for 2 months, then at room temperature for 2 weeks. *(Winter chilling followed by spring warmth.)*

(b) Seeds treated for 24 hours with hydrochloric acid, then sown and watered. *(Passage through an animal digestive tract, then defecation.)*

(c) Seeds germinate in light but not dark. *(Plant requires full or partial sunlight – seeds germinate if they fall on open ground with no larger plants around.)*

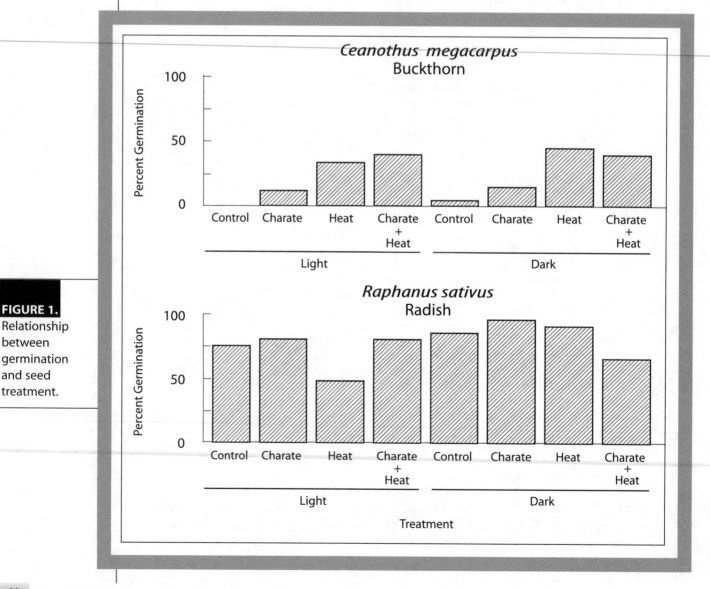

FIGURE 1.
Relationship between germination and seed treatment.

(d) Seeds germinate in light or will germinate in dark plus charate added. (*Plant requires full or partial sunlight. Once a seed is buried, charate signals that plants above have burned, and open ground exists.*)

(e) Seeds germinate after being heated. (*Plant requires full or partial sunlight. Heating seed signals that surrounding plants have been burned.*)

Be aware that some species will not germinate according to expected conditions. Occasionally, some species do not germinate at all. This may be because you have a subpopulation of seeds that were too old or too fresh. Even botanists have problems germinating seeds on occasion.

For this reason, students must test a variety of species and combine results for their lab report. Remind them that they are experimenting on organisms, and organisms do not always behave as we expect.

Figure 1 shows results obtained for radish and buckthorn in one experiment. A good reference for plants is Emery (1964), which describes how to germinate many hard-to-germinate species without regard to ecological conditions. To identify what your plants would look like if you were to grow them to maturity, see Munz's (1961, 1962, 1963 & 1964) excellent series on wildflowers. All seeds and books are available by mail. If other local plants are preferred, call a local arboretum and ask for information about fire-evolved ecosystems or hard-to-germinate species in your area of the country.

Acknowledgments

The authors gratefully acknowledge the National Science Foundation — Advances in Biological Science Fellowship program, Stephen B. Oppenheimer, and Dorothy Moot for providing assistance and support to Nancy L.C. Steele to develop this activity for high school students.

Original Source

This activity has been adapted from an original exercise by Nancy L.C. Steele and Jon E. Keeley (1991) titled "Chaparral & Fire Ecology: Role of Fire in Seed Germination" in *The American Biology Teacher, 53*(7), 432-435, and has been modified and reprinted with permission of the publisher.

Examining Bacterial Succession in Milk

Based on an original activity by
Alan L. Gillen and
Robert P. Williams

This investigation shows how pasteurized milk acts as a growth medium for bacteria and provides a wonderful ecosystem for scientific inquiry. The unit is designed to make the unseen world of microbes relevant to the average high school student. Many of the activities also can be adapted to middle schools. The laboratory uses materials that should be readily available at most middle or high schools. Materials and supplies required for this activity are relatively inexpensive. All activities in the unit are designed to challenge the students to think of the unseen as relevant to their own world.

Upon completion of the laboratory unit, students will be able to measure the pH of milk, observe and describe visible changes in milk, grow bacteria on nutrient agar plates, and identify bacteria growing in milk (by shape).

Ecological Principles Illustrated

- Succession

Introduction

Bacteria are important organisms to study because they are found everywhere, from hot springs to polar regions and from ocean depths to mountaintops. Since milk is an ideal medium for the growth of bacteria, it can be used to study microorganisms. Laboratory exercises developed to study bacteria can both improve student knowledge of microorganisms essential to our well being and improve students' inquiry skills.

There is probably no other food that is so important to man as milk. Milk is an essential form of nutrition in which bacteria have an important role. Most bacteria are killed in milk through pasteurization; however, some bacteria remain (Oram et al., 1983). This explains why even unopened milk in the refrigerator will soon spoil. Moreover, bacteria are used in many processes in the dairy industry. Products such as buttermilk, yogurt, sour cream, and some cheeses are usually made commercially by adding bacteria to milk (Alcamo, 1987). The changes of milk into other products are, in fact, types of milk spoilage.

Milk spoilage under proper conditions can lead to the formation of cheese. Nevertheless, the more common instance of milk spoilage often takes place in the kitchen refrigerator or in the dairy case at the supermarket. Bacteria multiply slowly and ferment lactose sugars in the milk into acid, thereby "spoiling" the milk (Alcamo, 1987).

Materials

- whole pasteurized milk
- skim milk
- chocolate milk
- buttermilk
- nutrient agar
- pH paper or pH probe
- compound microscope
- crystal violet
- cotton swabs or inoculating needles
- graph paper, data paper
- petri plates
- 250-ml beakers
- 250-ml Erlenmeyer flasks
- microslides
- gram stain kit (optional)

Procedure

1. Divide the class into groups of four students. Assign each group a particular type of milk and temperature for bacterial growth as follows:

   I - Whole milk, room temp. (25° C)

   II - Whole milk, refrigerator temp. (4° C)

   III - Whole milk, incubator temp. (37° C)

   IV - Whole milk boiled (100° C), then cooled to room temp. (25° C)

   V - Skim milk, room temp. (25° C)

   VI - Buttermilk, room temp. (25° C)

   VII - Chocolate milk, room temp. (25° C)

2. Place 125 ml of each type of milk assigned to the group in an Erlenmeyer flask.

3. Record daily observations of the milk with respect to date, temperature, pH, odor, color, and growth of bacterial colonies on agar plates on laboratory data sheets. As observations are made, students should pay particular attention to physical changes in the milk's composition and record any odors, particles, "growths," or new liquids forming in the milk.

4. Using a pH probe or pH paper, record the pH of milk daily. When using the pH probe, rinse the probe in distilled water between readings, and contamination will be so minimal as to not affect results. At the end of the experiment, graph the pH record, with pH on the Y-axis and time (days) on the X-axis. The experiment should be conducted over 10 to 14 days to see the range of changes in the milk.

5. Record the temperature using a Celsius thermometer.

6. Use cotton swabs or inoculating loops to transfer milk (some with bacteria) to petri dishes containing agar to grow bacteria. Count the number of colonies growing on the petri dish. This number will give a relative value of the amount of bacterial growth and is not meant to be quantitative.

7. Use a simple crystal violet stain or gram stain on the bacteria to help identify shapes of bacteria. Identify the bacteria as coccus, bacillus, or spirillum using a compound microscope with an oil immersion lens, if available. To perform a simple stain, a student places a small amount of bacteria in a droplet of water on a glass slide and dries the slide in air. Next, the slide is passed briefly through a flame in a process called "heat fixing." The slide is then flooded with crystal violet or methylene blue for about two minutes, washed with water, and blotted dry.

   A technique for advanced high school students is the gram stain. This technique differentiates bacteria into two groups – gram-positive and gram-negative (Alcamo, 1987). The procedure is described in most general microbiology textbooks (i.e., Alcamo, 1987 or Nester et al., 1978).

8. After the activity is completed, students should record their observations on a data table and graph the pH of milk through time (Figure 1). Observations should include the day and date experiment, descriptions of milk changes, temperature, pH, odor of the milk, description of bacterial colonies grown on agar in petri plates, and bacterial shape. A sample of such data is shown in Table 1 on page 49.

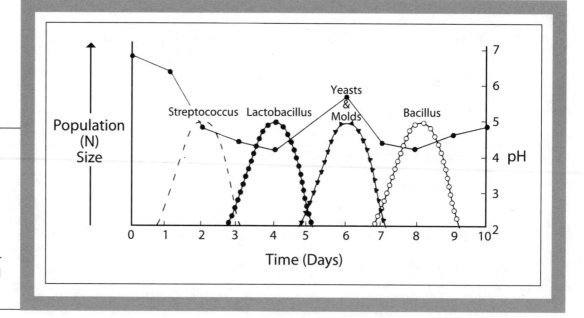

Questions for Discussion

A wide range of questions could be asked to help students make sense of this laboratory. Examples of questions that might be asked include the following:

1. What is pasteurization? Does pasteurization kill all the bacteria in milk? If not, what bacteria remain?

2. List three types of bacteria based on shape. Would you expect to find any of these in milk? Explain.

3. What is coagulation? At what time does it begin to occur at room temperature as milk changes? At what time does it occur at incubator and refrigerator temperatures?

4. What are four conditions for bacterial growth? Of these requirements for bacterial growth, which is naturally changed when you place milk in the refrigerator or incubator?

5. How do the results observed at room temperature compare with the results when milk is kept in the refrigerator? What advantage is there to keeping milk or other foods under refrigeration? Why?

6. Which milk changes the quickest? The slowest?

7. Of what benefit to the food industry is changed milk?

8. How long does it take for milk to change at room temperature? At refrigerated temperature?

9. Examine your pH graph. What is the relationship of milk pH to time (days)?

10. Look at your data and draw conclusions with respect to relationships between pH, temperature, types of milk, and time. For example, compare type of milk (whole vs. skim milk) or temperature ranges (refrigerated vs. room temperature).

Milk Specimen: Whole pasteurized, room temperature						Name: Jane Doe
Day	Observations Noted	Temp. (°C)	pH	Odor	Color	Bacteria Colonies Shapes & Gram Stain
0	normal milk color	11	6.7	fresh	solid white	none
1	little change	24	6.4	slight	white	in all quadrants/rods/ gram-positive
2	separation; solids and liquids	23	4.8	mild	variable white	in all quadrants/cocci and rods/gram-positive
3	coagulation	23	4.4	mild	white & dry	small colonies all quadrants/ cocci & rods/gram-negative
4	heavy coagulation	22	4.2	mild	solid white	no observation
5	like cottage cheese	24	5.1	sour	creamy white/ yellow liquid	in 3 quadrants/mixed-size cocci & rods/gram-negative
6	very chunky, like cottage cheese	23	5.7	mild	solid white/ dirty liquid	1 quadrant filled/cocci/ gram-negative
7	chunky, white, separation	24	4.4	mild	bright white	in all quadrants/cocci and rods/ gram-positive
8	chunky, white	24	4.3	mild	bright white	in all quadrants/rods, gram-negative/cocci and rods, gram-positive
9	chunky, white	24	4.9	mild	creamy white	in all quadrants/cocci/gram-positive
10	chunky, white	24	4.9	mild	creamy white	in all quadrants/cocci/ gram-positive/many yeast cells

TABLE 1. Data sheet for changes in milk.

Discussion

The post-laboratory discussion is an excellent opportunity to solidify students' knowledge of the bacteria they have studied. Go over the questions shown in the previous section that were prepared to guide students' thinking in the laboratory.

In the post-laboratory, questions should be asked and discussed, and conclusions should be drawn. The student should conclude that there is order in nature from the observation of the ecological succession of microbes. The ecological succession of microorganisms in unpasteurized milk was discussed by Nester (1978). The succession of microbes in pasteurized milk follows a similar sequence.

In milk, the changing conditions bring about an ordered and predicted succession of microorganisms: first, streptococci; then a second bacterium, lactobacilli; then a third group of microorganisms, such as yeasts and molds; and finally *Bacillus* species. This sequence of changes is due to a changing chemical environment produced by the metabolic processes of the preceding microorganisms.

Streptococci break down the milk sugar, lactose, to lactic acid. The bacteria produce so much acid that they eventually inhibit their own growth and make the milk ideal for lactobacilli growth. Lactobacilli multiply in this acidic environment and metabolize the rest of the lactose into more lactic acid until their growth is also inhibited by too much acid. Lactic acid sours the milk and curdles protein. Yeasts and molds grow well in this acidic environment and metabolize acid into nonacidic products.

Finally, *Bacillus* species multiply in the environment where the only nutrient available is protein. *Bacillus* species metabolize protein into ammonia products, and the pH rises (Figure 1). Also, *Bacillus* species excrete proteolytic enzymes that digest the remaining protein in milk (Nester et al., 1978). The odor of milk spoilage becomes apparent once this change has occurred.

Thus, milk pH goes through a succession of changes with time, first due to fermentation and then due to putrefaction. These changes were brought about by microorganisms which themselves have undergone a succession in their dominant population.

Another conclusion that could be drawn by the student is that cooling (refrigeration) retards but does not halt bacterial growth. This fact is evident from data tables and/or pH graphs. The milk at room temperature spoils in a matter of 1 to 2 days; whereas, the milk kept at refrigerated temperature may keep for 4 to 10 days before changing.

Answers to Post-Laboratory Questions

1. Pasteurization is the heating to 163° to 165° C or 170° C of a substance to kill bacteria. After heating the substance, it is rapidly cooled. No, the harmful bacteria are killed, but other bacteria remain. Bacteria that are heat resistant are left in milk. Particularly resistant are the species of *Bacillus* that produce endospores.

2. (a) cocci, (b) bacilli, (c) spirillum. You would expect to find cocci and bacilli in milk.

3. Coagulation is the clotting of liquid milk to form a semisolid. It occurs in milk at room temperature after about 3 days. It occurs within 1 day in the incubator and after 7 to 10 days in the refrigerator.

4. (a) temperature, moisture, nutrients, and proper atmosphere (oxygen),
   (b) temperature.

5. Milk kept at room temperature spoils in 2 to 3 days and, at refrigerator temperature, in 7 to 10 days.

6. Quickest to spoil - buttermilk. Slowest to spoil - refrigerated whole milk.

7. Manufacture of yogurt, cheeses, butter, and many other dairy products.

8. It takes 2 to 3 days for milk to spoil at room temperature and 7 to 10 days to spoil at refrigerated temperature.

9. The pH decreases through time (overall trend).

10. Conclusions. Answers will vary, but some conclusions that may be included are:

   (a) Cooling retards bacterial growth in milk.

   (b) The pH drops due to bacterial metabolism of lactose to lactic acid.

   (c) There is a predictable succession of microorganisms in milk due to changing environmental conditions.

Acknowledgments

Development of this lab was supported by the Houston Mathematics and Science Improvement Consortium (HMSIC) and funded through the National Science Foundation Grant #MDR-8319912 to Baylor College of Medicine. The authors also wish to note their appreciation to all the students who worked with them, especially Phan Duong, who did many of the trial experiments and helped in the preparation of the manuscript.

Original Source

This activity is based on an exercise by Alan L. Gillen and Robert P. Williams (1988) titled "Pasteurized Milk as an Ecological System for Bacteria" in *The American Biology Teacher*, 50(5), 279-282, and is modified and reprinted with permission of the publisher.

Measuring Discharge and Materials Transport in Stream Ecosystems

Based on an original activity by Frank T. Kuserk

Students enjoy this exercise because it gives them an opportunity to use a sophisticated but inexpensive hydrological instrument in an actual field situation. After collecting their data, the students proceed through a series of calculations and arithmetic conversions that challenge their mathematical abilities. The end result is a clearer understanding of the principles and methods used in watershed ecology.

Ecological Principles Illustrated

- Watershed ecology
- Materials transport
- Abiotic factors

Introduction

The transport of materials within and through ecosystems is an important topic covered in most introductory courses. Due to their complexity and the limitations of time, however, field exercises demonstrating cycling principles and techniques are often not included in such courses. Since streams are constant, rather steady conduits for matter through watersheds, measuring materials flux in them can be easily used to illustrate how these substances move in nature.

Flux is defined as the amount of matter passing a given stream transect in a given period of time. By measuring the fluxes of some material at two or more sites along a stream, it is possible to determine whether it is acting as a source or a sink for that element or compound. By performing these measurements at several points in the stream system, a materials budget for the watershed can be constructed (Lock & Williams, 1981).

The fluxes of many ecologically important materials, such as dissolved organic compound (DOC) and particulate organic carbon (POC), nitrate, phosphate, ammonia, silt, etc., can be measured by determining the concentrations of the substance in the water and the stream discharges (volume of water flowing past a given point per time period) at various sites along a reach. The concentrations of these and other materials can be determined by using standard chemical procedures (American Public Health Association, 1985) or commercial water analysis kits. Discharges at several points along a small stream can be measured by a class in 3 to 4 hours with a small current meter (see Figure 1), a 25-meter tape, a meter stick, and a stopwatch.

Materials

- current meter
- stopwatch
- 25-meter tape
- meter stick

Procedure

Measuring Stream Discharge

Calculating discharge requires knowing the velocity and the cross sectional area of a stream transect. A simple, although inexact way to estimate velocity is to determine the time it takes for a floating object to cover a known distance. Since velocity differs greatly across a stream due to frictional resistance and the eddies, pools, and rapids associated with streambed morphology, a better velocity estimate can be obtained by dividing the transect into smaller segments and estimating water velocities at several horizontal and vertical points (Gregory & Walling, 1973). Figure 2 illustrates a recommended velocity measurement plan for a typical stream.

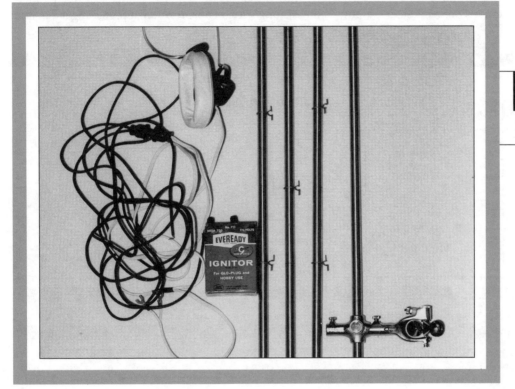

FIGURE 1. Pygmy-type current meter.

When placed in a stream, the meter acts much like a wind anemometer. For each revolution of the spinning cups, a click is produced that can be heard through the headset. For this model, velocity in m/min equals 0.3 times the number of clicks/min.

A team of two students assembles and places the meter at the desired location and depth in the stream. One student, wearing the headset, counts the number of clicks in one minute. The second student records the velocity data and measures the depth of the stream at each one-meter interval of the transect. This technique works best for streams in which the depth of flow exceeds 30 cm and velocity exceeds 5 m/min.

Estimates of discharge in each transect segment are calculated from the following (also see Figure 3):

Segment discharge = (m³/min)

$$\frac{V_1 + V_2}{2} \quad \frac{D_1 + D_2}{2}(B)$$

where:

1. V_1 and V_2 are the mean velocities in m/min at any two adjacent verticals along the transect.

2. D_1 and D_2 are the stream depths in meters at the two adjacent verticals.

3. B is the horizontal distance in meters between the two adjacent verticals.

Discharge estimates of the two end segments are made by assuming that they are triangles. Total stream discharge is then determined by summing the individual segment discharges.

Calculating Materials Flux

Determining materials flux is simply a matter of multiplying the concentration of the material in the water times the total stream discharge at the site. Since concentration is generally measured as units of mass per liter or milliliter, and discharge is expressed as m3/min, some arithmetic conversions need to be done.

The only information provided to the students is that one cubic centimeter of water equals approximately one milliliter. Since they are dealing with a cubic relationship, making a diagram

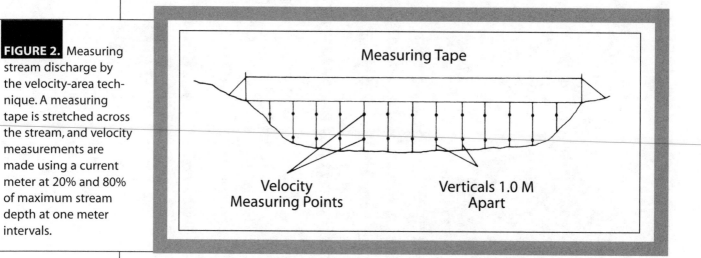

FIGURE 2. Measuring stream discharge by the velocity-area technique. A measuring tape is stretched across the stream, and velocity measurements are made using a current meter at 20% and 80% of maximum stream depth at one meter intervals.

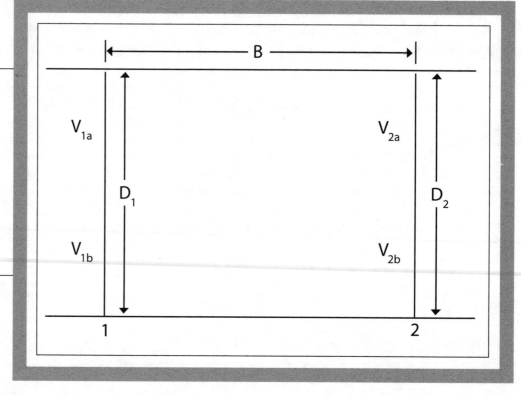

FIGURE 3. Mean-section method of calculating segment discharge. V_{1a}, V_{1b}, V_{2a} and V_{2b} are velocity measurements at verticals 1 and 2; D_1 and D_2 are stream depths at verticals 1 and 2; B is the horizontal distance between verticals 1 and 2.

to determine how many cubic centimeters are in one cubic meter (answer: 1 million) may be helpful. Since 1000 ml equal one liter, dividing this into 1 million ml/m³ yields 1000 l water /m³. Similar conversions for changing units of time from minutes to hours and units of mass from μg or mg to grams needs to be performed.

By determining fluxes at a number of sites within a stream system, a pattern of materials transport in the water emerges. Students can then hypothesize the reasons for these patterns and make predictions on how events at upstream sites can affect the water quality and biological community downstream (Vannote et al., 1980).

For example, if DOC concentration and total discharge at a particular site in a stream were measured as 0.8 mg DOC/l and 5.2×10^6 l/hr, DOC flux, the product of concentration and discharge, would equal 4.2×10^3 g DOC/hr. This represents the actual amount of dissolved carbon passing this particular site each hour.

If the same measurements were done at a site farther downstream and found to be 0.7 mg DOC/l and 6.4×10^6 l/hr, DOC flux would then be 4.5×10^3 g DOC/hr, and net flux would be $+0.3 \times 10^3$ g DOC/hr. This might be the expected result for a stream in which photosynthetic activity and subsequent release of DOC by algae were high or for a stream in which soluble carbon from either naturally occurring detritus or man-made pollutants were leaching into the water.

However, if the downstream measurements were 0.7 mg DOC/l and 5.8×10^6 l/hr, DOC flux would be 4.1×10^3 g DOC/hr and net flux would equal -0.1×10^3 g DOC/hr. These results would indicate a net uptake of dissolved carbon from the water, possibly through either physical or chemical processes or by the activities of heterotrophic streambed microorganisms (Kuserk et al., 1984).

These examples illustrate some of the principles involved in analyzing the transport of matter in watersheds and the importance of measuring materials flux rather than concentration in stream ecosystems. In both of these cases, the concentrations at the downstream site were identical. Because of differences in stream discharge, however, net fluxes were different to the point that they led to significantly different interpretations of what is occurring in the stream.

Original Source

This activity has been adapted from an original exercise by Frank T. Kuserk (1989) titled "Measuring Discharge & Materials Transport in Stream Ecosystems" in *The American Biology Teacher*, 51(2), 100-103, and has been modified and reprinted with permission of the publisher.

III

ENVIRONMENTAL ANALYSIS

Tools &
Techniques

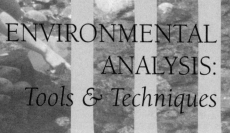

ENVIRONMENTAL ANALYSIS:
Tools & Techniques

In the following activities, students have opportunities to engage in ecological investigations by sampling, estimating, and analyzing — all things that must be done to more fully understand complex natural systems. It would be impossible for scientists to examine every aspect of the environment so we use techniques that permit a small sample to represent the whole. Samples allow the scientist or scientist-in-training to see more deeply into the balance between biotic, abiotic, and human-driven factors. These details can be integrated into the big picture balance of the given ecosystem. The cumulative and deleterious effects (e.g., drops in biodiversity, clearcutting, loss of habitat) over the last century have become the focus of much scientific study and general inquiry.

The sampling protocol, or the principles by and location at which samples are selected, differ based on the site, sampling objectives, and the substance in which the sample is found. For example, there are different sampling protocols for water, air, biologicals and solids, liquids, and sludges. Sampling involves a bit of statistics, and ways in which to select samples can be broken down to three: *simple random sampling, systematic sampling,* and *sampling with unequal probabilities.* Simple random sampling is most straightforward and the most commonly used sampling protocol. There are four basics and commonly accepted principles on which to base sample selection. First, the environmental samples must be representative of the portion of the environment being investigated. Second, since procedures for sampling and analysis influence each other, they must be planned together. Third, quality control samples must be representative of the environmental samples being analyzed. Finally, quality control samples are used to provide an assessment of the kinds and degree of bias and imprecision in data from analysis of the environmental samples (Keith, 1996).

The means of collection of environmental samples are as varied as the many different types of factors found in the environment. Samples and related data can be biological, chemical, physical, and geologic in nature. For example, tools involved in collection can vary from the very simple to the complex. Simpler environmental sampling tools include the thermometer, as well as pH and turbidity meters. Temperature, pH, and turbidity data can now be collected, stored, and presented through inexpensive computer interface equipment.

Analysis of samples is limited by the best available technologies. In addition to the sampling technologies presented above, best available technologies include the laboratory methods of analysis and the electronics used to sample, analyze, and draw conclusions from the data. Laboratory analyses performed include, but are not limited to, spectrophotometry, atomic absorption and emission, gas chromatography, mass spectrometry, chromatography, election microscopy and X-ray diffractometry. Increasing productivity through the use of technologies not only increases the data available for analysis, it frees the time formerly spent on performing simple mathematical functions for logical analysis of the interrelationships between the factors found in the environment of study. For example, in *Analyzing Ecological Data with a Spreadsheet,* students are asked to model the presentation of data in the practice of environmental science.

Measuring Species Diversity in Freshwater Plankton Communities

Based on an original activity by
John M. Kirby and Larry N. Reinking

A central theme in biology is the vast diversity of life. In recent years, it has become apparent that the decline of the Earth's biodiversity will be one of the important problems facing students in coming decades. This activity describes a simple exercise that gives students both field and classroom experience in measuring biodiversity.

Through this exercise, students can learn how to make and use a simple plankton sampling device; gain experience in counting microscopic organisms; use a species diversity index to compare plankton communities; develop and test hypotheses concerning plankton diversity in different aquatic ecosystems; and become familiar with an often overlooked, but diverse and dynamic, group of organisms.

Ecological Principles Illustrated

- Biodiversity
- Estimating diversity

Introduction

Presently there are about 1.4 million species of microorganisms, animals, and plants that have been studied and given scientific names. Of these organisms, the great majority are insects (approximately 750,000 species) and flowering plants (approximately 220,000 species). These numbers, however, may represent only a small fraction of the actual biodiversity on our planet; various estimates place the total numbers anywhere from 10 million to more that 100 million different types of organisms (Ehrlich & Wilson, 1991).

In the past few years, biologists have become very concerned over an accelerated rate of species extinction and reduction of biological diversity. This concern has been particularly focused on the destruction of habitat in the tropical rain forests. Estimates suggest that 4000 species may become extinct per year due to deforestation in the tropics alone (Wilson, 1989). On a global scale, it appears that we are losing 100,000 species annually due to human expansion and resultant loss of habitats. According to some estimates, the current rate of habitat loss will result in the extinction of 25% or more of all species on Earth in the next 50 years (Ehrlich & Wilson, 1991).

Most students are acquainted with the concept of biological diversity but often only have a vague definition that they can apply to it. Furthermore, they are under the impression that biological diversity is important only in tropical jungles or other exotic locales. In reality, the planktonic communities existing in local, temperate ponds or lakes are quite complex and are readily available for analysis at most times of the year.

Materials

- empty Ajax® liquid laundry detergent bottle, 64 fl. oz. size
- 8- to 12-foot pole (wood, plastic, or metal)
- duct tape
- meter stick or tape measure
- 1-foot latex tubing (7.5 mm outside diameter)
- tank ball
- 8 to 12 feet of cord (corresponding to length of pole)

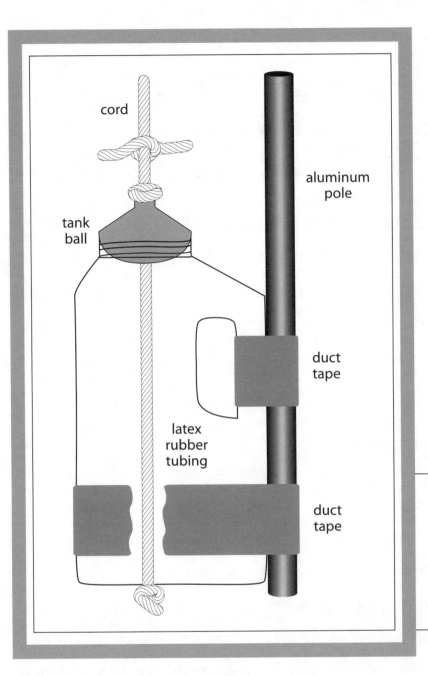

FIGURE 1. The Ajax® plankton sampler. A liquid laundry detergent bottle was taped to an aluminum pole and the bottle was sealed with a tank ball. The elasticity of the latex rubber tubing created a tight seal. At a specified depth, the cord was pulled to allow filling and then released to reseal the bottle.

The "Ajax®" Plankton Sampler

Several types of plankton sampling devices are commonly available but also are quite expensive. A simple and inexpensive sampler that is effective in collecting plankton at controlled depths can be made in the classroom (see Figure 1). This sampler is made from a plastic laundry detergent bottle (Ajax® liquid laundry detergent, 64 fl. oz.) that is taped to a pole (in this case, an aluminum pole with 0.5 in markings). The bottle is capped with a rubber tank ball that is held in place with a stretched latex tubing (7.5 mm, O.D.) . The elasticity of the latex tubing creates a tight seal. A gentle tug on a nylon cord, attached to the tubing above the tank ball, allows the bottle to fill at a specific depth. Releasing the cord reseals the Ajax® sampler.

The Counting Cell

In plankton studies, the Sedgwick Rafter counting cell is typically used to determine the number of organisms in a concentrated sample. Such counting cells are commercially

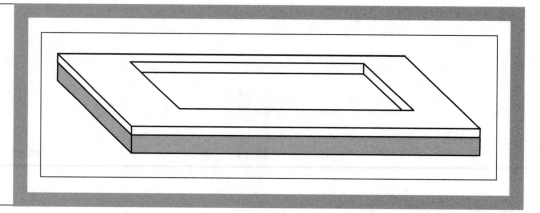

FIGURE 2. Counting cell. A plastic microscope slide with a rectangular cut-out was glued on top of a standard glass microscope slide. A second, intact plastic slide was used as a coverslip after a plankton sample was placed in the well.

available (see Lind, 1979 for a description); however, an inexpensive alternative that works well can be constructed (Figure 2).

This counting cell is made from a standard glass microscope slide of the same size. Using a razor blade, a rectangular opening (50 x 20 mm) is cut in the plastic slide; the remaining plastic border is bonded to the glass slide with a flexible, waterproof glue. A portion of the water sample is then placed in the "well," and an intact plastic slide is used as a cover slip. The volume held by the well depends on the type and amount of glue used. Uniform copies of the counting cell can be produced by carefully dispensing the glue and by placing weights on the counting cell as the glue sets; excess glue is easily trimmed with a razor blade after curing. Counting cells produced in this way comfortably hold 0.6 ml.

Plankton Identification

Identification of planktonic organisms to the genus or even species level is not really necessary to compute a species diversity index. As long as students can recognize one species as distinct from another, scientific names are not essential. However, identifying organisms to at least the genus level enhances the students' appreciation of this community of organisms. Some useful references that can aid students in plankton identification are listed in the "Plankton Identification Sources" section at the end of this activity. In the laboratory, photocopies of key pages from Needham and Needham (1962) are provided.

Simpson's Index of Diversity

In the study of an ecological community, one of the key questions deals with the type and abundance of species. In effect, the researcher asks, "How rich and varied is the community?" To help answer this question and to qualify species diversity, a number of species diversity indices have been developed (Magurran, 1988).

An easily-computed form of Simpson's index has been chosen to calculate plankton diversity in this activity (Krebs, 1985). This index is derived from probability theory and basically predicts the chance of simultaneously picking two members of the same species when sampling a large community. Little weight is given to rare species, and greater weight is given to the more common species. The numerical value for this index ranges from zero (low diversity) to a maximum of I-I-/S, where S is the number of species in the community.

$$D = 1 - [(p_1)^2 + (p_2)^2 + (p_3)^2 + \ldots (p_n)^2]$$

or

$$D = 1 - \sum (p_i)^2$$

where D = Simpson's Index of Diversity

p_i = the proportion of species i in the community (i.e., the number of individuals of species i divided by total number of individuals in the community)

This index is most meaningful when it is compared to the maximum theoretical diversity (I-I-IS) for the community.

Procedure

1. Collect water samples, at specified depths, using the Ajax® sampler. Usually 5 or more samples should be collected at a specific site, combined, and concentrated with a plankton net. If desired, the concentrated sample can be preserved by adding formaldehyde or alcohol (final concentration = 4% formaldehyde or 10% ethanol).

2. In the laboratory, transfer 0.6 ml (this volume may differ, depending on construction technique) to a counting cell and cover with a plastic slide. The sample vial must be gently stirred before taking this sample. At 100X, scan the entire slide and identify all observed plankton species (microscopes with mechanical stages are desirable for scanning the counting cell). Use the "Organism Guide" to identify each species. This identification and counting procedure works well if students work in pairs; one student scans the slide and identifies the species while the other student records data.

3. Repeat this procedure for each field sample.

4. For each field location, determine the following from the sample counts:

   - Number of species
   - Total number of individuals
   - Density of organisms (#/liter) =

$$\frac{\text{total \# of indiv. counted}}{0.0006 \text{ liters}} \quad X \quad \frac{\text{volume in sample vial}}{\text{volume filtered (1)}}$$

5. Students should be made aware of environmental variables that may affect plankton distribution and density. Therefore, physical and chemical data, such as water temperature, light penetration (turbidity), wind speed and direction, pH, and substrate characteristics, should be collected at each sampling site.

An Example

The Ajax® sampler was used to collect plankton from three lentic ecosystems: a small spring pond (approximately 60 m^2), a campus research pond (approximately 0.4 hectare), and a lake of several hundred hectares located on a wildlife refuge. At each location, five Ajax® plankton samples were collected at a depth of one meter, and the samples were combined and concentrated into a vial by filtering through a plankton net. These samples were preserved in formaldehyde solutions, although 10% ethanol would also suffice. In the laboratory, three subsamples were analyzed from each site, and the number of species and number of organisms per species were determined.

Tables 1 to 3 show the plankton community data collected from each location and the computations needed to determine Simpson's Index of Diversity. (These tables could be used as models to construct student worksheets.) Comparison of Simpson's diversity indices shows that two of the lentic ecosystems have nearly identical diversities – values representing 81% of maximum theoretical diversity. This is due to the similar number of species at both locations and the even distribution of individuals among these species. The small spring pond has a relatively low diversity (48% of maximum) since the community is dominated by one species.

An alternative expression of the species diversity formula (Cox, 1980) has been included with an example data set (Table 4). This formula may be useful if the students do not have a solid math background.

Suggested Student Projects

The general experimental procedure presented in this activity can be used by students to test hypotheses concerning the species diversity of aquatic ecosystems. Some factors that affect plankton diversity which can be incorporated into student studies include vertical distribution, temporal distribution, light penetration (turbidity), nutrient enrichment, other forms of pollution, water temperature, and pH. This exercise is especially well-suited as a scientific investigation and writing project.

The activity has been used in an introductory level college biology laboratory with successful results but could also be incorporated into an advanced high school biology or ecology course. At least 4 hours of laboratory time are needed for most student teams to count and identify organisms in the counting cells. For this reason, this exercise may be of greatest value as a longer-term project, covering perhaps 6 to 8 hours of class time (including both field and lab portion).

Plankton Identification References

Edmonson, W.T. (Ed.). (1959). *Freshwater Biology.* New York: John Wiley & Sons.

Fitzpatrick, J.F. (1983). *How to Know the Freshwater Crustacea.* Dubuque, IA: Wm. C. Brown Co. Publishers.

Needham, J.G. & Needham, P.R. (1962). *A Guide to the Study of Freshwater Biology,* 5th ed. Oakland: Holden-Day, Inc.

TABLE 1. Plankton counts from a spring pond sampled at a depth of one meter with the Ajax® sampler.

Sample Description: 60 m² Spring Pond

SPECIES	NUMBER	PROPORTION (p_i)	$(p_i)^2$
Algae			
Synedra	500	.7645	.5845
Navicula	55	.0841	.0071
Gyrosigma	27	.0413	.0017
Frustulia	33	.0505	.0025
Rotifera			
Philodina	18	.0275	.0008
Crustacea			
Chydorus sphaericus	21	.0321	.0010

Total Individuals = 654 $\sum(p_i)^2 = .5976$

Number of Species = 6

Max Diversity (1-1/6) = .83

Simpson's Index = .40   Simpson's Index as % of max. = 48.3%
$(D = 1 - \sum(p_i)^2)$

Sample Description: Small Pond (0.4 hectare)			
SPECIES	NUMBER	PROPORTION (p_i)	$(p_i)^2$
Algae			
Synedra	27	.1007	.0101
Fragilaria	123	.4590	.2160
Gomphonema	13	.0485	.0024
Navicula	3	.0112	.0001
Oedogonium	27	.1007	.0101
Ulothrix	3	.0112	.0001
Protozoa			
Strombidium	3	.0112	.0001
Rotifera			
Asplanchina	13	.0485	.0024
Pleurotrocha	5	.0187	.0003
Keratella cochlearis	5	.0187	.0003
Filinia	3	.0112	.0001
Crustacea			
Chydorus sphaericus	19	.0709	.0050
Bosmina longirostris	3	.0112	.0001
Daphnia pulex	5	.0187	.0003
Nauplius larvae	16	.0597	.0036

Total Individuals = 268 $\sum (p_i)^2 = .2455$

Number of Species = 15

Max Diversity (1-1/6) = .93

Simpson's Index = .75   Simpson's Index as % of max. 80.8%
$(D = 1 - \sum (p_i)^2)$

TABLE 2. Plankton counts from a small research pond sampled at a depth of one meter with the Ajax® sampler.

Pennack, R.W. (1989). *Freshwater Invertebrates of the United States,* 3rd ed. New York: John Wiley & Sons.

Prescott, G.W. (1983). *How to Know the Freshwater Algae,* 3rd ed. Dubuque, IA: Wm. C. Brown Co. Publishers.

Original Source

This activity has been adapted from an original activity by John M. Kirby and Larry N. Reinking (1994) titled "A Field & Classroom Exercise for Measuring the Species Diversity of Freshwater Plankton Communities" in *The American Biology Teacher,* 56(5), 298-301, and has been modified and reprinted with permission of the publisher.

Sample Description: Wildlife Refuge Lake (> 100 hectares)

SPECIES	NUMBER	PROPORTION (p_i)	$(p_i)^2$
Algae			
Synedra	70	.1449	.0210
Asterionella	38	.0787	.0062
Navicula	3	.0062	0
Cynibella	9	.0186	.0003
Pediastrum	41	.0849	.0072
Rotifera			
Asplanchina	9	.0186	.0003
Keratella cochlearis	14	.0290	.0008
Brachionus calyciflorus	14	.0290	.0008
Polyarthra	11	.0228	.0005
Crustacea			
Chydorus sphaericus	14	.0290	.0008
Bosmina longirostris	41	.0849	.0072
Daphnia pulex	3	.0062	0
Nauplius larvae	216	.4472	.2000

Total Individuals	= 483	$\sum (p_i)^2 = .2451$
Number of Species	= 13	
Max Diversity (I-1/6)	= .92	
Simpson's Index	= .75	Simpson's Index as % of max. = 81.8%
$(D = I - \sum (p_i)^2)$		

TABLE 3. Plankton counts from a wildlife refuge lake sampled at a depth of one meter with an Ajax® sampler.

$$D = \frac{N(N\text{-}1)}{\sum n(n\text{-}1)}$$

Where: D = diversity index

N = total number of individuals of all species

n = number of individuals of a species

Example (Data from Table 1)

SPECIES	NUMBER (n)	$n(n\text{-}1)$
Algae		
Synedra	500	249500
Navicula	55	2970
Gyrosigma	27	702
Frustulia	33	1056
Rotifera		
Philodina	18	306
Crustacea		
Chydorus sphaericus	21	420

$\sum n(n\text{-}1) = 254954$ $N=654$

$N(N\text{-}1) = 427062$

$D = \dfrac{427062}{254954} = 1.67$

TABLE 4. Alternative form of Simpson's Index of Diversity.

Using Species Diversity To Assess Stream Water Quality

Based on an original activity by Dwight Moody

The techniques and equipment necessary to study the water quality of a running water ecosystem are often highly sophisticated and/or very expensive. The following study is inexpensive, involves virtually no equipment, and produces consistent and easily interpreted results.

Ecological Principles Illustrated

- Water quality
- Species diversity

Introduction

This field investigation rests in part on the premise that the benthos region of a stream or river develops characteristics which are directly related to sediments carried in the stream. Fast moving streams, streams in their upper reaches, and streams that carry little sediment will usually exhibit substrates which are more solid. Streams in their lower reaches, slow-moving streams, or streams that carry large amounts of sediment will have substrates of fine sand, silt, organic deposits, or a combination of all three. The substrate composition will necessarily be formed of the sediments carried in the stream (Reid, 1961).

Another major premise is that each substrate type contains living organisms unique to that substrate. For example, organisms of the benthos in a stream that carries and deposits large amounts of organic debris will be primarily detritus feeders (Reid, 1961).

The final premise is that the types of organisms which inhabit the substrate of streams are directly related to the condition of the water. A river that constantly carries sewage will eventually develop a deposit of organic materials along the bottom. Only a few organisms will live in this sewage sediment. On the other hand, a relatively clean stream or river will have bottom sediments with little organic matter and a representative group of organisms that generally inhabit cleaner waters (Coker, 1954; Sykes & Skinner, 1971; Wagner, 1978; Willoughby, 1976).

An organism living in polluted water may also live in clean water, but in clean water, the competition is more intense, and the abundance and variety of organisms intolerant of pollution are greater (Coker, 1954). This greater variety found in clean water is a good indicator of water quality. A greater diversity correlates with clean water, and less diversity is usually associated with unclean water (Coker, 1954; Finstein, 1972).

Materials

- meter sticks
- small glass containers
- eye droppers
- tweezers
- microscopes

- celsius thermometers
- gallon containers or 2 to 3 lb. coffee cans
- light-colored trays or white enamel pans
- hand lens
- slides

Field Procedure

1. With the class divided into groups of about 3 to 5 students each, take each group of students to a different point on a stream. Each group should make a study sample about a

mile apart from the nearest group. If possible, begin the first group at a known source of pollution, with the other groups located downstream from the first.

2. Upon arrival, have the students observe and record the following: point number, water color, water velocity (fast, slow, nearly stationary, or actually calculate), water depth (estimate or actually calculate), water temperature, abundance of aquatic animals and general types, abundance of plant life and location, and other conditions (odor, scum on water, etc.).

3. With a can or jar, students must collect sediment from the stream bottom, scraping off only the top 1 to 2 inches of the substrate. It is important to get only the top 1 to 2 inches because, below this depth, there will be very little life. Confine the sampling to a one-square-meter area. Scrape several times in different places within the square meter area until about one-half gallon of material (3 lb. coffee can two-thirds full, or 2 lb. can full to the top rim) is obtained.

Lab Procedure

1. Upon returning to the lab, students should dump the collected material into trays or pans and examine it, recording the point number and a description of the stream bottom soil (color, odor, type and size of particles, and other observations).

2. Following the physical inspection, the samples should be very carefully sorted and all living organisms removed. This procedure should be done the same day the sample is taken because many insect larvae and some worms will die and be extremely difficult to identify after 24 hours.

3. To describe the animal life, animal specimens should be divided into groups or into small glass containers, taking care to separate specimens by species. A list of all animal species found should be made and sketches or descriptions made for the species that cannot be identified. (The *Pond Life* paperback by Reid, part of the *Golden Guide* series, and *A Guide to the Study of Fresh-Water Biology* by Needham and Needham are excellent sources for animal identification. Various other library references catalogued under *water pollution, aquatic biology, freshwater biology,* and *limnology* will also prove helpful.

4. After the specimens have been catalogued, the following numerical determinations should be recorded: the number of specimens of each species; the total number of specimens of all species (N); and the total number of species (S).

5. The final step is to determine the species diversity for each point. Use the following formula to calculate the diversity index:

$$d = \frac{S-1}{\log_e N}$$

   d = diversity index
   N = number of specimens per square meter
   S = number of species per square meter
   (MacKay & Kalff, 1969)

6. If a logarithm to the base of 10 ($\log_{10}$) is used for table purposes, the formula to convert the $\log_{10}$ to the natural logarithm ($\log_e$) is: $\log_e = \log_{10} \times 2.3$. For example, if N = 40, then $\log_{10} 40 = 1.60206$, and $1.60206 \times 2.3 = \log_e N$.

7. An optional activity that may contribute valuable information is *microorganism sampling*. Have students prepare microscope slides of several drops of water from the sample and identify protozoans, copepods, algae, fungi, etc. found on the slides.

Laboratory Analysis

Post a large chart so that each group of students can record their results for the entire class to view. It may also be a good idea to display a map of the stream so that students can orient themselves and more accurately pinpoint their sampling point.

Have students analyze their investigation by recording the following results:

1. Post the results from the investigation of the point studied by their groups. List numbers and types of organisms, stream and substrate descriptions, species diversity, and any other pertinent information. Post the water quality at the point.

2. Explain their reasoning for the water quality determination that was made at their points.

3. Provide answers to the questions, "Does the water quality improve after the water has run for a mile? Why or why not?"

4. Draw a map of the stream or river section showing all points that were sampled. Use a key and symbols to make the map easily understood. Be sure to show through symbols the condition of the water from the first to the last point.

5. Explain the map and make a list of conclusions from this field investigation.

Conclusion

The description of the preceding technique has been written for high school biology classes and introductory college environmental studies courses. But, with modifications, the investigations can be attempted at other levels. For example, in an upper-level college ecology class, longer-term studies that include more rigorous identification of plant and animal specimens may be done. For all age groups, analysis and interpretation of the field work is essential.

A measurement of species diversity should be conducted. As discussed previously, there is a direct relationship between the diversity of animal life and the degree to which a stream is polluted. Odum (1971) reported on a research study in which the diversity index dropped drastically for benthos samples taken immediately downstream from a pollution source. At points farther downstream, the diversity increased as the river became cleaner. Sixty miles from the pollution source, the diversity index was nearly as high as it had been upstream from the point of discharge.

Table 1 on page 71 is a fairly complete composite of the characteristics that indicate the degree of organic sediments and solutes in running water. However, it is not the ultimate description of stream quality, and teachers who use this investigation should use local publications and other manuals and keys to supplement Table 1. Finally, the organisms listed in the table are printed as common names, family, and genera names. This was done to facilitate cross referencing in the event that other sources are consulted. The names listed are those most commonly found in the literature.

Original Source

This activity has been adapted from an original exercise by Dwight Moody (1985) titled "Assessing Stream Water Quality" in *The American Biology Teacher,* 47(6), 359-361, and has been modified and reprinted with permission of the publisher.

Characteristic	Water Quality			
	Heavily Polluted	**Moderately Polluted**	**Slightly Polluted**	**Clean Water**
Water Condition	brown; possibly with scum or frothy	brownish; film or scum possible	may be nearly clear or slightly muddied	fairly clear
Mud Condition	black; sewage, oily or chemical odor	black; fairly strong odor	dark brown; may have slight odor	should not have a foul odor
Diptera Larvae	mosquito (*Culex*), rat-tailed maggot (*Eristalis*)	Midge (*Chironomidae* and *Dixidae*), black fly (*Simulidae*), mosquito, dance fly (*Empididae*), *Eristalis*	a few chironomids, dixids, and simulids, mosquito, horsefly, dance fly, *Eristalis*	possibly mosquito, chironomid, cranefly
Worms	sludge or tubiflex worms (*Oligochaeta*)	tubiflex and other/oligochaetes, leeches, possibly roundworms	leeches, oligochaetes, flatworms	possibly none, may be oligochaetes
Crustaceans/Mollusks	none living, may find empty shells	pea shell clams; air breathing snails on algae and exposed rock; some *Copepoda*, particularly cyclops; some *Branchiopoda*, particularly *Daphnia*; limpets	*Daphnia*, aquatic snails, crayfish, many copepods, many ostracods, some amphipods, freshwater mussels, limpets	crayfish, good copepod variety, freshwater mussels, aquatic snails, limpets
Other Insect Larvae	none	probably none	possibly some dragon-flies and damselflies, caddisflies, water striders, water scorpions, dobsonflies, whirligig beetles, riffles beetles	caddisfly, mayfly, damselfly, dragonfly, stonefly, water strider, water scorpion, water boatmen, giant water bug, dobsonfly, water penny, predaceous diving beetle, whirligig beetle, riffles beetle, water scavenger beetle
Protozoans/Rotifers	*Euglena, Amoeba*, and some rotifers	*Paramecium, Euglena, Amoeba*, rotifers	*Stentor, Paramecium, Euglena*, rotifers	a few *Euglena, Dinobryon, Difflugia, Chlamydomonas, Gonyaulax*, not many ciliates
Fish	none	may see some carp, minnows (Cyprinidae), buffalo fish, and possibly catfish	carp, catfish, minnows, buffalo fish, gars, stickleback, suckers	carp, catfish, minnows, buffalo fish, gars, stickleback, suckers, blue gill, darters, and game fish
Algae	possibly *Melosira* and *Oscillatoria*	*Oscillatoria, Spirogyra*	*Pandorina*	*Oedogonium, Navicula*
Diversity Index	0-2	1-3	2-5	4-10
Miscellaneous	great numbers of bacteria (*Sphaerotilus*), or may be entirely lacking life	possibly algae floating on the surface; bacteria (*Beggiatoa*)	rooted plants may be present	good variety of rooted plants

* The numbers for the diversity index are approximates based on a slow moving river. Various conditions other than pollution can cause the diversity to fluctuate. For example, extremely fast moving water and very cold water can lower diversity (Allee et al., 1949; Coker, 1954; Hynes, 1970, 1971; Klots, 1966; Needham & Needham, 1977; Odum, 1971; Sykes & Skinner, 1971; Wilkes, 1983; Willoughby, 1976, Zimmerman, 1983).

TABLE 1.
Characteristics that determine water quality.

Estimating Population Density in the Laboratory and Field

Based on an original activity by John Cruzan

The following three exercises were developed as part of an experimental ecology laboratory based on microcosms. They require no field work by students and are geared toward the testing of hypotheses.

Ecological Principles Illustrated

- Sampling techniques
- Population density

Materials

- Materials required are dependent on the activity being performed.

Procedure

Using Random Quadrats

Prepare for this laboratory by establishing 200 to 500 ml microcosms of pond water along with a small amount of pond detritus (cultured on a sunny windowsill) or 200 to 300 ml hay infusions. Hay infusions are made by boiling 3 grams of timothy hay or equivalent material for 10 minutes in 1,000 ml of pond water or spring water. Divide among culture dishes, wait 24 hours for them to cool and reaerate, then inoculate each dish with 2 to 3 ml of pond water including some pond detritus.

The organisms in these microcosms tend to become stratified, with some on the bottom among the detritus, some on the container walls, and some near the surface where there is maximum oxygen. To obtain an "average" sample from the microcosm, thoroughly (but gently) agitate it to mix all these microcommunities together. Immediately withdraw a few drops with a pipet and place it in a Palmer counting cell that holds 0.1 ml of sample when full. Scan the entire cell using the mechanical stage and the 10X objective. An alternative technique is to put 0.05 ml on a plain glass slide using a calibrated pipet. Add a coverslip and examine under the microscope. Most organisms can be identified using various guides to pond organisms. The density of each organism in the culture can be calculated in number per ml. The entire class can sample the same culture, and a class mean can be calculated.

Introduce an experimental variable by treating two microcosms differently, such as introducing a small amount of some pollutant into one. Field applications of this technique include counting plankton in plankton hauls over a measured distance and counting plants in randomly selected quadrats of one square meter or other-sized area, depending on the size of the plants.

Removal Sampling

The preparation for this experiment involves establishing a 20 ml culture of vinegar eels (microscopic nematodes). This can be done by inoculating a sample of the medium with several milliliters of a stock culture. (Both medium and culture are available from most biological supply companies.) Each student group needs to have its own culture.

The students gently agitate the culture to even out the distribution of the vinegar eels. Then a 0.5 ml sample is removed with a calibrated pipet and placed in a small watchglass. Examination under the microscope will reveal that the nematodes are wriggling too rapidly to readily count. The animals are immobilized by placing the slide on a warm hotplate for a couple of minutes. The sample can then be scanned using the compound microscope and the nematodes counted.

After each count, 0.5 ml of medium should be added to the culture to replace the volume that was removed. After agitation, a second sample is removed and counted like the first. As this process is repeated 8 to 10 times, the number counted each time should decline due to the constant removal of individuals.

Data should be recorded in two parallel columns: a = the number removed in each sample and b = the total number removed after each sample. Plot *a* on the Y axis and *b* on the y axis. The points should be roughly in a straight line which can be extended until Y = 0. The X value at this point is the population estimate.

In the field, this approach could be used for any population of animals that is localized in distribution and from which a significant proportion can be removed. One application is the removal trapping of small mammals from a population over a period of 3 or 4 days. Another would be netting of tadpoles from a small pond. In all cases, the removal effort must be uniform from one sampling to the next.

Mark-Recapture Method

In the field, this approach is used for mice, larger insects, fishes, and almost any kind of animal that can be tagged, dyed, dabbed with a spot of nail polish, or otherwise marked. The population is sampled, and all captured individuals are marked and returned to the population. The number of marked individuals is recorded. At a later time, the population is resampled, and the number of marked and unmarked individuals is recorded. With this data, the total population density can be calculated by the following formula:

$$\text{\# recaptured/\# marked} = \frac{\text{total in second sampling}}{\text{total population}}$$

This method can be modeled in the laboratory by using a healthy population of mealworms. The population needs to be established a couple of months ahead of time by placing a pound of bran (found in health food stores) in a covered aquarium. Introduce 100 or more mealworms (from a pet store), along with a quarter of a potato for moisture, and cover the bran with shredded paper. An instant population can also be created by buying a much larger number of mealworms.

Students remove about 50 mealworms by dipping up samples in a small beaker and sifting them through a sieve. A spot of red nail polish is put on each worm's dorsum for identification purposes. The mealworms are kept in a container until the nail polish has dried and are then returned to the aquarium. On a subsequent day, approximately the same number are removed from the aquarium in a similar manner, and the number that are marked with nail polish are determined.

Original Source

This activity is based on an original exercise by John Cruzan (1988) titled "Teaching Ecology with Microcosms" in *The American Biology Teacher, 50*(4), 226-228, and has been modified by the author for this publication.

Analyzing Ecological Data with a Spreadsheet

Based on an original activity by Linda A. Sigismondi and Cynthia Case

The following laboratory exercise and computer application was developed to encourage science students to use their basic computer skills in their science classes. Although the application described in this activity uses a specific example — analysis of ecological data — the technique can easily be extended to other types of data analysis in other courses.

The specific computer application outlined here is used to analyze data on plant community composition from the point quarter sampling.

Ecological Principles Illustrated

- Using computers in ecology

Materials

- materials necessary for point quarter sampling
- spreadsheet program, such as Excel, Lotus 1-2-3, etc.

Procedure

1. Data are collected in the field using the point quarter sampling method (Brower & Zar, 1984). Students are given data sheets to use in the field that are constructed as templates from the database used in the analysis. (See Figure 1.)

2. Students bring their field data to the next lab period, where they demonstrate the technique of data entry and analysis using sample data. For small classes, students can simply gather around the computer screen. For large classes, projecting the computer screen onto a classroom screen is helpful. The data are entered in a database with the necessary fields as illustrated in Figure 2.

3. When all data have been entered, a command such as "Show List" displays the data in a chart format. For future calculations, it is helpful to list the data alphabetically by species name with a sort routine. The resulting chart is shown in Figure 3.

4. The data set is next transferred to a spreadsheet to perform the necessary calculations. The area of each tree is calculated from the circumference using the formula $A = (circumference)^2/ (4 \times \pi)$. This is entered for the cells in the first column $[= E3*E3/(4*3.14)]$.

   The area occupied by each species is calculated manually, selecting cells containing area for the same species and then summing. Next, the total point to plant distance and mean point to plant distance are calculated using *sum* and *average* commands. These values are needed for future calculations. The spreadsheet can be formatted as to column size, number of decimal places, etc. Figure 4 illustrates this spreadsheet.

5. The next step is to construct an additional spreadsheet to summarize the data. This is the same summary as Table 3c.3 in Brower and Zar (1984). In our example, the table is turned sideways to allow for graphing of the data. The final spreadsheet is illustrated in Figure 5. To conserve time, part of this spreadsheet is usually constructed prior to class and construction of a small number of rows only is demonstrated during the regular class period. Note that the values for n, j, a, and mean distance in Figure 5 come from the previous spreadsheet (Figure 4), while the remaining values are newly calculated.

The formulas used to calculate the spreadsheet in Microsoft Works™ are given in Figure 6. (Other spreadsheets may require slightly different formulas as indicated in their manuals.) The formulas in Column C are input manually. Columns D through G are made with *fill right* command. Column H is the sum of Columns C through G. The letter number designation in the formula refers to the column and row of a cell. For example, C2 indicates the number in Column C, Row 2. When the *fill right* command is used, this will change to D2, E2, etc. A $ in front of a cell designation means to keep the same cell designation throughout the row when *fill right* is used.

6. Once the final spreadsheet is constructed, the data can be graphed to illustrate importance values or other parameters as desired. Figure 7 is an example of a graph made from the spreadsheet illustrated in Figure 5. Graphing is a feature that is part of many, but not all, integrated packages.

7. After our demonstration, the students work in groups entering and analyzing their data. Once the students generate their tables and graphs, they can *paste* them directly into the word processing part of the program and write their report. In the word processor, students can also put headings on the tables and add boxes and lines to the tables.

point	quadrant	species	dist (m)	circum (CM)
1	1			
1	2			
1	3			
1	4			
2	1			
2	2			
2	3			
2	4			
3	1			
3	2			
3	3			
3	4			
4	1			
4	2			
4	3			
4	4			

FIGURE 1. Portion of data sheet for use in field.

Discussion

This lab was done in a junior-senior level ecology class. Students who had previous experience with spreadsheets did not have difficulty with this exercise. Students who had little experience with spreadsheets or computer use in general required much more time and instructor supervision. If a class has a large percentage of students with little computer experience, analyzing a simpler data set first is recommended. Alternatively, one should allocate more than one lab period for this exercise.

Overall, this lab activity has proven to be successful. Students demonstrate significant improvement in computer skills and confidence as the exercise progresses, and some students continue to analyze data sets by computer throughout the semester, even though it is not a requirement.

Original Source

This activity has been adapted from an original activity by Linda Sigismondi and Cynthia Case (1990) titled "Integrating Basic Computer Skills into Science Classes: Analysis of Ecological Data" in *The American Biology Teacher, 52(5)*, 298-303, and has been modified and reprinted with permission of the publisher.

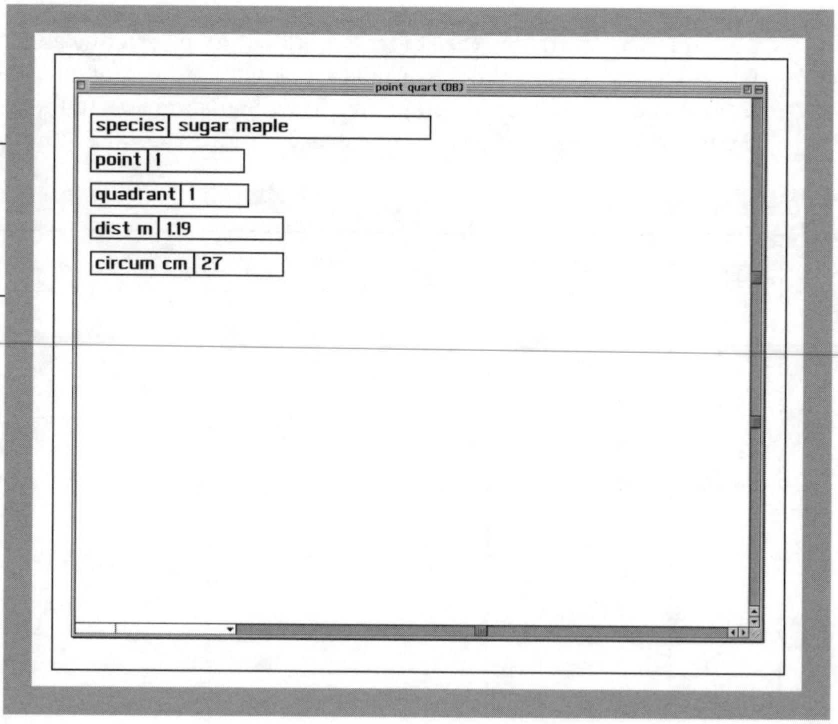

FIGURE 2. Sample screen for database entry.

point quart (DB)

species	sugar maple
point	1
quadrant	1
dist m	1.19
circum cm	27

species	point	quadrant	dist m	circum cm
dogwood	4	4	2.85	5.9
hawthorn	1	3	1.30	5.00
sassafras	1	4	2.95	24.7
sugar maple	1	1	1.19	27
sugar maple	1	2	1.34	17.0
sugar maple	2	1	1.22	10.1
sugar maple	2	2	1.49	4.5
sugar maple	2	3	3.11	27.7
sugar maple	2	4	4.47	88.0
sugar maple	3	1	1.83	9.5
sugar maple	3	2	1 02	58.4
sugar maple	3	3	1 .56	60.2
sugar maple	3	4	1.53	17.2
sugar maple	4	1	1.49	51.6
sugar maple	4	2	1.77	25.7
yellow poplar	4	3	3.05	29.7

FIGURE 3. Screen of database in list format sorted alphabetically by species name.

	A	B	C	D	E	F	G
1	species	point	quadrant	dist m	circum cm	area cm²	sum species
2						A=(C*C)/4π	area (a)
3	dogwood	4.0	4.0	2.85	5.9	2.77	2.77
4	hawthorn	1.0	3.0	1.30	5.0	1.99	1.99
5	sassafras	1.0	4.0	2.95	24.7	48.57	48.57
6	sugar maple	1.0	1.0	1.19	27.0	58.04	1623.83
7	sugar maple	1.0	2.0	1.34	17.0	23.01	
8	sugar maple	2.0	1.0	1.22	10.1	8.12	
9	sugar maple	2.0	2.0	1.49	4.5	1.61	
10	sugar maple	2.0	3.0	3.11	27.7	61.09	
11	sugar maple	2.0	4.0	4.47	88.0	616.56	
12	sugar maple	3.0	1.0	1.83	9.5	7.19	
13	sugar maple	3.0	2.0	1.02	58.4	271.54	
14	sugar maple	3.0	3.0	1.56	60.2	288.54	
15	sugar maple	3.0	4.0	1.53	17.2	23.55	
16	sugar maple	4.0	1.0	1.49	51.6	211.99	
17	sugar maple	4.0	2.0	1.77	25.7	52.59	
18	yellow poplar	4.0	3.0	3.05	29.7	70.23	70.23
19							
20				Sum	32.17		
21				Mean	2.01		

FIGURE 4. Spreadsheet of data from point quarter sampling with some preliminary calculations.

FIGURE 5.
Spreadsheet of
summary data
on point quarter
sampling.

	A	B	C	D	E	F	G	H
1	**Parameter**	**Formula**	**Dogwood**	**Hawthorn**	**Sassafras**	**Sugar Maple**	**Yellow Poplar**	**Total**
2	# individuals	n	1.00	1.00	1.00	12.00	1.00	16.00
3	relative density	RD=n/sum n	0.06	0.06	0.06	0.75	0.06	0.99
4	density	D=RD*TD	1.55	1.55	1.55	18.56	1.55	24.76
5	# pts w/species	j	1.00	1.00	1.00	4.00	1.00	8.00
6	frequency	f=j/# pts	0.25	0.25	0.25	1.00	0.25	2.00
7	relative frequency	RF=f/sum f	0.13	0.13	0.13	0.50	0.13	1.02
8	sum species area	a	2.77	1.99	48.57	1623.83	70.23	1747.39
9	coverage	C=a*D/n	4.29	3.08	75.14	2512.05	108.65	2703.21
10	relative coverage	RC=C/sum C	0.00	0.00	0.03	0.93	0.04	1.00
11	importance value	IV=RD+RF+RC	0.19	0.19	0.22	2.18	0.23	3.01
12								
13	# sampling pts	4						
14	mean distance	2.01						
15	A=mean sq	4.04						
16	TD=100/A	24.75						

FIGURE 6.
Formulas used
to calculate
spreadsheet in
Figure 5. Note
that column A
was omitted.

	B	C	D	E	F	G	H
1	**Formula**	**Dogwood**	**Hawthorn**	**Sassafras**	**Sugar Maple**	**Yellow Poplar**	**Total**
2	n	1.00	1.00	1.00	12.00	1.00	=SSum(C2:G2)
3	RD=n/sum n	=C2/$H2	=D2/$H2	=E2/$H2	=F2/$H2	=G2/$H2	=SSum(C3:G3)
4	D=RD*TD	=C3*$C16	=D3*$C16	=E3*$C16	=F3*$C16	=G3*$C16	= SSum(C4:G4)
5	j	1.00	1.00	1.00	4.00	1.00	=SSum(C5:G5)
6	f=j/# pts	=C5/$C13	=D5/$C13	=E5/$C13	=F5/$C13	=G5/$C13	=SSum(C6:G6)
7	RF=f/sum f	=C6/$H6	=D6/$H6	=E6/$H6	=F6/$H6	=G6/$H6	=SSum(C7:G7)
8	a	2.77	1.99	48.57	1565.79	70.23	=SSum(C8:G8)
9	C=a*D/n	=C8*C4/C2	=D8*D4/D2	=E8*E4/E2	=F8*F4/F2	=G8*G4/G2	=SSum(C9:G9)
10	RC=C/sum C	=C9/$H9	=D9/$H9	=E9/$H9	=F9/$H9	=G9/$H9	=SSum(C10:G10)
11	IV=RD+RF	=C10+C7+C3	=D10+D7+D3	=E10+E7+E3	=F10+F7+F3	=G10+G7+G3	+SSum(C11:G11)
12	+RC						
13	# samp. pts.	4					
14	mean distance	2.01					
15	A=mean sq	=C14*C14					
16	TD=100/A	=100/C15					

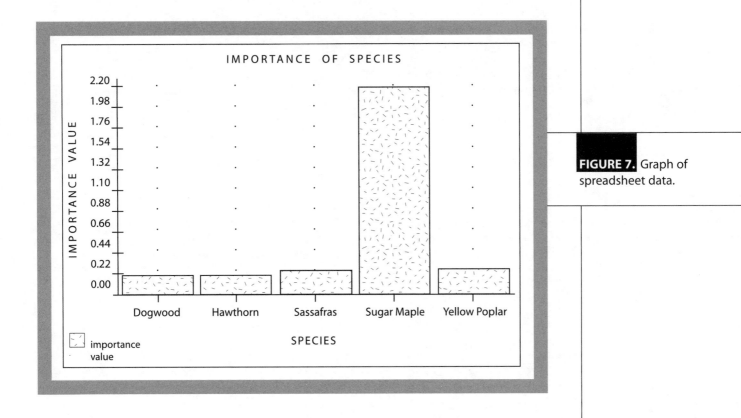

IV

POPULATION & COMMUNITY ECOLOGY

Organisms Interacting

POPULATION & COMMUNITY ECOLOGY: *Organisms Interacting*

Organisms do not live in isolation. Rather, they are in a constant state of interaction with the physical world, with other members of their same species, and with other species. These intra- and interspecific interactions serve as forces that tie species together into communities (Campbell, Mitchell & Reece, 1997). A community, simply defined, is a "group of populations of plants and animals in a given place" (Krebs, 1972), and may consist of a relatively simple artificial community established in a laboratory or a complex community established in a tide pool, an oceanic kelp forest, a garden, a pond, or a climax forest, for example. The key feature of any community is interaction among organisms. The major interactions fall into three general categories: competition, predation, and symbiosis.

Competition refers to those types of interactions that involve "striving for the same thing" (Odum, 1975), with the net result that the competitors are hampered in some way. Competitive interactions may be direct or indirect, may involve some form of conflict for food, light, living space, nesting sites, etc. and may result in coexistence via resource partitioning or complete exclusion from a specific habitat (Odum, 1975). Predation and its counterpart parasitism are defined as "two-species interactions in which one species is directly harmed by the other" (Starr, 1994). Both predators and parasites kill their prey or host species, respectively; the difference is one of size, for prey species are usually smaller than the predator while host species are usually much larger than their parasites (Campbell, Mitchell & Reece, 1997). Symbiosis, an interactive relationship in which one species lives in or on another species, may be of benefit to both organisms (mutualism) or may benefit one but neither help nor harm the other (commensalism) (Campbell, Mitchell, & Reece, 1997). Parasitism may be considered a harmful symbiotic interaction.

The laboratory activities in this section, intended for both general and advanced biology students, deal with all three types of community interactions. In *Investigating Species Interactions* by Cruzan, students study community structure, competition, predation, and commensalism in aquatic and soil communities that are set up in the lab using materials collected from the field. In *Demonstrating Predator-Prey Relationships and Food Selection with Fish* by Kotila, students are introduced to a technique for determining the diet of a natural population of predators and then use this technique to determine the selection and variety of prey consumed relative to the availability of prey. Students are also shown a method for quantitative analysis of prey selection and calculation of an electivity index. In *Investigating Predator-Prey Relationships with Cobra Lilies and Drosophila* by Pratt, students study the feeding mechanism and factors affecting the consumption success and rate of a carnivorous plant. In *Herbivores, Predation, and Biological Control* by Murphy, Canington, and Walker, students study the population growth of insects and food plants under conditions of uncontrolled herbivory (no predation) and biological control (predation). In *Investigating Insect-Plant Relationships* by Fry and Wratten, students study the relation of historical and current geographical range, host-plant selection, succession, palatability, insect feeding rates, and other insect-plant relationships. In *Investigating Population Growth and Competition with Paramecium sp.* by Cruzan, students study the growth rates of two protozoan competitors when cultured alone and together.

The activities demonstrate a wide variety of techniques to study community ecology, use readily available or easily attainable supplies, and provide suggestions for alternative or extension activities. The activities can be used for a whole class or as independent study projects.

Using Spreadsheets To Model Population Growth

Based on an original activity by
Ashley J.R. Carter

One of the most basic elements of a study of ecology is the population – a focus of any ecological models. This activity will introduce discrete (that is, measured once per generation instead of continuously) models for population growth as presented by Robert Ricklefs (1993). Starting with a simple exponential growth model for one species, we will build up to a model that considers two competing herbivore species and a predator species that preys on them both.

The equations considered can be placed into a spreadsheet that performs the calculations quickly and easily. Spreadsheet programs can graph columns of values and we will graph the populations of each species over time to observe the effects of the population interactions. Minimal experience with spreadsheets is assumed, including defining equations, referencing cells, and generating plots – all of which can be learned and taught in a matter of minutes.

The models and spreadsheets will encourage students to make the connection between a purely mathematical model and the real population it represents. Students will consider the qualitative effects of changing a value in equations, and their spreadsheets will present the quantitative effects. Environmental issues can be discussed by their effects on the equations and predicting or observing the resulting population crashes or booms (seen from the graphs of the populations over time).

Ecological Principles Illustrated

- Population interactions
- The mathematics of population interactions
- Competition
- Computer simulations of ecological relationships

Materials

- Personal computer with spreadsheet program such as Quattro® Pro or Lotus 1-2-3

Background Information

Population Equations

If we start with a population of size N and an intrinsic rate of population growth (r) in percent (r = .04 is 4% increase per generation), we can calculate N' (the next population size) from r and N. The discrete exponential equation for a population of N organisms is:

$$N' = N + rN$$

One can see from this equation that the population will grow exponentially without bound until the entire Earth would be covered (Figure 1 shows the case with a 5% growth rate, r = 0.05 and an initial population of 20). This is clearly unrealistic; the students may wish to offer their opinions as to what is wrong. What the equation is lacking is a notion of a maximum sustainable population size that can be supported in an environment (carrying capacity).

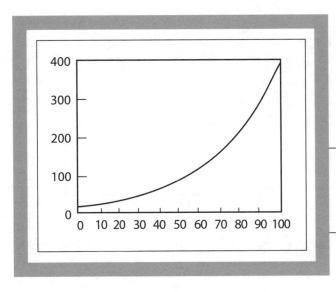

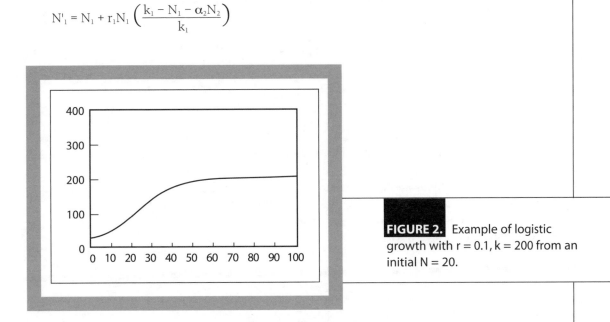

FIGURE 1. Example of exponential growth with r = 0.05 from an initial N = 20.

This notion of an environment's carrying capacity was used by Pearl and Reed (1920) in their equations to explain the population growth of early America. The discrete version of the logistic equation they proposed for population growth in a population of N organisms and a carrying capacity k is:

$$N' = N + rN\left(\frac{k - N}{k}\right)$$

From this equation you can see that when N < k the population would grow until k − N = 0. At that point the second term is zero so that N' = N and the population stops increasing. Likewise, if the population were above the carrying capacity for some reason, N > k and the second term is negative and N' < N, the population starts to decrease. Figures 2 and 3 demonstrate the shape of these two cases; the flattened s-shaped curve in Figure 2 is a sigmoid curve that is the hallmark of the logistic equation. This model seems more realistic, but treats the organism as if it is alone and is the only organism that is consuming resources in the environment.

The notion of competition was introduced by A.J. Lotka (1932) and G.F. Gause (1934) in the following way. For a pair of competing organisms the appropriate equations would be:

$$N'_1 = N_1 + r_1 N_1 \left(\frac{k_1 - N_1 - \alpha_2 N_2}{k_1}\right)$$

FIGURE 2. Example of logistic growth with r = 0.1, k = 200 from an initial N = 20.

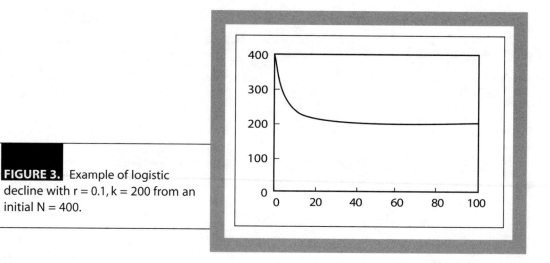

FIGURE 3. Example of logistic decline with r = 0.1, k = 200 from an initial N = 400.

$$N'_2 = N_2 + r_2N_2 \left(\frac{k_2 - N_2 - \alpha_1 N_1}{k_2} \right)$$

The subscripts indicate which population the r, N, and k values would correspond to if they were modeled alone, as in the previous paragraph. The α_1 and α_2 values show the impact of the other population on the resources that the given population uses. The $\alpha_2 N_2$ and $\alpha_1 N_1$ values represent competing organisms expressed as equivalent organisms of the original species. For example, if $\alpha_2 > 1$, that means that each individual of population 2 consumes more of population 1's resources than an individual population 1 does, depressing population 1's growth greatly. Similarly, if $\alpha_2 < 1$, individuals of population 2 consume less of population 1's resources than each member of population 1 does. The students may wish to consider factors such as organism size and food preference overlap that determine α_1 and α_2.

Predation was independently considered by A.J. Lotka (1932) and Vito Volterra (1926). This final case is a discrete version of a model combining their work with the results above, considering one population of predators (P) consuming two populations of herbivores (H_1 and H_2). The appropriate equations for this would be:

$$H'_1 = H_1 + r_1H_1 \left(\frac{k_1 - H_1 - \alpha_2 H_2}{k_1} \right) - \gamma_1 H_1 P$$

$$H'_2 = H_2 + r_2H_2 \left(\frac{k_2 - H_2 - \alpha_1 H_1}{k_2} \right) - \gamma_2 H_2 P$$

$$P' = \gamma_1 H_1 P \in_1 + \gamma_2 H_2 P \in_2 - DP$$

Where γ indicates the rate of a successful kill per encounter (the number of which are expressed by H*P) between the two organisms. The $\in$'s represent the conversion ratio between successful kills and new predators. D is the death rate of the predators. The form of these equations can lead to discussions about what the factors really mean, for example, would a larger body size for H_1 increase or decrease $\in_1$? (Increase.) If H_2 gets faster, what would happen to γ_2? (Decrease.)

	A	B	C	D	E	F	G	H	I
1									
2		H1		H2					
3	r1=	0.4	r2=	0.1					
4	k1=	1000	k2=	400					
5	a1=	0.1	a2=	0.3					
6	g1=	0.005	g2=	0.001					
7	e1=	0.15	e2=	0.3					
8	D=	0.2							
9	Generation	H1	H2	P					
10	0	100	100	2					
11	1	133.8	107.05	1.81					
12	2	177.2293	114.3382	1.687762					
13	3	231.6297	121.8042	1.632443					
14	4	297.5444	129.3713	1.649197					
15	5	374.0763	136.9485	1.751398					
16	6	458.3103	144.4341	1.964441					
17	7	545.17	151.7236	2.331915					
18	8	628.0716	158.7192	2.925141					
19	9	700.3622	165.3368	3.857295					
20	10	756.9012	171.5037	5.303289					
21	11	794.8542	177.1459	7.526041					
22	12	813.2715	182.162	10.90737					
23	13	811.8849	186.3919	15.97496					
24	14	789.9674	189.5847	23.40063					
25	15	745.9344	191.3771	33.91572					

FIGURE 4. Example of a spreadsheet set up to demonstrate population growth.

Setting up Spreadsheet Models

Apart from discussing the equations in general terms, these equations can be programmed onto a spreadsheet that will allow the students to set values and watch the populations of the organisms thrive or die. The spreadsheet program I have used to model the equations and to generate the figures is Corel® Quattro® Pro 7.0. I will describe the modeling of the two herbivores/one predator case because other cases are simplified versions of this and easily modeled if this example is understood. When being taught to students it is probably best to present the models in the order above, especially if the students are unfamiliar with spreadsheets.

Figure 4 shows a setup for the calculations. The cells are identified by their coordinates (for example, in Figure 4, cell B5 is 0.1). Rows 2 through 8 contain the labels for the constants or the constants themselves as defined in the equations above: r1 and r2 represent r_1 and r_2, k1 and k2 represent k_1 and k_2, a1 and a2 represent α_1 and α_2, g1 and g2 represent γ_1 and γ_2, e1 and e2 represent $\in_1$ and $\in_2$, and finally D represents D. Row 9 contains labels for each column below. Row 10 contains the generation number in column A and the starting population of each organism in B10, C10, and D10. Row 11 is where the calculations begin.

In cell B11 the equation is: B10 + $B$3*B10*[($B$4-B10-$D$5*C10)/$B$4]-$B$6*B10*D10 which corresponds to the equation shown earlier. The dollar signs are used to prevent the cell references from changing when the cell is dragged down (to the long columns).

In cell C11 the equation is: C10+$D$3*C10*[($D$4-C10-$B$5*B10)/$D$4]-$D$6*C10*D10.

In cell D11 the equation is: D10 + $B$6*B10*D10*$B$7 + $D$6*C10*D10*$D$7-$B$8*D10.

Once all the equations are entered, drag the cells down to generate a series of cells that re-evaluate the equations with each generation using the population values from the previous one.

The graph is generated simply by highlighting the population columns (I recommend creating the graphs out of at least 100 generations in order to see long-term changes) and clicking the graph icon above the spreadsheet. Adding the generation column as a series for x-values gives a good x-axis.

Experiments with the Spreadsheet

Once a spreadsheet and linked graph have been set up, the students can experiment by changing the values of the constants and starting populations. Once a block of cells and graph are linked, the graph should automatically change when the values in the block do. The students should consider what characteristics the organisms would have to change in order to change the values. Would a larger γ mean that the organism was better or worse at escaping predators? (Worse) Would a smaller, shorter-lived organism have: a larger r? (Yes), smaller ∈? (Yes), larger γ? (Maybe), etc. The goal is for the students to be able to make the connection between the mathematical model and the reality it represents.

Figure 5 shows 100 generations using the same values as in Figure 4. From these values perhaps herbivore 1 is small (rabbit) and herbivore 2 is larger (moose) and the predator is a wolf. Note that cycling of population size is common for models with predators and quickly reproducing prey. Note that the more quickly reproducing organisms (larger r) cycle more severely with the predator.

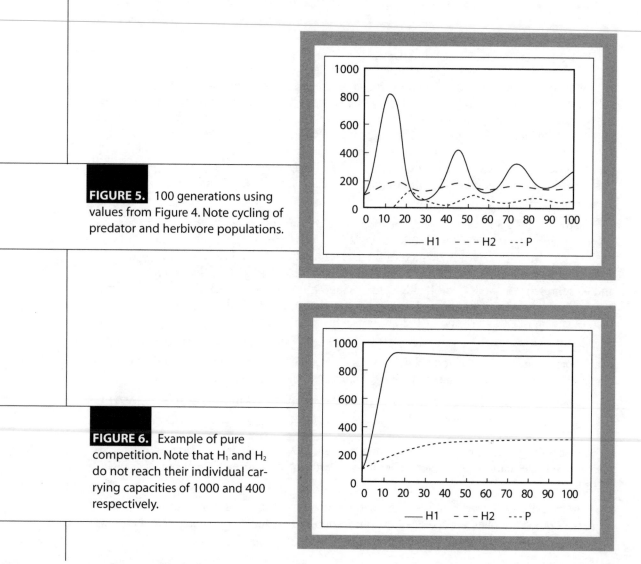

FIGURE 5. 100 generations using values from Figure 4. Note cycling of predator and herbivore populations.

FIGURE 6. Example of pure competition. Note that H₁ and H₂ do not reach their individual carrying capacities of 1000 and 400 respectively.

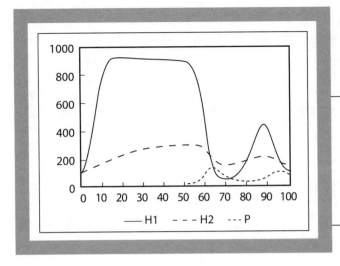

FIGURE 7. The introduction of two predators at generation 50 into a pure competition situation as in Figure 6. Note the drastic decline in herbivore 1, almost driving it to extinction.

If there are no predators, we set the initial value of P to zero (with the same values we have been using for other constants as in Figure 4) and get Figure 6. This represents pure competition without predation. The final populations of the herbivores can be seen to be below their individual carrying capacities (k) due to their competition with each other. Changing the values of α_1 and α_2 would result in different final proportions of the populations. We can also see the effects that the predator in Figure 5 had on the final populations of the herbivores.

We could model the introduction of a new predator or herbivore by setting the initial value of the species to be introduced to zero and inserting a value at some later generation to represent the introduction. Figure 7 shows the introduction of two predators (at generation 50) into the competition situation in Figure 6. We can see the drastic reduction in the number of organisms in this ecosystem. In fact, herbivore 1 comes close to extinction. This is an example of what can happen when humans are careless and introduce unsuitable species into new environments.

I would encourage the students to explore many situations and values for the mathematical constants. There are many different looking graphs that can arise out of this model and each makes a different statement about what happens to these organisms in their shared ecosystem. It is actually surprising how many situations are unstable; perhaps this is a testament to the fragility of nature. The students could prepare reports about the shape of the graphs for different values. They could try to predict the shape of the graphs for certain values of r, $\in$, γ, etc., and then accept or reject these hypotheses. If the graphs do not meet their expectations they may want to explain why they think they were mistaken.

Original Source

This activity has been adapted from an original by Ashley J. R. Carter (1999) titled "Using Spreadsheets To Model Population Growth, Competition and Predation in Nature" and appeared in *The American Biology Teacher*, 61(4), 294-296. It has been reprinted and modified with permission of the publisher.

Investigating Species Interactions with *Daphnia* sp.

Based on an original activity by John Cruzan

In natural communities species often interact in a variety of ways, some of which may reduce populations (competition; predation for the prey) and some of which may increase them (commensalism; predation for the predator). These types of interactions can be illustrated by examining microcosms established with or without a potential competitor, commensal, or predator.

Ecological Principles Illustrated

- Competition
- Predation
- Commensalism

Materials

- 500 ml pond water
- cheesecloth
- pipet
- *Daphnia*
- microscope slides
- coverslips
- Palmer counting cell
- microcrustaceans
- hydras or tiny fish
- 4-L jar
- topsoil
- Styrofoam™ box
- Berlese funnels
- earthworms, centipedes, or a small salamander
- 15-watt bulb
- petri dish
- dissecting microscope
- guides to pond organisms

Procedure

Aquatic microcosms can be established with 500 ml of pond water maintained in a lighted location. Microcrustaceans, such as cladocerans and copepods, can be removed by filtering through several layers of cheesecloth and then picking out with a pipet those that subsequently appear. Reintroducing *Daphnia* into one microcosm and leaving another as a control permits analysis of the impact this micropredator has. Examine samples from each microcosm by stirring the culture, removing a small sample, and examining either a drop on a glass slide with a coverslip or 0.1 ml in a Palmer counting cell. Protozoa and algae can be identified using various guides to pond organisms. Positive identification is less important than recognizing different organisms, even if they are "named" A, B, C, etc. Students can calculate densities, species richness, and a species diversity index (such as Shannon-Weiner) to compare the two microcosms.

A variation of this experiment leaves the microcrustaceans in and introduces hydras or tiny fish into the experimental culture. A larger volume container, such as a 4-liter jar, works better for this experiment.

Species interactions can also be examined in soil microcosms. To establish them, freshly collected topsoil is brought into the laboratory and placed in a plastic or Styrofoam™ box with an area of 0.1 square meters or greater. The soil brings with it populations of soil microarthropods, such as various types of mites, springtails, and other small insects. Now a potential predator or commensal can be introduced. Some possibilities include earthworms, centipedes, and small salamanders.

After 4 weeks, soil cores are removed from the containers and placed in Berlese funnels. A Berlese funnel is a plastic funnel large enough to hold the sample with a shelf of wire mesh that holds the sample above the bottom of the funnel. The soil core is placed on cheesecloth in the funnel, and the funnel is suspended over a vial or small jar of preservative (70% ethanol). A 15-watt bulb over the soil slowly dries it out, forcing the soil animals to burrow downward, ultimately falling out the bottom into the alcohol. The organisms are examined in the preservative in a petri dish under a dissecting microscope. Identification of species is usually not possible, but major groups can be identified and obvious variants identified as A, B, C, etc. Again, the different treatments can be characterized as to numbers of organisms, richness, and diversity. The number per soil core may be relatively low, so pooling of class data will be helpful.

Original Source

This activity is based on an original exercise by John Cruzan (1988) titled "Teaching Ecology with Microcosms" in *The American Biology Teacher, 50*(4), 226-228, and has been modified by the author specifically for this monograph.

Investigating Population Growth and Competition with *Paramecium* sp.

Based on an original activity by John Cruzan

The purpose of this laboratory exercise is to closely determine how the growth of a population approximates the sigmoid growth curve predicted by the logistic equation and to observe how competition between species influences population growth.

Ecological Principles Illustrated

- Competition
- Population growth

Materials

- 6 tubes of medium
- *Paramecium multimicronucleatum*
- *Paramecium aurelia*
- protozoan food
- cotton
- parafilm
- calibrated dropper
- microscope slides
- warming tray or hotplate

Procedure

The experimental organisms are two species of paramecium, *P. multimicronucleatum* and *P. aurelia*. These two can be easily distinguished on the basis of size, *P. aurelia* being much smaller. Student pairs will each be provided with 6 tubes of medium in which to grow protozoans. Two are to be inoculated with *P. multimicronucleatum*, 2 with *P. aurelia,* and 2 with a mixture of equal numbers of the 2 species. Each population should be started with 10 ml of medium containing a total of 200 paramecia. Each tube should be plugged loosely with cotton and labeled. Mark the level of the medium on the outside of each tube.

Census the contents of each tube 3 times a week until the populations have all declined to near zero. It is essential that no census periods be skipped, especially in the early stages of the experiment. Censusing is done by removing the cotton plug and replacing it with a square of parafilm. Placing a thumb over the parafilm, gently agitate the contents of the tube and immediately remove a sample with a calibrated dropper.

Place one 0.05 ml of the sample on a slide and count the number of paramecia on the slide. If the paramecia per slide are too active to count, warm the slide for a couple of minutes on a warming tray or warm hotplate. As the volume of medium is reduced, return it to its original level with new medium from the refrigerator. Each student pair should maintain a record of population densities with the cultures.

Submit population growth curves for each population. Discussion of the growth curves should relate results to the logistic equation and competitive exclusion. Do both species exhibit similar growth? Can the carrying capacity for each one be estimated? If they are not the same, why? Which species seems to be the superior competitor? Any ideas why? Why did all the populations eventually decline?

The final report should include 3 graphs of population growth:

1. *P. multimicronucleatum* alone and in competition.

2. *P. aurelia* alone and in competition.

3. *P. multinucleatum* and *P. aurelia* in competition.

Graphs should have the following form:

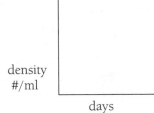

To prepare the medium, boil one Carolina™ protozoa pellet in 1000 ml of spring water or other water for 10 minutes. With frequent stirring or agitation to keep it suspended, dispense 10 ml portions into test tubes. Place one grain of boiled wheat in the bottom of each tube.

Original Source

This activity is based on an original exercise by John Cruzan (1988) titled "Teaching Ecology with Microcosms" in *The American Biology Teacher, 50*(4), 226-228, and has been modified by the author specifically for this monograph.

Simulating Predator-Prey Interactions

Based on an original activity by
M.C. Calver and R.D. Wooler

Introduction

Knowledge of predation is key to an understanding of basic ecology. Predation is a major ecosystem process, underlying such important concepts as food web structure and community stability, the theory of the niche, and foraging theory, as well as having important applied functions in understanding biological control, harvesting, and optimal yield. Furthermore, by their choice of prey, predators influence the rate of cycling of important nutrients through ecosystems. While some useful guides to fieldwork for teaching predation biology are available (e.g., Sellers & Allen, 1991), practical work involving predation presents special ethical problems for both professional researchers and teachers. There may also be logistical problems in planning and executing such studies.

Alternative paper and pencil classroom exercises are available (e.g., Calver & King, 1986; Calver & Porter, 1986) as well as some excellent computer simulations (e.g., Cook, 1993), but access to a suitable number of computers is not always available and both computer simulations and paper and pencil exercises lack the excitement and stimulation of using real animals, even if the experimental animal is a human! Tranter (1982) and Barker (1983) present simple but enjoyable simulations for classroom studies of mimicry and crypsis as anti-predator defenses using humans as the predators, while Gendron and Staddon (1984) and Knill and Allen (1995) used humans as models of visual studies in research projects that could be modified for teaching situations.

Overview

Here, we follow this approach by adapting for classroom use the experiments of Holling (1959a) and Rogers (1972), in which a predator (a blindfolded assistant) hunted for prey (discs of sandpaper or polythene) on a large desktop under time constraints. This simulates a number of real situations, including, for example, a wading bird probing a beach for invertebrates in the face of a rising tide. The initial purpose is to determine and interpret the relationship between prey density and number of prey taken by the predator, which is known as the functional response. Thereafter, the simulation can be modified to explore the effects of changes in predator behavior and prey distribution on the shape of the functional response curve.

This strategy may be used at several different levels. Advanced students can be challenged by asking them to design modified simulations which will produce specific functional responses or by fitting theoretical functional response equations from the literature to their data. More sophisticated exercises requiring skills in non-linear curve fitting and significance testing are possible, which would challenge senior undergraduate students in biometry.

Ecological Principles Illustrated

- Population interactions
- Predator-prey relationships
- Mathematical expressions of ecological relationships

Materials

Students should work in pairs or small groups, each needing:

- 50 x 9 cm diameter paper discs. Filter papers are ideal. (7 cm squares cut from used pieces of photocopy paper also work, and if these inexpensive sheets are crumpled during the exercise they can be replaced.)

- 50 paper clips

- a blindfold

- an empty margarine tub or small box

- a stopwatch

Background Information

Functional Responses

The functional response is the relationship between an individual predator's consumption rate (defined as the number of prey eaten per unit time) and the density of its prey. Holling (1959a) recognized four different categories, although only three of these, known simply as Type 1, Type II, and Type III (Figure 1), are widely discussed in undergraduate textbooks. The shape of a functional response curve is influenced by the primary factors of predator attack rate and the time taken to locate, catch, and consume prey. Subsidiary factors such as learning, hunger, and fatigue may also influence the functional response.

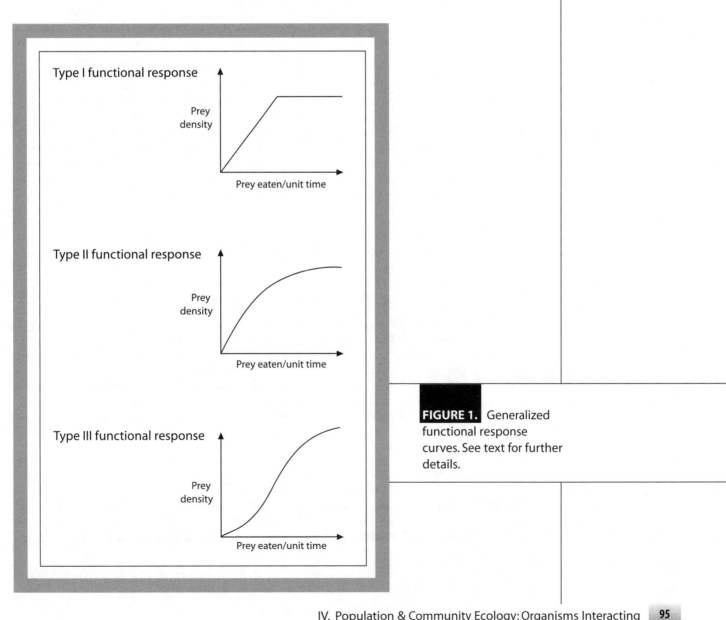

FIGURE 1. Generalized functional response curves. See text for further details.

Type I is characteristic of filter feeders and shows a constant increase in the number of prey taken at increasing prey densities, followed by an abrupt plateau when the predator's filters are saturated. Many animals feeding predominantly on one species of prey show a Type II functional response, in which the predator takes greater numbers of prey as prey density rises, although the number of prey taken ultimately reaches a plateau. The rate of increase in the curve is determined by the attack rate of the predator at different prey densities, and the ultimate ceiling is related to the time taken to capture, subdue, and eat each prey (handling time). At the plateau level, under the time restrictions that may affect predators, they are essentially constrained by how fast they can catch and eat their prey.

Type III functional responses can occur when a predator's attack rate or handling time improve at higher prey densities, which might happen if the predator switched the focus of its attention from one prey type to another. The predator initially records only a small increase in the number of prey taken as prey density rises, but then above a critical prey density the number of kills rises sharply before leveling off. Overall, this gives an S-shaped functional response curve. Some earlier textbooks refer to Type II as the invertebrate response and Type III as the vertebrate response, which can be misleading since the response depends on the number of prey species in the system and not the taxonomic classification of the predator.

Type II is probably the most widely studied of the functional responses and Holling (1959a, b) summarized the curve mathematically with the expression:

$$P_e = \frac{a'\,NT}{1 + a'\,T_h N}$$

where P_e is the number of prey eaten during a specified searching time; T, a' is the attack rate; N is the density of prey; and T_h is the handling time. The equation assumes prey replenishment as they are eaten (N is assumed constant), but alternative models are available for those cases where this is untrue (e.g., Rogers, 1972). Comparisons of functional responses, in particular estimates of the constants a' and T_h, can be used to predict which of a range of predators is more likely to have an impact on a target prey population. Approaches to statistical significance testing in this area are given by Butler and Burns (1993), Juliano (1993), and Casas and Hulliger (1994). Accounts of current research questions in functional response theory, including a fuller discussion of methodology and relevant equations, are given in Fan and Petitt (1997) with references.

The Simulation

Aims

The initial aim of the simulation is to produce a Type II functional response. Students may then vary aspects of the methodology to see if this alters the steepness of the curve, or produces a different functional response altogether. By their involvement as the active predators, students should have a greater insight into the aspects of predator behavior that lead to their results than would result from using a computer simulation, which although faster, does not allow them to share the predator's experience. The description below applies to the basic simulation we use with undergraduate university students (c. 19 years of age) studying an elective in animal behavior; we also give suggestions for adapting it to a wide range of teaching situations.

Basic Procedure

We describe first the basic procedure we have used in our laboratory classes, followed by brief summaries of other approaches given in the research literature. If 2 to 3 hours are available for the complete exercise, each group member may take a turn as the predator and be tested at prey densities for 5, 10, 15, 20, and 25 prey spread on a bench or table of 2.25 m². However, if time is more pressing, only one person per group need be a predator and the class results can be combined.

The predator is blindfolded, then the others spread the required number of papers on the surface. It is helpful if the predator remains blindfolded through the whole procedure to avoid detecting any subtle cues about the density of prey to be placed in the next trial. For instance, those positioning the prey should be careful to take roughly the same amount of time on each occasion, so that a cunning predator cannot use the time between trials as a likely indicator of the density of prey available. Similarly, predators should not be told the outcome of any trial until they have completed their sequence of 5 trials.

Randomizing the presentation sequence and the position of the papers on the surface is vital. Such a technique will control for the possible effect of predator learning and ensures that the distrubution of prey does not vary during the trials. Planning how this will be accomplished can be introduced as part of the exercise.

Once the arena is ready, the blindfolded predator should be positioned, together with the margarine tub and paper clips, and begin searching by tapping with the fingers of one hand on the surface to locate prey. Sliding fingers on palms over the surface rapidly to sweep up prey is cheating! Some predators find it useful to roll up long sleeves to avoid brushing prey off the surface. The aim is to capture as many prey as possible in 2 minutes. Once encountered, each prey is captured, killed, and eaten by picking up the paper, folding it into quarters, securing the loose edges with a paperclip, and dropping the secured paper into the stomach (margarine tub). The predator should then resume the search. When the time is up, the number of prey eaten is recorded, the prey for the next trial are positioned, and the procedure is repeated until all group members have been tested at all prey densities.

Paper prey caught in an earlier trial become easier to capture as they are crumpled, and do not lie flat on the bench. Such prey can be rationalized as having escaped wounded from an earlier encounter, the injury making them easier to recapture. Alternately, fresh prey can be supplied for each trial. The number of prey eaten is plotted against prey density, either as a group mean or with a separate symbol or color for each individual predator. A curve can then be fitted by eye to the points. Students can be asked to explain the shape of the curve, and guided discussion used to help them appreciate that the curve plateaus when the predator is spending very little time searching, and virtually all its time in processing prey. If data for individual predators have been plotted, individual variation between predators might provide an interesting topic for discussion.

Holling's original experiments (Holling, 1959a) used sandpaper discs of 4 cm diameter, distributing 4, 9, 16, 25, 49, 81, 100, and 256 of them in turn over an area of 9 ft.^{2} (c. 0.83 m^2). Rogers (1972) used polythene discs of 4.5 cm diameter in a square arena of 0.83 m^2, distributing in turn 4, 8, 16, 32, 64, and 128 of them. In both cases, subjects placed a paper clip on discs found but did not fold them. The use of very high prey densities in these experiments helps in confirming the plateau in the Type II functional response, but extends the preparation time for each trial considerably if the discs are positioned randomly. We chose to use randomization and a smaller number of discs, although other instructors may have different preferences. A sample data set generated by our students is shown in Figure 2, together with examples from Holling (1959a) and Rogers (1972) to illustrate likely results and help others judge the value of including high prey densities.

Modifications and Enhancements

Many modifications are possible depending on the ability of the students and the points the instructor wishes to emphasize.

1. **Prey replenishment.** The simulation described here does not involve the replacement of prey that are lost, so that prey density falls during a trial. Students may wish to speculate on the effect of this and test their predictions by repeating the experiments with prey being replaced as they are captured. Doing this, without sending subtle cues to the predator, requires ingenuity!

2. **Prey distribution.** Is the functional response curve altered if prey are aggregated or dispersed, instead of random? Students can generate and test their own hypotheses.

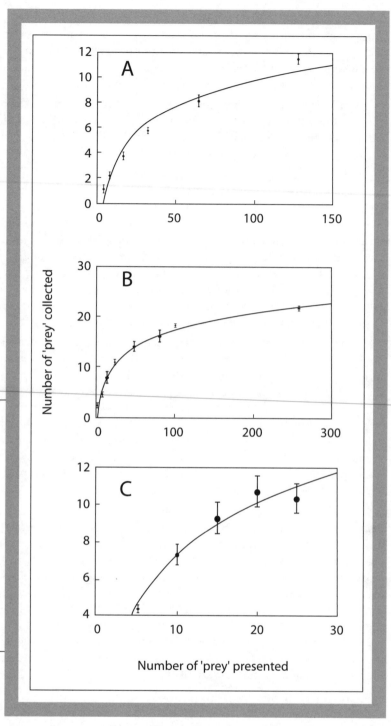

FIGURE 2. Examples of Type II functional response curves generated from simulation data. 'A' uses data from Rogers (1972) n = 8, 'B' uses data from Holling (1959a) n = 8, and 'C' presents data collected by our students n = 3 (from one practical group). Points correspond to means and the error bars to standard errors. The precise methodology used in collecting each data set is described in the text. Logarithmic curves were fitted to the data for simplicity, but Holling (1959a), Rogers (1972), and references included in Fan and Petitt (1997) give specialist functional response equations that can be fitted if desired.

3. **Alternative search techniques.** Fingers may be walked over the surface, rather than stabbed at it, to provide a different search technique. Holling (1959a) includes a fascinating variation in which the predator searches for the prey by tapping with a pencil, making prey detection auditory rather than tactile. What difference do these techniques make to the functional response curve?

4. **Predator satiation.** If paper clips are kept in the margarine tub with folded paper prey, the clips become harder to find as the stomach fills with prey. This may prompt discussion about whether ingestion of prey slows down as the stomach fills and the predator becomes satiated.

5. **Prey refuge.** These can be simulated by placing 50 envelopes randomly on the surface. The required prey are placed inside some of the envelopes. What effect does this have on the functional response? Astute students will recognize that the search time of the predator will rise considerably under this system, thereby reducing the attack rate.

6. **The Type III functional response.** We give our students the challenge of modifying the simulation so that the data fit a Type III functional response rather than Type II. The key to a successful modification is to simulate the predator switching from one prey type to another, a common cause of a Type III curve. We have not tested this thoroughly, but one approach that may work is to provide two different prey refuges, such as equal numbers of envelopes and Petri dishes (50 each). The dishes can contain an alternative prey at a constant number of 7 per trial, while the target prey, at densities from 5 to 25, are always concealed in envelopes. As the density of the target prey rises, the predator should learn that the envelopes are far more likely to contain prey and switch to searching in them alone, thus producing a Type III curve for the prey type concealed in envelopes. It may be desirable to present trials in sequence from low to high target prey density and to increase the search time per trial for this to succeed, but such an approach would be analogous to temporal changes in prey abundance.

7. **Fitting functional response curves and significance testing.** If good computing facilities are available, senior students with some biometrical training may attempt to model their data using the different equations given in Holling (1959a, b), Rogers (1972), Juliano (1993), and Casas and Hulliger (1994), noting the specific assumptions of each equation in deciding which should give the best fit to their data. The equations can also be used to estimate handling time and attack rates for each simulation, and the methods of Butler and Burns (1993) and Juliano (1993) can be used to test for significant differences in these factors in different simulations. For example, does providing a prey refuge make a significant difference to either or both of these variables? If biometrical approaches are to be a major feature of the work, instructors could set one or more readings from Fan and Petitt (1997) and included references, which debate significant issues in this area.

Original Source

This activity has been adapted from an original activity by M.C. Calver and R.D. Wooller (1988). It was originally titled "A Nondestructive Laboratory Exercise for Teaching Some Principles of Predation" and appeared in *The Journal of Biological Education, 33*(1), 45-48. It has been reprinted and modified with permission of the publisher.

Demonstrating Predator-Prey Relationships and Food Selection with Fish

Based on an original activity by Paul M. Kotila

The exercise involves a nonlethal technique for collecting consumed prey from stream fish while, at the same time, gathering samples of invertebrates near the fish collection site. This allows students to compare the fishes' available food with their actual consumption. Students will learn a technique for determining the diet of a natural population of predators, the variety of prey consumed, and the selective nature of predation and its quantification using an electivity index.

Ecological Principles Illustrated

- Predator-prey relationships
- Food selection

Materials

- 7.5-1 pump sprayer (H.D. Hudson Manufacturing Company, 500 N. Michigan Ave., Chicago, IL 60611); 1.0-ml hypodermic syringe attached to sprayer nozzle using 0.8 mm ID Tygon tubing and ring clamp; 18 gauge needle with 4 to 6 cm of 1.4-mm ID plastic tubing (larger needle and tubing may be substituted for larger fish)

- D-frame or triangular dip net with net mesh of 500 μm or less

- miscellaneous field equipment – shallow white pans, forceps, 70% alcohol, squirt bottle, 100-ml sample jars with labels, bucket, hip boots, fish measuring board (optional)

- lab equipment – watch glasses, dissection microscopes, identification keys, data sheets

Procedure

Sculpins (*Cottus* spp.) are good fish to use for this exercise because of their small size (generally <10 cm long), ease of collection, and relative abundance. Other fish species may be equally suitable, and the following procedures can be modified easily to accommodate larger fish. A fishing license and collecting permit often are required for this type of work, and instructors should check with local fish and game authorities before beginning this exercise.

Sculpins are common benthic (bottom-dwelling) fish of shallow riffle areas of medium-sized streams where they are predators on benthic invertebrates, small fish, and fish eggs. These fish can be collected by placing a flat-edged dip net on the bottom just downstream of any large, loose stone. The stone is then kicked over, and any sculpin present will be swept by the current into the net. The fish then can be transferred to a holding bucket. Ten to 20 sculpins can be collected in an hour using this technique.

Benthic invertebrates can also be collected near the fish collection site. Place the dip net firmly on the bottom and agitate the substrate immediately upstream of the net with a stick or foot. Dislodged organisms will drift into the net. This technique will collect most benthic invertebrates of fast water that are accessible to fish (Hynes, 1970). Three bottom samples are usually sufficient to collect a hundred or more invertebrates. More samples may be necessary if benthic populations are sparse. A net with a mesh of >500 μm should not be used because it will not retain many of the smaller invertebrates likely to be consumed by sculpins.

Invertebrates are separated from debris by dumping the collected sample into a white pan containing stream water and picking out the organisms (photo developing trays work well). Alternatively, samples can be preserved in 70% alcohol for later sorting in the lab.

Gut contents of collected fish are obtained by using a stomach washing (gastric lavage) technique (Light, Adler & Arnold, 1983). The pump sprayer with an attached hypodermic syringe is used to wash food items from fish stomachs. A damp cloth or cotton glove is used to hold each fish firmly against the bottom of the white pan. The plastic tubing attached to the syringe needle is inserted through the fish's mouth into the stomach until resistance is encountered. This should be done carefully to avoid puncturing the stomach or passing the tube out through the gills. The sprayer valve is depressed for 3 to 5 seconds to wash any gut contents into the pan. This technique causes little mortality (Meehan & Miller, 1978) and avoids the regurgitation that can occur when fish are killed in formaldehyde or alcohol for later dissection.

The fish can be measured at this time, if desired, before returning the fish to the stream or placing them in a holding bucket. The food items are rinsed into a labeled collection jar using a squirt bottle filled with water. Each fish's gut contents must be placed in a separate jar. Later, transfer these samples to 70% alcohol but do not use alcohol as a pan rinse because this could harm the fish.

Invertebrates should be identified at least to the order level (Edmondson, 1959; Needham & Needham, 1962; Pennak, 1978), and family determinations of common groups may be useful (Table 1). Identification usually requires use of a dissection microscope. Organisms in the benthic samples should be identified first. This will enable students to associate body parts in the guts with whole organisms. The number of prey consumed by each fish is then determined from the identification of these parts. Do not count duplicated parts (e.g., 6 legs/insect) as more than 1 individual. While more rapid digestion of soft-bodied prey can bias these data (Hyslop, 1980), there is no way to correct for this effect without conducting studies of digestion rates.

A labeled display of invertebrates collected from the stream will speed identification of specimens and body parts by students. The instructor should check identifications before students record them. Experience indicated that a class of 15 students can complete gut washing (using one sprayer), invertebrate identification and enumeration, and discuss data analysis within a 3-hour lab period if fish and benthos are collected ahead of time and brought to the lab. An additional 2 to 3 hours will be necessary if the whole class participates in the collecting.

Data Analysis and Interpretation

Students should examine the tabular data before they begin the following calculations, noting the variety of food items, the number of fish with empty guts, and the presence of unconsumed "foods." The absence of a gut item from the benthic samples may indicate that sampling was inadequate.

The numbers of food items in the stomachs can be standardized to fractions or percentage values in two ways (Table 2). The Frequency of Occurrence (FO) is the fraction of those guts with food in them that contained a particular item. (Note that fish #2 is not included in this calculation.) This indicates how widespread a particular food is in the guts of all fish collected and how variable diet is from fish to fish. Mayflies, for example, occurred in 5 of 11 fish collected (Table 1), giving a FO of 0.45 (Table 2).

The Fractional Composition (or Percent Composition) by numbers indicated the fraction of all food items belonging to a particular category. These values can be calculated for gut contents (r_i) and benthos (n_i). Gut fractional composition values (r_i) indicate the relative importance of the various food types to the group of fish examined, while n_i values indicate the relative abundances of foods in the environment. Eight mayflies, for example, occurred in both the guts and benthos, giving r_i and n_i values of 0.032 (8/248) and 0.066 (8/122), respectively.

Spearman's rank correlation test (Siegel, 1956) can be used to compare relative abundances of foods in the guts and the benthos. Consumed prey and benthic organisms are separately ranked in decreasing order of abundance with the most common type receiving the highest rank of one. Less abundant prey receive progressively higher ranks (2, 3, etc.), and tied categories are assigned the average of their ranks. The differences in the ranks of each prey type (guts vs. benthos) are used to calculate a correlation coefficient (r_s) (Siegel, 1956). The prey in Table 2, for example, exhibit significant rank correlations between abundances in the guts and abundances in the benthos ($r_s = 0.85$, $p < 0.05$), as well as between frequency of occurrence in guts and benthic abundance ($r_s = 0.80$, $p < 0.05$). It therefore appears that sculpins consume prey in relative order of their abundances in the environment.

The food preferences of sculpins also can be examined using any of a number of selectivity or electivity indices (Lechowicz, 1982). Ivlev's (1961) Electivity (E) is one such index that compares the fractional composition of a particular food item (i) in the guts (r_i) to its fractional composition in the available food supply (p_i):

$$E_i = (r_i - p_i)/(r_i + p_i)$$

TABLE 1. Invertebrates collected from sculpin guts and benthos.

Taxon (common name)	1	2	3	4	5	6	7	8	9	10	11	12	Tot.	1	2	3	Tot.
					Fish										Benthos		
Chironomidae (*midge larvae*)	9		7	1	3	10	2	2	11	2	9	2	58	58	106	26	190
Simuliidae (*black fly larve*)	6		1				13	1	13	2	3	39	20	5	4	29
Other Diptera (*true fly larvae*)			2	1	1						1		5	9			9
Trichoptera (*caddisfly larvae*)	1		3		2	1	1	1			3		12	2	4	1	7
Coleoptera (*beetles*)													0	1			1
Ephemeroptera (*mayfly nymphs*)			3	1		1	1					2	8		2	6	8
Plecoptera (*stonefly nymphs*)													0	1	1	2	4
Total	16	0	16	3	6	12	4	16	12	15	15	7	122	91	118	39	248

Values of E can range from -1 to 1. A value of less than zero indicates possible avoidance of a food type, while a value greater than zero indicates an apparent preference. A value of zero indicates that a prey is being consumed in the same proportion as it is found in the environment. While high electivity implies that a fish "looks for" this particular food, such a value could also indicate a particularly accessible or easily found prey. Low E values might indicate active avoidance, poor visibility, or good defense by the prey (Ringler, 1979). Further study would be necessary to determine why a predator selects certain foods.

Note that the same E value can occur for very different composition values (e.g., $E = 0.33$ for $r_i = 0.8$. $p_i = 0.4$ or $r_i = 0.1$, $p_i = 0.05$). Thus, E indicates selection for or against a prey but not its importance in the diet. While other indices have been proposed to incorporate an importance component (e.g., Strauss, 1982), the use of such indices does not result in any apparent improvement in measures of relative prey preference (Lechowicz, 1982).

Once students realize that E is not a measure of feeding intensity, they should understand intuitively the meaning of relatively high or low E values. The ranking of foods based on E values can be compared to a ranking based on availability using Spearman's test. This correlation is not statistically significant for my example (Table 2) ($r_s = 0.38$, $p > 0.05$), thus indicating that food preferences are not merely a reflection of abundance.

A close examination of the data frequently turns up some interesting "contradictions," such as a commonly consumed prey (high r_i) that exhibits a low E (e.g., Chironomidae). Such data can be used as a basis for a discussion of how r_i, FO, and E measures differ, what they can and cannot tell us, and how they can be used together to determine the importance of various prey and how fish feed.

| Taxon | Gut Contents | | Benthos | |
	Frequency of Occurrence (FO)	Fraction of Total (r_i)	Fraction of Total (p_i)	Electivity (E)
Chironomidae	1.00	0.475	0.766	-0.23
Simuliidae	0.64	0.320	0.117	0.46
Other Diptera	0.36	0.041	0.036	0.06
Trichoptera	0.64	0.098	0.028	0.56
Coleoptera	0.00	0.000	0.004	-1.00
Ephemeroptera	0.45	0.066	0.032	0.35
Plecoptera	0.00	0.000	0.016	1.00

TABLE 2. Electivity (E) values and relative composition of invertebrates found in sculpin guts and benthos.

It should be possible to see significant size differences among individuals in some taxa. The mass of various species of dipterans, for example, may differ by two orders of magnitude or more. Such differences introduce students to concepts of biomass, nutrients, and energy content. They also indicate a potential problem when only higher taxonomic categories are used in food selection studies or numbers of individuals are used to quantify trophic relationships.

Once students realize that predators are both selective and flexible in their feeding habits, they can begin to understand why many questions in predator-prey relationships remain unresolved. The effects of predators on prey numbers, distribution, genetic composition, and evolution are vigorously debated issues that have important implications for the management of endangered species, game animals, and pests. This laboratory will introduce students to techniques used in predator-prey studies and some approaches for data analysis.

Original Source

This activity is based on an exercise by Paul M. Kotila (1987) titled "Using Stream Fish to Demonstrate Predator-Prey Relationships and Food Selection" in *The American Biology Teacher,* *49*(2), 103-106, and is modified and reprinted with permission of the publisher.

The experiments described here deal with the feeding mechanism of a carnivorous plant and allow students to examine the impact of both predator and prey characteristics on the capture success of the predator. This approach can be used as a laboratory exercise or the subject for an independent study/research project.

Ecological Principles Illustrated

- Predator-prey relationships

Introduction

"Cobra lily" (*Darlingtonia californica*) is a carnivorous plant restricted in range to northern California and southern Oregon (Schnell, 1976; Juniper et al., 1989). The cobra lily traps insects in a tubular, hooded leaf that curves in such a fashion as to resemble the head of a striking cobra. The leaves have small oval-shaped openings on the underside of the curved hood through which insects enter the trap. Extending below the opening is a forked appendage that is covered with nectaries, presumably for attracting prey. Insects can be observed to land on or crawl onto the "tongue-like" structure and then enter the trap.

Once in the trap, escape is impeded by two mechanisms. In the upper, curved region of the leaf opposite the entrance hole, there are areas that lack chlorophyll and are known as "areolae" or "fenestra." These areas are regions that permit light to enter the inside of the leaf, much like a window (after which the structures were named), and serve as light sources to confuse potential escaping prey by directing them away from the entrance hole. The other anti-escape mechanism is the downward pointing hairs that form a dense lining on the inner surface of the leaf tube. These hairs appear to impede insects from climbing up and out of the leaf tube.

Under natural conditions, *D. californica* attracts a variety of prey items, depending upon its location and the season. Prey include ants, grasshoppers, flies, moths, and spiders (Juniper et al., 1989).

Materials

- cobra lily (*Darlingtonia californica*) [available through biological supply houses]
- ether or Fly-Nap® (also available through biological supply houses)
- *Drosophila virilis, D. melanogaster,* or other similar-size insects
- 9-inch plastic pots filled with a mixture of sand and peat moss
- 3-liter plastic soda container or 250-ml flask with clamp and appropriate support stand
- foam sponge or nonabsorbent cotton to plug either of the above containers' openings
- fluorescent growth light (optional)

Teacher Background

Drosophila virilis is cultured in a standard fashion using prepared instant media and virtually any size bottles or containers. *Drosophila virilis* is used as the prey in the following experiments because they are somewhat larger than *D. melanogaster,* but there is no reason other insects could not be used if they are available.

Cobra lilies do not have extensive root systems and will grow readily in individual 9-inch plastic pots filled with a mixture of sand and peat moss. The soil mixture should be kept moist at all times. Additional plant care information can be found in Schnell (1976). Plants may be maintained in a greenhouse, if available, but a sunny windowsill also works equally well. However, during experimental trials — when more controlled environmental conditions are desired — the plants should be placed on a laboratory bench under fluorescent growth lights connected to a timer to provide a 12-hour photoperiod. Length of the experimental trials varies, but most often a 24-hour period is used. After an experimental trial is complete, the plants are returned to the greenhouse or window for recuperation.

In order to provide background, stimulate interest, and establish an intellectual framework for initiating experiments, assign a number of readings in the area of carnivorous plants and predator-prey systems. Heslop-Harrison (1978) provides a good introduction to the carnivorous habit in plants. Articles dealing with feeding behavior of the pitcher plant (*Sarracenia*) by Cresswell (1991), Wolfe (1981), and Plummer and Kethley (1964) will provide sufficient information to stimulate interest and help generate possible hypotheses for testing. Most general ecology textbooks (e.g., Smith 1990) and some introductory biology texts (e.g., Campbell et al. 1997) provide sufficient background on the concepts of predator and prey systems and, in particular, the role of prey density in predator success.

Preparation

Two different experimental arrangements are used, depending upon the experiment and the hypothesis under investigation. The first experimental setup employs a plastic 3-liter soda container with the bottom cut off to form a dome over the entire plant. The cut bottom of the bottle is pressed into the soil surface to prevent flies from escaping. The bottle cap is removed and replaced with a foam sponge or nonabsorbent cotton plug. The plug prevents flies from escaping, allows ventilation during an experimental trial, and provides a means for introducing an anesthetic to the flies at the end of a trial.

Flies are etherized and counted; known densities of flies are introduced into the dome. Anesthetized flies are introduced into the dome on a piece of white paper placed on the substrate surface. After an appropriate trial length, usually 24 hours, the flies not trapped by the plants and thus still visible within the dome are counted, etherized, and re-counted. Flies are etherized by placing large cotton swabs saturated with ether into the dome through the top opening. For those who prefer not to use ether because of obvious hazards, products such as Fly-Nap® should also work.

By introducing different densities of flies into the dome, one can investigate the capture success as a function of prey density. The use of a 3-liter bottle to form a dome over the entire plant is simple and effective for examining the capture success of entire plants but does not allow examination of individual leaves. In addition, students may encounter some difficulty in accounting for all the flies released within the dome.

The second experimental design is perhaps an improvement over the first. In this setup, individual leaves are enclosed within laboratory flasks. The size of the flask can vary, but 250-ml flasks appear to work best.

The flask is carefully placed over an individual leaf, and the mouth of the flask is closed with a foam plug through which a hole has been bored to allow it to be slipped around the base of the leaf. Alternatively, nonabsorbent cotton may be used to form a plug in the mouth of the flask and around the leaf base. The flask is held in place with a laboratory clamp and appropriate support stand.

This experimental setup offers an advantage over use of the 3-liter bottles because uncaptured flies are readily visible through the wall of the flask, in many cases eliminating the necessity to etherize flies remaining in the flask at the end of an experimental trial. Accuracy of data collection is increased when the flasks are used because all flies not visible within the flask can be assumed to have been captured since there are no escape routes and no hiding places. The use of flasks also allows examination of capture rates of individual leaves. Therefore, one may examine the role of individual leaf characteristics (such as leaf age, size of opening, condition of tongue-like appendage) on the success of the capture.

Another important advantage to using flasks on individual leaves is that several replicates of the same experimental trial may be performed simultaneously on the same plant, or if plant material is in short supply, students may share plants and conduct their own experimental trials. Moreover, the use of enclosures on individual leaves allows students to view the capture rate as it happens, allowing time-course studies of capture.

Leaves of cobra lily are very successful at attracting, capturing, and retaining flies. Capture success of 100% for densities up to 40 flies per flask for 24 hours is not uncommon. In fact, preliminary data suggest that the cobra lily operates in a strict density-dependent manner as a so called "type I" predator (Smith, 1990) and displays a mean capture success of 85.7% over densities ranging from 10 to 40 flies per leaf.

Suggested Experiments

Several investigations are possible with this experimental system. The variety of hypotheses to be tested is limited only by the creativity of the investigators. A sample of possible hypotheses follows.

The major thrust of most investigations using this system is to examine the factors that influence the success of the plant in capturing insects. Characteristics of the cobra lily that are likely to influence the efficiency of capture are:

- Size of the leaf opening.
- Size of the leaf.
- Importance of the tongue-like appendage.
- Functioning of fenestra in preventing prey escape.
- The age of the individual leaves.

Other factors that may also influence capture success are prey size, prey density, and the presence of previously captured prey in the base of the leaf tube, as captured prey may provide olfactory clues to attract additional prey.

As a sample investigation, examine the influence of prey density on the capture success. In a laboratory setting, it may be best to have students work in groups in order to efficiently distribute the workload. To provide sufficient replication, select a plant with a minimum of 4 to 5 leaves of similar size and general appearance. Record the leaf height, head dimensions, and diameter of opening for each leaf and be careful to select leaves with similar characteristics. Insert individual leaves carefully into flasks, holding the flasks in place with clamps and a laboratory stand. Place known numbers of anesthetized *Drosophila virilis* into the laboratory flasks enclosing individual leaves. Seal the flasks with foam sponge (or nonabsorbent cotton) stoppers and place the plants under fluorescent growth lights with 12-hour photoperiods.

At the end of a 24-hour period, record the number of flies visible within each flask. Subtract the number of remaining flies in each flask from the original number of flies placed in that flask and calculate a percent capture success. The procedure is repeated for each prey density of interest, and other variables may be introduced into the experiment by removing the tongue-like appendage from leaves to test its importance in prey attraction or covering the fenestra on the leaf hood to determine its importance in deterring prey escape.

Summary

The experimental setup described in this article allows for hands-on experience in investigating an important ecological concept: the relationship between a predator and its prey. It can be used to quantitatively analyze a variety of factors that may influence the ability of a predator to successfully capture prey. The techniques and materials employed are simple, inexpensive, and readily adaptable to high school or college ecology laboratories.

Acknowledgments

The author would like to thank W. Mostafa for her work with the plants, R. Cassetta for thoughtful comments on the manuscript, and the College of New Rochelle for providing the opportunity to conduct this work. The manuscript also benefited from the careful and constructive comments of the reviewers.

Original Source

This activity is based on an exercise by Carl R. Pratt (1994) titled "Use of Cobra Lily (*Darlingtonia californica*) & *Drosophila* for Investigating Predator-Prey Relationships" in *The American Biology Teacher*, 56(1), 38-40, and has been modified and reprinted with permission of the publisher.

If you were to take your students for a walk to record their observations of your schoolyard today, what would they write? Most students would record seeing trees, flowers, fungi, squirrels, birds, and other obvious organisms. Some more insightful students might note the direction of the wind, humidity, amount of sunshine, or the layout of the land, or report seeing a hawk catching a mouse. This directed inquiry activity takes students beyond simple observation by having them investigate how living organisms capture prey. Students learn about the methods of science by stating and testing their hypotheses, while at the same time posing in the role as "predator" catching their macaroni "prey."

Investigating Predator-Prey Relationships with Macaroni

Based on an original activity by M. Oyler, J. Rivera, M. Roffol, D. J. Gibson, B.A. Middleton, and M. Mathis

Ecological Principles Illustrated

- Population interactions
- Food web and food chain
- Predator-prey relationships

Materials

- 2 boxes of a variety of plastic utensils
- forceps (about 5)
- timer (with a "bell" is helpful)
- colored pasta such as macaroni (although other types of pasta mixed in might provide an interesting variation of this activity)
- portable chalkboard (or large paper with stand)
- chalk
- eraser
- outdoor activity site

Teacher Preparation

1. Introduce the concepts of "food chain" and "food web," including a discussion of how a disturbance such as farming, logging, or fire might change predator-prey relationships by altering habitat structure.

2. Introduce the concept of "biotic" and "abiotic" factors and how these interact. Include a brief discussion of which abiotic factors could affect predator-prey relationships.

3. Familiarize your students with the scientific method, particularly the development of a hypothesis.

4. Arrange for use of an outdoor site.

5. Warn your students to dress appropriately for working outdoors.

6. Spread "prey" (macaroni) out before class! We find that one 16 oz. bag is sufficient to adequately "seed" approximately 5 m².

7. For homework two days prior to the activity, have your students make their own food web using drawings and pictures from magazines. These student creations can be used for the food web discussion the day before. Students can volunteer to "show and tell" their food web. You can choose two or three posters to demonstrate the devastating effects of the removal, reduction, or addition of one link in a food web.

Selection of Activity Site

The outdoor site that you choose for this activity should include differences in habitat structure, e.g., grass height, amount of woody material. At least two different structural types are necessary.

Specific Procedures

Day One

After a short review of the material from the day before, bring the students and the necessary materials to the site chosen for the activity. Begin by asking, "What factors can limit the success of a predator?" A wide variety of answers is acceptable, such as: the weather, speed of the prey, color of the prey, technique or mechanism the predator uses to capture prey, and location of the prey (e.g., in a tree, under leaves on the ground, in a hole).

Write the responses of the students on a portable chalkboard. To assess whether your students fully grasp the great extent to which members of a food web are interconnected, ask a question such as, "What effects would a fire have on the predator-prey relationship between a red-tailed hawk and a cotton-tail rabbit?" (*Possible answers include: fire would increase predation due to lack of cover for rabbits, increase mortality of rabbits, increase red-tailed hawk population due to immigration to the area, and a sharp decrease in rabbit population as more rabbits are captured in the open habitat, followed by a decrease in red-tailed hawk population.*)

Activity

Begin by explaining to your class that animals face multiple obstacles while trying to capture prey or to avoid becoming prey. The nature of the animal's habitat impacts its ability to find food. For instance, it would be easier for a fox to spot a rabbit in an area with little vegetation than in an area with dense vegetation. Density of the vegetation, the space and density of the food item, the color of the food in relation to its background, and the type of appendage (e.g., claws, teeth, beak, tongue) predators use to obtain prey also affect prey capture rate. The purpose of the activity is for students to develop a hypothesis, test the hypothesis, analyze data, and draw conclusions based on that data.

Gathering Data in the Field

Note: This activity could be extended over several laboratory periods (days) by having the students gather data first and analyze it later.

- Before the students arrive, spread the macaroni at the site.

- After the students arrive, ask them to pair up.

- Inform students that the purpose of the activity is to simulate the predator/prey relationships. They can play the role of a predator with any of the following appendages for prey capture: fork, spoon, knife, forceps, or fingers. Colored macaroni will represent their prey. The students will choose habitat types within which to locate prey (e.g., mowed, unmowed, bushy, etc).

- Have each pair of students develop a hypothesis concerning the success of prey capture using various types of prey capture devices (e.g., forks, spoons) within two habitat types.

- If students develop a hypothesis dealing with aspects other than area and appendage, that is good! Here is an example: Spoons who search for prey close to the ground (squatting) will catch more prey than spoons who search for prey high off the ground (standing).

- After three minutes, have one or two of the groups read their hypotheses out loud to their classmates.

- All groups should then test their hypotheses individually.

- The groups need to spread out a little. One group member will act as a "predator" (e.g., spoon, fork) while the other records the data. The "predator" will have 45 seconds to capture at least seven "prey" with his/her appendage to avoid starvation. "Prey" should be picked up *one at a time* (in reality, most predators can only capture and eat one prey at a time!) without using fingers. Then, the prey is brought back to an area set aside as a "nest." At the end of 45 seconds, the recorder for the pair writes in the number of prey caught by his/her partner. This process will be repeated five times in each of the two habitat types (*Example: Five 45-second trials of forks in the mowed area and five 45-second trials of forks in the unmowed area*).

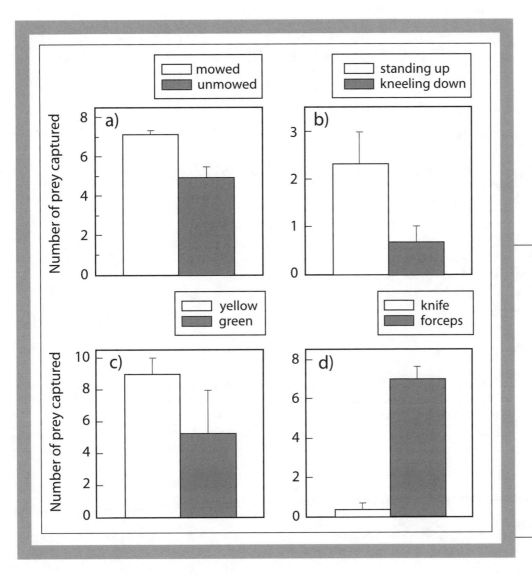

FIGURE 1. Representative data collected by students in an undergraduate nonscience majors biology class, Summer 1997. Student groups were comparing a) mowed and unmowed areas, b) high flying (student searches standing up) and low flying (student searches kneeling down), c) yellow versus green (camouflaged) prey, and d) knife versus forceps as a feeding appendage. Data are the mean number of prey items captured per minute +/- 1 SE.

Analyzing Data

Ask students to summarize their findings. The students will regroup into pairs. The students should graph the means of their data in a histogram (bar graph [e.g., Figure1]). Leave it up to them how to organize the histogram; however, you might provide a few guidelines (title, "x" and "y" axes labeled, neat and organized, overall good representation of their data set). This provides students a means to visually analyze the data collected. Students should be asked to summarize results in complete sentences and respond to the following questions:

1. What conclusions can you deduce from these results?

2. Was your hypothesis supported? Explain thoroughly.

3. What are some abiotic factors that may affect the success or failure of predators in their ability to capture prey?

Ask for pairs to volunteer to share their findings with the rest of the class.

Additional Suggestions

1. Keep up the pace! Without rushing the students, keep a close watch on time. Make sure time in between 45-second trials is minimal to reduce down time and the opportunity for students to stray off task.

2. Keep students close enough together so they can hear you and stay on task, yet not so close as to cause confusion during the trials.

3. Designate some minimum number of macaroni capture per trial for the predator to keep its nestlings alive. This will add drama to the exercise.

Acknowledgments

We would like to thank Mike Oyler for assisting in the development of this activity. Financial support was provided by the National Science Foundation (DUE-9554807). Additional information is available at (http://www.science.siu.long-term/).

This activity is a modification of a foraging/flocking behavior lab described by Smith (1993) that has proven very successful for undergraduate nonscience majors at Southern Illinois University at Carbondale (Gibson et al., 1999) and can be easily modified for use through the eighth grade. Not only does this activity engage students in actually "doing science," it also builds their inquiry skills by allowing them to think for themselves (see Ebert-May et al., 1993).

Original Source

This activity has been adapted from an original by M. Oyler, J. Rivera, M. Roffol, D. J. Gibson, B.A. Middleton, and M. Mathis (1999) titled "The Macaroni Lab: A Directed Inquiry Project on Predator-Prey Relationships" and appeared in *The American Biology Teacher, 61*(1), 39-41. It has been reprinted and modified with permission of the publisher.

Herbivores,
Predation, and
Biological Control

*Based on an original activity by Terence
M. Murphy, Deborah Canington, and
Douglas E. Walker*

This exercise is designed to test the quantitative effects of herbivory and predation in a simple experimental ecosystem. The results may be used to estimate the effectiveness of biological control. It joins three species, in different combinations, in an environment designed to exclude other species. The three species are cabbage plants (*Brassica oleracea capitata*), turnip aphids (*Hyadaphis pseudobrassicae*), and midges (*Aphidoletes aphidimyza*).

This activity describes a set of controlled ecosystems that can be used to demonstrate the effects of herbivory on the health and growth of a plant population and of predation on the growth of a primary consumer population. The system also shows the effectiveness of biological pest control measures in a dramatic way. In addition, this exercise demonstrates the population growth of insects, exhibits the effects of uncontrolled herbivory and biological control on the net productivity of a plant species, shows sampling techniques for an ecological experiment, and applies descriptive statistics and statistical tests to the data from an ecological experiment.

Ecological Principles Illustrated

- Effects of herbivory and predation

Introduction

Herbivory and predation, like symbiosis, are basic interactions among living organisms. They are responsible for the flow of matter and energy from the producers to primary consumers (herbivory) and from primary to secondary consumers (predation). They are interactions so fundamental to human life ("What's for dinner?") that it is easy to miss the point that they play major roles in shaping communities. The health of plants and the amount of biomass they accumulate and the relative numbers of animals of different species may be controlled to a large extent by the availability of food and the presence and efficiency of animals that eat it.

From a practical standpoint, herbivorous insects can be considered man's most effective competitors in harvesting the nutrients produced by crop plants. The voracious appetites and rapid reproduction of certain insect species allow them, in the absence of any hindrance, to completely divert all the value (nutrient and commercial) of a particular crop. Yet, in nature, it is quite unusual to see a plant species being wiped out or an insect species growing explosively. It is reasonable to hypothesize that crop fields are especially fragile in their simplicity and that, in natural communities, herbivorous insects are kept in check by their natural predators and parasites. The strategy of recruiting insect predators or parasites to protect crops is called biological pest control.

Materials

- 4 cages screened with 40-μm mesh polyester (Figure 1) in a greenhouse or other site suitable for plant growth (The cages should hold about 50 pots each.)

- cabbage seedlings (one seedling per 6-cm pot, grown to the 2- to 3-leaf stage)

- 200 6-cm pots

- aphids
- midges
- trays
- cotton batting

Background

Cabbage is a fast-growing producer. As a biennial, it grows in a rosette habit, storing a large amount of photosynthate in specialized leaves. Aphids are small (0.5 min to 2.5 mm) green herbivores. An aphid has a specialized tubular proboscis, which it can insert through the epidermis of a plant, between mesophyll cells, and directly into a sieve tube member (a sugar-conducting cell in the phloem tissue; a longitudinal series of these cells forms a sieve tube). Hydrostatic pressure in the sieve tube forces the rich sucrose into the aphid's digestive tract. Under permissive conditions (lots of food), aphid females reproduce asexually by parthenogenesis. Under restrictive conditions (less food), winged forms develop, and these forms reproduce by a normal sexual process.

Midges are obligate carnivores, and the species used in this activity preys specifically on aphids. Adult females locate colonies of aphids and lay eggs among them. In 2 to 3 days, the eggs hatch, and the orange larvae find the aphids, inject a toxin that paralyzes and kills them, and then suck the aphids dry. If there are plenty of aphids, the larvae kill more than they can eat. After eating 5 to 15 aphids and growing to their full size (3 mm), the larvae fall to the ground, burrow into the soil, and form cocoons. The pupal stage lasts for 10 to 14 days; then the new adults emerge from the cocoons.

Aphids are pandemic and can be collected by placing cabbage seedlings outside in the spring. They can be maintained, primarily in the asexual form, in a separate cage (to exclude midges and parasites) by adding cabbage seedlings at weekly intervals. The turnip aphid,

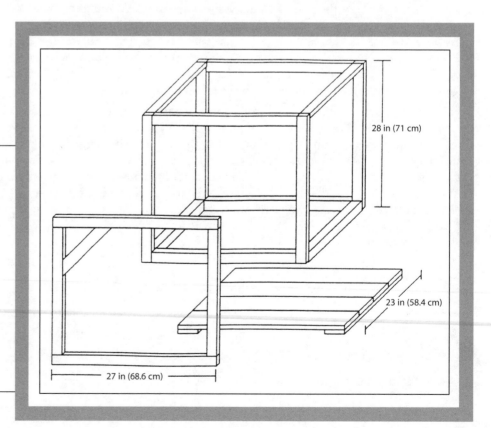

FIGURE 1. Schematic of the frame of a screened cage used to isolate insect-plant ecosystems. For cages that will last many seasons in the humidity and high light intensity of a greenhouse, use rough-cut redwood (or equivalent), galvanized nails, and polyester (not nylon) mesh. To prevent escape and invasions, use silicone caulk to seal all cracks. For a materials list, see Table 3 on page 118.

28 in (71 cm)

23 in (58.4 cm)

27 in (68.6 cm)

which is clear green, is the better subject because it is more restricted in its diet. The cabbage aphid, whose waxy cuticle makes it gray-white, is a worse pest to have in one's greenhouse.

Midges can be obtained from supply companies specializing in biological control. They can be maintained in separate cages, using aphid-infested cabbage as a food source. To obtain pupae that can be distributed to students, leaves with larvae are detached and placed on a tray covered with wet cotton batting. It may be possible to keep pupae for long periods in the refrigerator, although this method has not been tested.

Procedure

1. Table 1 below describes the timing of preparation for this experiment.

2. Divide each class into groups of 4 or 5 students. Make each group responsible for preparing and analyzing 2 pots, each given a different treatment. In smaller classes, each group could have more pots. The treatments are: A = cabbage plants only; B = cabbage + aphids; C = cabbage + aphids + low midge inoculum; D = cabbage + aphids + high midge inoculum.

3. Ask students to set up the experiment 3 weeks before data is to be collected. Instruct them to select cabbage plants randomly. If setting up an A pot, encourage them to check

Day 0	Plant seeds.
Day 3	Collect leaves with 3rd to 4th-instar midge larvae; place on trays.
Day 5	Seedlings emerge.
Days 13-15	Give plants and insects to students.
Days 27-34	Analyze results.

TABLE 1. Timeline for the experiment. Steady-state stocks of asexual aphids and midges in the larval stage should be available at the start of the experiment. Greenhouse conditions are 17 to 28° C, 16-hour photoperiod, no insecticide.

the leaves carefully, top to bottom, to make sure there are no aphids on them. Carry pots to the greenhouse and place them in the A cage before handling aphids or midges.

4. When setting up a B, C, or D pot, instruct students to carefully place 10 aphids from the stock supply on the leaves, using a brush to transfer the insects without crushing them. If setting up a C pot, have students add 1 midge pupa from the stock supply to the pot; if setting up a D pot, add 10 pupae to the pot.

5. Since the stock of midge pupae is on cotton, direct students to cut the cotton (small scissors work best) around the required number of pupae and place the cotton, with attached pupae, on the soil surface of the pot.

6. Place the B, C, and D pots in the appropriate cages.

7. At the end of the experiment, have the student groups remove the appropriate pots and, in the laboratory, cut off the leaves at the base of the petiole one at a time, starting from the bottom of the stem (outside leaves on the rosette). For each leaf and for the remaining stem, have the students:

- Count the total number of midge larvae.

- Count the total number of aphids.

- Determine the mass of the leaf or stem.

- Record the data in a table.

8. Students total the measurements to report them on a per plant basis. All measurements for each treatment and each laboratory section should be made available to all members in the class.

Report

In order to complete a written report of this activity, instruct your students to:

- Summarize the reasons for conducting the experiment.

- Using accumulated data from all groups and classes, prepare three bar graphs showing mean and standard error for each aphid population density (aphids/plant), midge population density, and plant mass.

- Write out and test null hypotheses regarding:

  (a) The effect of aphids on plant biomass.

  (b) The effect of midges on aphid population sizes.

  (c) The difference between low and high inoculum of midges on aphid population size.

  (d) The effect of midges on plant mass (choosing one inoculum size).

  (Students can also use the t test or the nonparametric Mann-Whitney U test to analyze their results.)

- Summarize their conclusions from this activity.

Typical Results

Table 2 shows the results from two classes (Winter 1991: 305 students in 18 laboratory sections; Spring 1991: 600 students in 22 laboratory sections). Fresh masses of the plants varied most dramatically and consistently. The aphids reduced the plant biomass by at least 60%, and the introduction of midges ameliorated the effect of aphids significantly.

The numbers of aphids were less predictable. In Spring 1991 (a two-week experiment), the numbers of aphids varied as expected (except for significant contamination of some plants in A cages, which probably occurred when the cages were opened to water the plants), with the high inoculum of midges reducing the number of aphids by more than 99%. In Winter 1991 (a three-week experiment), the numbers of aphids varied in an unexpected way. Because the plants in cages B and C were so debilitated, few aphids were found on their leaves. The number of aphids was highest on the healthy plants in cage D, suggesting the possibility of oscillations in plant health and aphid population size if the experiment is allowed to continue for longer periods.

The results of this activity can be compared with recent data on the effects of predator fish on populations of herbivorous insects and producers (algal mats) in a northern California river (Power, 1990). The original idea that the biomass of an ecosystem (mostly in plant matter) depends on the number of trophic levels, with odd numbers of trophic levels giving more biomass than even numbers, is attributed to Fretwell (1977). A more comprehensive discussion of trophic levels and community structure is found in Krebs (1985).

Cage	Number of aphids	Number of midges	Plant mass (9 g)
Winter 1991			
A	0.024 ± 0.024	0 ± 0	8.0 ± 0.5
B	0.053 ± 0.037	5.8 ± 2.2	0.32 ± 0.08
C	1.8 ± 0.78	34.3 ± 13.6	0.40 ± 0.05
D	8.8± 1.1	3.3 ± 2.4	4.00 ± 0.33
Spring 1991			
A	49 ± 17	0.1 ± 0.08	6.2 ± 0.3
B	578 ± 78	1.2 ± 0.6	2.2 ± 0.2
C	182 ± 26	8.2 ± 1.5	3.1 ± 0.3
D	2.6 ± 1.1	10.7 ± 2.50	4.2 ± 0.3

TABLE 2. Results from Winter and Spring 1991 trials. Cages: A, plants only; B, plants plus aphids; C, plants, aphids, plus low (1x) midges; D, plants, aphids, plus high (10x) midges. Data represent means ±SE, n = 40 pots (Winter), and n = 50 pots (Spring.)

Summary

This exercise provides a clear illustration of the effects of herbivory and predation in a set of controlled ecosystems. It also provides data that students can use for statistical analysis, although in the trials, the conclusions were evident without statistical tests. The system can be modified in many ways (for instance, using different plants or plants of different ages, or sampling over a wider time span to test for oscillations in aphid and midge populations), making it useful for truly experimental, individual student projects. Finally, there is a practical advantage to setting up the experiments. Once established, the midges can be used for aphid control in a greenhouse, so long as no insecticides are also employed.

Acknowledgments

Preparation of this experiment for classroom use was originally supported by grants from the University of California, Davis Undergraduate Instructional Improvement Program, and the Hughes Foundation.

Original Source

The activity has been adapted from an original exercise by Terence M. Murphy, Deborah Canington, and Douglas E. Walker (1992) titled "Herbivory, Predation & Biological Control" in *The American Biology Teacher, 54*(7), 416-419, and has been modified and reprinted with permission of the publisher.

TABLE 3. Materials list for one screened cage (see Figure 1 on page 114).

Redwood Lumber	Length
2" x 2"	7'4"
1" x 2"	29'2"
1" x 6"	9'

Hardware	Number
2" angle irons	8
2" hinges	2
hook and eye	1
foam rubber (door gasket)	8'8"
aluminum screen framing & spline	41'8"
clear silicone caulk	ca. 1 lb.
assorted screws (to attach angle irons, hinges and aluminum screen frame to the wooden frame, and to assemble the door frame securely)	

Polyester screen	
polyester organza (available through retail outlets from Hyman Hendler & Sons, Inc., 1440 Santee St., Los Angeles, CA 90015)	
48" width	5'8" length

The background to current theories concerning the evolution of insect plant relationships is described, followed by a series of experiments based on recent publications in this field. These experiments have been tested with students and school teachers. They concern the relationships between herbivore number and plants' successional status, geographical range, geological history, and stage of growth, and they also include experiments on the chemical basis of host-plant selection by insects. Modified explanations for published results are given to emphasize the value of such experiments in the teaching of evolution, ecology, and applied biology. Suggestions for the extension of these short-term experiments as projects are also given.

Investigating Insect-Plant Relationships

Based on an original activity by G.L.A. Fry and S.D. Wratten

Ecological Principles Illustrated

- Insect-plant relationships
- Succession
- Geographical range
- Host-plant selection

Introduction

Plant species vary considerably in the number of herbivorous insect species they support. This initially casual observation has prompted numerous studies that have attempted to look for ecological reasons for this variation. Some plant species appear to be virtually ungrazed, while others seem prone to fairly regular defoliation. Because severe insect damage is familiar to most of us, it seems reasonable to assume that grazing has been an important selection pressure in plant evolution.

Obviously, leaf spines and hairs or a thick cuticle can affect a grazing insect, but many plants employ more subtle defenses, frequently chemical. Such chemicals sometimes have no obvious role in the plant's metabolism but do deter potential grazers. For this reason, they are called "odd substances" or "secondary plant substances," and their origin, taxonomic and geographical distribution, and biological properties have prompted much work and speculation. A group of such chemicals is responsible for the familiar cabbage smell that can be detected near a field of these plants or from the odor of overcooked cabbage!

Using the successional sequence of plants that appears during the colonization of new areas (e.g., annuals - woody shrubs - trees) as a framework, we can consider some of the major concepts of insect-plant biology.

Materials

- Among the wide choice of plants from the three broad classes of successional status, the following are easily obtained:
  EARLY – **clover** (*Trifolium* spp.), **hogweed** (*Heracleum sphondylium* L.), **dandelion** (*Taraxacum officinale* Weber).
  MID – **hazel** (*Corylus avellana* L.), **bramble** (*Rubus fruticosus* L.), **elder** (*Sambucus nigra* L.), **birch** (*Betula* spp.).
  LATE – **oak** (*Quercus* spp.), **ash** (*Fraxinus excelsior* L.), **beech** (*Fagus sylvatica* L.), **sycamore** (*Acer pseudoplatanus* L.).

- white plastic trays

- forceps
- beating tray or umbrella
- stout stick
- oak leaves
- distilled water
- polyethylene bags
- deep freeze
- plastic sandwich boxes
- sinigrin powder (a mustard-oil glucoside occurring in *Cruciferae* that can be obtained from biological supply houses)
- agar powder
- petri dishes
- leaf powder
- 'Nipagin M'
- ethyl alcohol
- snails and slugs

Background

Plants' Successional Status and Their Defense Against Grazing

A study by Cates and Orians (1975), for instance, has suggested that there is a trend in the occurrence of secondary plant substances within the successional series mentioned above. The authors postulate that early successional plants, such as annuals, have a higher palatability to herbivores than late successionals because of their low odd substance content. These "early" plants can be considered to be opportunists whose strategies of survival and success are based on rapid growth, short generation time, and high fecundity. They are thought to devote little of their metabolic energy to the production of defensive chemicals because they do not persist long enough for destruction by large numbers of grazers to be a serious problem. In contrast, late successionals, like many trees, may have a generation time of tens of years and, therefore, occupy a site for a much longer time. Insect grazers, with their shorter generation time and high fecundity, could in theory develop devastatingly high populations in the absence of a plant-based restraint. This restraint is thought to be provided by a high level and variety of odd substances. An experiment described later in this activity attempts to test the above assumption by assessing the palatability of leaf discs from a range of plants using a general herbivore.

Plants' Geographical Range and the Number of Herbivores

At any one stage in the successional series, there is still a large variation among plant species in the extent of insect grazing. Among the possible reasons for this, geographical range and taxonomic isolation (number of species per genus, family, etc.) have been investigated by Lawton and Schroder (1977). They found that, for several plant groups, geographical range of the species has a marked effect on the number of herbivores feeding on it. This too can be tested by students using insect collections made in summer and plant distribution data from a flora or botanical atlas.

Historical Abundance and the Number of Herbivores

Although the work of Lawton and Schroder (1977) demonstrates the importance of the current abundance and distribution of a plant in determining its herbivore "population," there is evidence that historical abundance in geological time can also be reflected in current herbivore burden. Some trees in Britain, for instance, have been important components of the flora for thousands of years while others have always been rare or are recent arrivals or introductions. Southwood (1961) used the total number of sites from which fossil records had been obtained (Godwin, 1956) as an index of trees' historical abundance and related to this the herbivore number obtained from a literature search. There was an increase in the number of herbivore species with increasing abundance of the tree (Figure 1). The points for some tree species, however, are of additional interest because they lie considerably above or below the line, suggesting unusually high or low palatability. This hypothesis can be tested by using the general grazer technique of Cates and Orians (1975) for these "outliers."

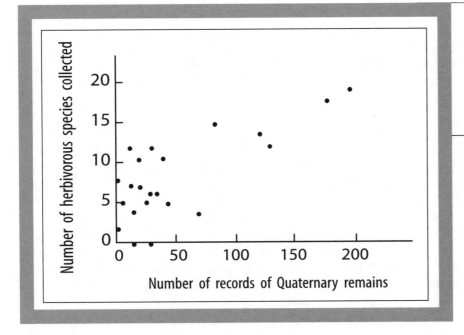

FIGURE 1. The relationship between the number of herbivorous insect species collected from tree species of different recent geological abundance; data collected on a South Devon field course.

Temporal Changes in a Plant's Palatability

Even within a tree species, there are temporal changes in the suitability of its foliage for herbivores. In oak (*Quercus* spp.), the concentration of proteins and tannins in the leaves increases from bud-burst to leaf maturity and then declines with the onset of senescence (Feeny, 1970). The number of insect grazers follows this pattern, too, especially in that they decline after a spring peak. Land mollusks can be used in a bioassay of leaves collected and frozen through the season. We can determine an association between leaf chemistry and herbivore number by allowing land mollusks to graze in the leaves of different physiological ages and measuring the percentage eaten.

The possession of particular odd substances by plants helps taxonomists define particular plant groups (Bell & Tirimanna, 1965). Odd substances are used by some insects to locate the plant species with which they have evolved. It is tempting to suggest that such chemicals are now less of an advantage to the plant species in which they occur than they originally were. They now serve as recognition stimuli for specialized insect groups which have evolved to deal with them, although these chemicals presumably still deter a large number of unadapted species. In this context, it is of interest that in two aphid species which can feed on *Cruciferae*, one feeds only on this family while the other is a generalist with a wide host-plant range. The growth rate of the former is accelerated by a crucifer odd substance while that of the latter is retarded (van Emden, 1972). We can show the vital importance that some of these chemicals now have for the adapted insect by incorporating them in artificial diets made from non-host, but relatively innocuous plant species, and measuring the effect on feeding rate.

Is Grazing Always Detrimental to the Plant?

If some apparently useless plant chemicals are now used by insects to identify their food, why do they persist? One reason could be that they will still deter a large number of nonspecialists and, therefore, are still useful. In addition, it has been suggested recently that grazing by insects may not always be wholly detrimental to the plant and that some plants may regulate insect grazing at a fairly low level rather than prevent it completely. Three examples are given by Owen and Wiegert (1976), at least one of which (dealt with in more detail by Owen, 1978) could easily be tested at the school level. They suggest that the presence of leaf-feeding insects on trees may extend the period of leaf fall and, therefore, insure an almost-continuous, small supply of recycled nitrogen to the soil. In poor soils, this could benefit the tree.

The history of plants and their grazers shows a process of dynamic evolution, with continuous pressure being exerted on the plants by grazers. The experiments that follow can all suggest something of the extent and mechanisms of plant defense against the grazers.

Procedures

1. Successional Status of Plants and Their Palatability

One-centimeter-diameter leaf disks (cut with a cork borer) or 1-cm squares (cut with a razor blade) are placed in sandwich boxes containing 1 to 2 cm damp soil. Two disks of an "early" species are placed with two of a "mid." In other boxes, "mid" species are compared with "late" and "late" with "early." It is not necessary to compare every early species with every mid and late species. This will depend on the number of students. Replicate comparisons at least once, however. Introduce two snails with a shell diameter of at least 2 cm or 2 slugs each 3 cm long into each box. A trial run will determine how long to leave the experiment. Twenty-four hours is often suitable, but in warm conditions, this may be too long, and most disks may be entirely eaten.

At the end of the grazing period, place each disk on metric graph paper and draw its outline in pencil. Counting the squares or weighing the paper will indicate the area consumed. The mollusks may move the disks, and intact leaves should be retained so that surface characteristics of partially-eaten disks may be compared with them for identification. Then collate results and tabulate them either as in Table 1 or with the details of the plant species. An analysis of variance can be used to compare the mean area consumed for the three stages. As well as indicating that plants early in the series are more likely to be eaten, data in Table 1 also suggest that the amount eaten is influenced by the category with which the plant is compared. Such experiments can be developed in many ways, such as comparing congeneric plants with different successional niches. Collections of herbivores made in the field could also provide clues (see Wratten & Fry, 1979, for further ideas).

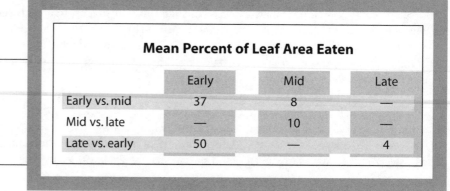

TABLE 1. Results of snail, *Helix aspersa* (Miller), palatability trials completed during a field course in South Devon.

Mean Percent of Leaf Area Eaten			
	Early	Mid	Late
Early vs. mid	37	8	—
Mid vs. late	—	10	—
Late vs. early	50	—	4

2. Geographical Range and the Number of Herbivores

In summer, visit a range of wild herbaceous plants of hedgerows and fields. Collect as many as possible of the insects living in or on at least 4 individual plants of each species. This can be done by bending the plant carefully over a tray (e.g., a white photographic dish) and tapping it sharply several times to dislodge the insects. If the plant is short-stemmed and common, cut it carefully at ground level and shake it over the tray. Examine the plant for remaining insects, such as lead miners. Using forceps (Bennett & Humphries, 1974), collect the most mobile invertebrates first, followed by the rest. Pool collections from different plants of the same species.

On return to the laboratory or classroom, carry out an initial sorting of herbivores and nonherbivores, and release the nonherbivores. This segregation of the catch is not as difficult as it may seem, even for a non-entomologist. For instance, all spiders, ladybirds, flower bugs (*Anthocoridae*), earwigs, and adult flies can be discarded. This is a crude separation, but the first 4 are mainly predatory, and most fly larvae are saprophagous. Chinery (1973) should be helpful for the more difficult taxonomic problems.

The remaining groups should now be largely Lepidoptera and sawfly caterpillars, plant-feeding bugs (including aphids), beetles, and the leaf miners recorded in the field. Count the number of herbivore species on each plant species, paying close attention to whether or not immature bugs belong to a species of which the adult has already been included in the total.

Plot the herbivore number against a measure of the geographical distribution of the plant; the number of occupied vice-counties could be used (see Clapham, Tutin & Warburg, 1962) or the number of occupied 10-km squares in a plant atlas (Perring & Walters, 1962). Data collected this way by entomological novices are plotted in Figure 2. There seems to be a clear curvilinear relationship with two "outliers."

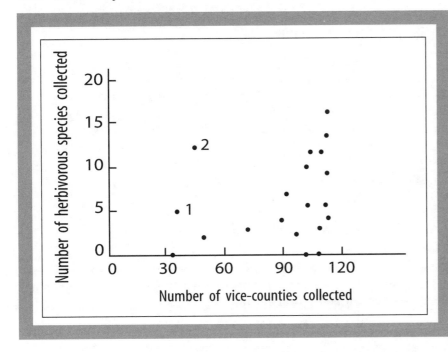

FIGURE 2. The relationship between the number of herbivorous insect species collected from herbaceous species of different geographical range in Britain; data collected on a South Devon field course. l = sea rocket, *Cakile maritima*, and 2 = sea beet, *Beta vulgaris*.

It is fascinating that the two species from which more herbivores than expected were collected were sea rocket (*Cakile maritima*) and sea beet (*Beta vulgaris*), coastal species with a large *latitudinal* range, even though they do not occupy many vice-counties or 10 km squares. They are also both closely related to crop plants (sea beet is the same species as sugar beet, and sea rocket is a crucifer, like cabbage, etc.). Their relatively large fauna may be related to the ubiquity of their cultivated relatives.

Figure 2 is not immediately comparable with the figures of Lawton and Schroder (1977) because their axes are both on a log scale; our plot would be comparable if the data were similarly transformed, but leaving them on arithmetical axes is more interesting because students can more easily discuss the biological reasons for the nature of the relationship (see Discussion). With data transformed to logarithms, a linear regression can be calculated if required.

3. The Geological History of Tree Species and Their Herbivore Fauna

A procedure similar to that in the previous experiment is followed, collecting and segregating the herbivores from a wide range of tree species. This time, however, use an entomological beating tray or inverted umbrella to catch the fauna knocked from branches by sharp blows from a stout stick. Do not collect from the same branch more than once. Collect the active animals first, as before. Visit new trees within a species as necessary until three successive "beats" do not yield a new species, as judged by visual inspection of the catch through the walls of the collecting vessel. A common group in this catch that occurs rarely in herbaceous vegetation is the booklice (*Pscoptera*); they feed on fungi and lichens, so they can be discarded.

Plot the herbivore species number for each tree species against the number of pollen records (see Appendix 1). Look for an upward trend (see Figure 1) and pay particular attention to the species well above or below the line (which can be fitted by eye or a calculated regression).

4. Palatability of Trees to Herbivores

Using the techniques of Procedure 1, make leaf disks of as many as possible of the tree species sampled in Procedure 3 and test their palatability using mollusk grazers. The results from this could have an important bearing on the interpretation of the trend in Procedure 3 because further information may modify Southwood's (1961) interpretation.

5. Temporal Changes in a Tree's Palatability to Herbivores

Collect oak leaves at 2 week intervals from just after bud burst, when they are about 2 cm long, to just prior to leaf fall. Wash each batch in distilled water, dry it on a paper towel, and freeze it in an air-free polyethylene bag. Remove these from the freezer 24 hours before the start of the experiment. Mollusks graze the leaf disks as in Procedure 1. The details will depend on pupil number; the leaf collections can be divided into just 4 categories, such as early-, mid-, and late-season, and senescent. In this case, an analysis of variance would be an appropriate statistical test.

A collection of herbivores made from the oaks at the same time as the leaf collections may provide useful additional information.

6. Effects of Odd Substances on Insect Feeding Rate

Easily measure the feeding rate of caterpillars by counting their frass (fecal) pellets. By using this method, one can incorporate different foods and chemicals in agar media and assess their acceptability to caterpillars. The standard quantities of materials for possible inclusion in the agar mixture are, for two petri dishes (25 cm³ mixture in total); 3% agar (0.75 g); 2% leaf powder (0.5 g); 0.1% sinigrin (0.025 g); 1 % 'Nipagin M' solution (0.25 cm³). Make the leaf powder in a pestle and mortar or a kitchen grinder from leaves dried at 40° C. 'Nipagin M' is an antifungal agent. Make a 10% w/v solution in 70% ethanol and include 0.25 cm³ of this in the above mixture.

Heat the agar and distilled water to 85° C to dissolve the former and then cool it to 55° C before stirring in sinigrin, plant material, and 'Nipagin M'. Then pour the mixture into 2 petri dishes. Fit circles of filter paper tightly into the lids, close the dishes, label, and leave to allow the contents to cool and set.

Addition to mixtures	Number of frass pellets
Cabbage	108
Broad bean	8
Cabbage and sinigrin	209
Bean and sinigrin	125
Bean, sinigrin and sugar	482
Agar only	7
Tomato	38

TABLE 2. The number of frass pellets produced in 24 hours by 3 larvae of *Plutella xylostella* on standard agar mixtures with plant or chemical additions.

Once the agar has set, mop up surplus water from the surface. Then, add 4 small larvae of *Pieris brassicae* (large white butterfly) or medium-sized larvae of *Plutella xylostella* (the diamond back moth), replace the lid, and invert the dish. *Pieris* can be obtained from laboratory supply companies and *Plutella* possibly from insecticide company entomology laboratories. Count the frass pellets on the paper at regular intervals. Possible combinations of the mixture are: cabbage without sinigrin; broad bean (*Vicia faba*) leaf with or without sinigrin; potato leaf with or without sinigrin (leaves of the family Solanaceae contain alkaloids that are poisonous to insects other than specialist feeders); sucrose (e.g., 0.5%), an important nutrient that may have a role in food selection in some insects as well.

Using these techniques in replicated experiments, relatively unpalatable plants like broad bean can be converted into reasonably acceptable food sources by the addition of a very small quantity of odd substance. Also, sucrose, a widespread nutrient, can be shown to have large effects on larval feeding rates.

Discussion

Most of the experiments outlined previously have in common the comparison of some measure of palatability to insects (numbers, feeding rates, etc.) with an unmeasured but assumed plant attribute. They, therefore, share the drawback that such correlations are not necessarily *causal*. It is this fact that makes them useful teaching aids. The assumptions can be discussed and, in some cases, tested further by pupils who suggest hypotheses and test these with new experimental data. There are alternative and equally plausible explanations of many of the results.

For instance, the interpretation of the snail grazing experiments has been cogently criticized by Maiorana (1978), who argues that one cannot assume that a slug or snail is a general herbivore no more likely to encounter plants of a particular successional stage than of others. If, however, a herbivore is largely confined to the woodland canopy or, in the case of terrestrial pulmonates, to the herbs of the ground layer, then there is no selective pressure for the herbivore to overcome the defenses of plants outside its own grazing regime.

Feeny (1976) demonstrated that there are chemical differences in the defense strategies of woody and herbaceous plants, and Maiorana (1978) showed that there were significant differences in palatability to mollusks between woody and herbaceous plants of the same successional stage. In other words, growth form (e.g., herbaceous, climbing, woody, etc.) could be at least as important as successional status in determining plant palatability to a slug or snail. Since late successional species tend to be woody, the two interpretations are obviously not independent. The leaves of woody plants do become available to slugs and snails at leaf fall, but at this stage, breakdown of leaf constituents is well underway, and the odd substances of the green leaf may no longer be present.

The relationship between the number of "associated" herbivore species and the geographical area occupied by a plant, proposed by Lawton and Schroder (1977), has relevance to the interpretation of the tree/herbivore relationship of Southwood (1961). It could be argued that current geographical distribution is the most significant factor in both studies (Opler, 1974; Claridge & Wilson, 1978). The current distribution of British trees, as recorded in the *Atlas of British Flora* (Perring & Walters, 1962) provides a significant correlation with herbivore number (Strong, 1974). Equally, one could argue that present distribution reflects past distribution and abundance. The relative roles of abundance in space and time will take much work to unravel.

New forests of non-native species recently planted throughout Britain could provide evidence of the mechanisms involved in determining a plant's herbivore complement in "taxonomic isolation" (see Lawton & Schroder, 1977). For instance, herbivore numbers on ash are lower than would be expected from its distribution, but this tree belongs to the olive family (Oleaceae) of which there are only two native species in Britain. These papers do not negate the conclusions drawn by the original workers but essentially are all part of the view of Feeny (1976) that a plant's "apparency" (a combination of a plant's abundance, persistence, and the general likelihood of it being found) is the main factor in determining its herbivore complement.

The origin and role of odd substances in insect host-plant selection have also been the subjects of much debate in recent years. For instance, the assumption that they have no metabolic role in the plant is not always valid (Brown, 1964; Neish, 1964; Towers, 1969). Also, if they evolved as anti-grazing chemicals, later to be used by specialist insects as host recognition stimuli, how did insects recognize their hosts before the evolution of such chemicals?

The answer may be associated with the role of nutrients as plant recognition factors, for although amino acids and sugars are common across a wide taxonomic range of plants, there is evidence that insects can respond to changes in the concentration and relative proportions of such chemicals in their diet (House, 1969). An adaptation of the caterpillar/agar experiments where a range of nutrient/agar mixtures was offered to caterpillars in the cells of a "Replidish" (a square petri dish divided into a grid of small compartments) could test the ability of different caterpillar species to select food on the basis of odd substances/nutrients.

The ideas in this presentation should provide a useful starting point for a wide range of investigations both in the field and the laboratory. Reference to the published work in the bibliography should provide additional stimulus. Further details of experimental technique and suitable extension projects are described in Wratten and Fry (1979).

Original Source

This activity is based on an original exercise by G.L.A. Fry and S.D. Wratten (1979) titled "Insect Plant Relationships in Ecological Teaching" in the *Journal of Biological Education,* 13(4), 267-274, published by the Institute of Biology in London and has been modified and reprinted with permission of the editor.

Oak (*Quercus robus* and *Q. pertraca*)	197
Birch (*Betula* spp.)	182
Hazel (*Corylus avellana*)	136
Willow (*Salix* spp.)	134
Alder (*Alnus glutinosa*)	87
Hawthorn (*Crataegus* spp.)	67
Ash (*Fraxinus excelsior*)	59
Pine (*Pinus sylvestris*)	54
Holly (*Ulex aquifolium*)	44
Yew (*Taxus baccata*)	42
Sloe (*Prunus spinosa*)	30
Poplar (*Populus* spp.)	30
Elm (*Ulmus* spp.)	30
Beech (*Fagus sylvatica*)	27
Common maple (*Acer campestre*)	18
Hornbeam (*Carpinus betulus*)	17
Juniper (*Juniperus communis*)	17
Spruce (*Picea ables*)	15
Lime (*Tilia* spp.)	14
Mountain ash (*Sorbus aucuparia*)	13
Fir (*Abies* spp.)	10
Sweet chestnut (*Castanea sativa*)	10
Apple (*Malus* spp.)	7
Walnut (*Juglans regia*)	3
Holm Oak (*Quercus ilex*)	2
Larch (*Larix decidua*)	1
Sycamore (*Acer pseudoplatanus*)	1
Horse chestnut (*Aesculus hippocastanum*)	11
Acacia (*Robinia pseudacacia*)	0
Plane (*Platanus orientalis*)	0

APPENDIX 1. The number of pollen records of British trees recorded by Godwin (1956).

Herbivory-Induced Alteration of Community Structure – A Classroom Model

Based on an original activity by
John R. Porter

The effects of excessive grazing by herbivores is a topic frequently discussed in a consideration of ecology. Because of striking examples in western North America, Australia, and especially the Sahel region of Africa, this topic is particularly relevant. Since the increased herbivore pressure that leads to ecosystem degradation and subsequent desertification is frequently caused by human populations seeking increased economic wealth, an understanding of this phenomenon also becomes part of discussions on sociology, economics, and world government. The conclusion of these discussions is clear: herbivore pressure beyond the carrying capacity of the habitat can lead to pronounced regional ecosystem degradation with ensuing disastrous effects on local and regional human populations.

Ecological Principles Illustrated

- Loss of vegetation

- Alterations in the species composition of a community

- Impoverishment of a community with respect to desirable food plant species when herbivore feeding exceeds the rate of vegetation regrowth

- A rapid and convenient technique for the study of diatoms

Background Information

Discussions and observations of changes in the environment are, of course, essential in developing a sense of relevance to ecological investigation. The "tragedy of the commons" is frequently used in each of its variations to demonstrate the potential for catastrophe when people forsake ecosystem health for social wealth. However, unless one lives in or has ready access to such a disturbed area, it is difficult to demonstrate with certainty the nature and scope of the ecosystem alterations. Even if such study sites are available, changes are frequently slow and subtle, so that students in a single lab or even a single year of observation come away with little appreciation of the problem or consequences. It was for these reasons that I developed a group of lab exercises to demonstrate the ability of introduced herbivores to alter community structure and character within the course of a few weeks up to a few months. The goals of this investigation were accomplished by manipulation and observation of an aquarium.

Aquaria are frequently used to study ecology in the classroom. They are found in a large number of classrooms from grade school to college because they are relatively cheap to set up and maintain. Besides the obvious esthetic value, a carefully designed aquarium can be used to illustrate a number of biological phenomena, such as animal behavior, species interactions, the importance of species diversity, and the competitive exclusion principle. The aquarium can serve as a model of a closed-type ecosystem because of the need to supply food. The current investigation uses the aquarium to examine the role and effects of herbivores in an environment and also provides experience in taxonomy, plant and animal ecology, and microscopy.

Materials

- 15 gallon aquarium
- external mounted power filter (optional)
- activated charcoal
- crushed oyster shell substratum
- cool-white fluorescent lamp
- opaline gourami, ~6 cm in length

- frozen brine shrimp or squid
- 2 Chinese algae eaters
- lettuce or cooked spinach
- clean glass slides

- Bunsen burner
- Muffle furnace
- Permount
- #1 coverslip

The aquarium used has a 15-gallon capacity and was filtered and aerated by an externally mounted power filter. Commercial filter materials containing activated charcoal were used to protect the fish from stressful ammonia concentrations. The pH was buffered near neutral (pH 6.6) by the use of a crushed oyster shell substratum. The aquarium was maintained at 76 to 78° F (24 to 25.5° C) with a 12- to 16-hour day length (cool-white fluorescent lamps).

At the beginning of the investigation the tank contained a single opaline gourami (*Trichogaster trichopterus* spp. *sumatranus*) approximately 6 cm in length. This fish is both attractive and hardy. Other species and a larger number of specimens could certainly be used, although no principally herbivorous fish, such as mollies (*Molliensia* spp.), platies and sword-tails (*Xiphophorus* spp.), or certain of the loricariid catfishes should be present. The cichlids (*Cichlasoma* spp. and relatives) are also to be avoided, since most are very aggressive and their constant "housecleaning" activities usually prevent the survival of algae or other plants.

Consultation of a standard reference on tropical fish, such as *Exotic Aquarium Fishes* (Inness, 1966) or the more extensive *Exotic Tropical Fishes* (Axelrod et al., undated) will provide a wealth of information on diet, behavior, and optimum conditions for most fishes commercially available. The use of a power filter is also optional, although some form of filtration including activated charcoal should be provided.

To induce a luxurious growth of algae, the fish was fed with about twice as much food as would normally be supplied. This consisted mainly of high nitrogen foods such as frozen brine shrimp or chopped, frozen squid. This maintained the tank at a high level of dissolved nitrate (40 mg/l) as determined with a Hach kit (Hach Chemical Co.). The use of activated charcoal kept ammonia levels below 0.1 mg/l.

Within about a month of the beginning of this regimen, heavy growths of algae were present on the glass, substrate, and stones. Samples were taken from glass scrapings, the surface of the gravel and stones, underneath the gravel surface, and the open water. The latter was accomplished by pouring approximately 4 l of water from the tank through a plankton net. All samples were examined microscopically and algal genera were identified using Prescott (1970). As shown in Table 1, there were relatively few species, the most abundant being *Microspora*. Diatoms and planktonic forms were noticeably absent, although the latter is easily explained by the efficiency of the power filter. Contrary to expected results, there did not seem to be a difference in the species of alga observed and the type of substrate, i.e., glass, oyster shells, stone, or open water. Also associated with the algal surfaces were numerous mites, probably of the genus *Hydrochares* and apparently feeding on the algae.

When abundant algal growth was present, two Chinese algae eaters (*Gyrinocheilus aymonieri*) were introduced to the tank. Within a week, the algae were quite noticeably reduced and within about two weeks the algae were virtually gone. The fish were maintained throughout this period on the same feeding regimen as before. Depending on the nature of the individual herbivorous fish, they may begin to eat the animal foods supplied when their primary food supply is depleted, or they may need additional vegetable matter such as lettuce or cooked spinach. Again, some variability is possible by using different herbivorous fish, such as loricariid or *Plecostomus*-type catfishes.

After a month or so, a fine green to brown algal growth began to appear. This was sampled as before and the various genera of algae determined (Table 1). Unlike the preherbivory

TABLE 1. Algal diversity and abundance before and after introductions of the herbivorous *Gyrinocheilus aymonieri.*

Genus	Abundance	
	Before	After
Green algae		
Microspora	+++	+
Rhizoclonium	+	+++
Chlorococcum	-	++
Ulothrix	++	-
Blue-green algae		
Oscillatoria	++	-
Phormidium	++	-
Diatoms		
Navicula	-	+++
Stauroneis	-	++
Fragillaria	-	++
Cocconeis	-	++
Nitzschia	-	+++
Cymbela	-	+
Protozoans		
Paramecium	+++	+++
Stentor	-	++
Others		
Hydrochares	+++	+

+++ abundant
++ occasional
+ rare
- absent

conditions, *Rhizoclonium* was the most abundant filamentous green alga, and numerous diatoms were present on all surfaces. *Microspora,* abundant before, was seldom seen. There were also numerous protozoans, such as *Paramecium* and *Stentor,* but the *Hydrochares* mites were infrequent. Although some algal genera may have been introduced with the algae eaters, occasional water changes, or airborne dust, it is more likely that they were present before but too infrequent to be discovered during the less-than-exhaustive sampling. These data suggest that the algae eaters show a distinct food preference, eating *Microspora* and perhaps the blue-green algae, but apparently avoiding *Rhizoclonium* and diatoms.

Although the diatoms can be observed microscopically under high power, their identification is much easier with the use of the oil immersion and permanent mounts of the cells. Diatoms are classified based on the size and ornamentation of the frustule, a quite tough, silica cell wall. The ornamentation can be clearly seen if the cells are first cleared of their organic contents. The traditional way to clear diatoms is by boiling in a sulfuric acid solution to digest the organic material. This is both messy and dangerous, and often damages the more delicate or complex frustules. A better way is to ash the contents using the muffle furnace method of

Zoto et al. (1973). Several drops of the sample containing diatoms are successively dried onto a clean glass slide. Diatoms may be air dried or dried gently over a Bunsen burner. The slide is then placed in a preheated 500° C muffle furnace for 30 minutes. The slide is then removed to a warm place away from drafts to cool. It may then be made permanent by dropping on a few drops of Permount, followed by a #1 coverslip and heating to evaporate the solvent. The diatoms are then observed normally under high or oil-immersion magnification.

This exercise demonstrates clearly the changes that can occur in a community due to excessive herbivore pressure. The abundance of the preferred foods declines almost to the point of extinction while other species less palatable to the herbivore increase, probably due to the decreased competitive pressure. Other herbivores native to the community (*Hydrochares*) also show a decrease in abundance while species seemingly uninvolved in the plant community (*Stentor*) may increase or decrease due to changes in the habitat. The biomass not only decreases overall, but the diversity of species also changes (in this case it apparently increased) to a new community that is less capable of supporting the introduced herbivores, and so, less capable of supporting species dependent on either the herbivores or the original vegetation.

The design presented can be modified in a number of ways to suit the facilities, expertise and level of the class, and the goals of the instructor. The study can be made more quantitative by the addition of known amounts of selected algal species from pure cultures to a tank already containing herbivores. The taxonomy could be considerably simplified by adding a few known species to seed the tank. It would also be interesting to compare the preferences of different herbivorous species by direct observation (different species of algae "planted" into different parts of the tank) or by comparison of two or more tanks containing the same algae but different fish species. For example, the species selection and ecosystem effects might be quite different for "lawnmower" types such as *Plecostomus* compared to selective "weeders" such as the mollies. Several species of snails also are effective at eating algae as well as other tank debris.

The observations from this exercise are likely to lead to much discussion of the results and the implications. In discussion of this exercise with the class it is appropriate to substitute grass for *Microspora* and cow for Chinese algae eater with humans as the controlling agent in both cases.

Original Source

This activity has been adapted from an original by John R. Porter (1989) titled "Herbivory-Induced Alteration of Community Structure — A Classroom Model" and appeared in *The American Biology Teacher, 51*(5), 300-302. It has been reprinted and modified with the permission of the publisher.

V

ENERGY & ECOLOGY

Resource Flow in the Environment

ENERGY & ECOLOGY:
Resource Flow in the Environment

Energy, the capacity to perform work, is the force that enables organisms to live and ecosystems to function. Like matter, energy is governed by physical laws. It cannot be created nor destroyed, only changed in form. However, unlike matter, each time it changes form, some of it is dissipated as heat and is no longer useful to organisms (Avila, 1995; Raven & Johnson, 1991). This creates a need for energy to be constantly imported into the ecosystem. Energy enters primarily as sunlight, and it flows through the environment from organism to organism, with less of it available each time it moves. The flow of energy and the interactions that result form the foundation of ecosystems. These relationships create community structure, effect evolutionary outcomes, and shape most life processes (Ehrlich & Roughgarden, 1987).

The following four activities presented in this section permit students to investigate resource flow through the environment with energy transfer as the unifying theme. Food webs, the foundation of community dynamics and energy flow through living organisms, are nicely illustrated in the first activity by Leonard, *Investigating Ecosystem Energetics.* Trophic relationships in aquatic ecosystems can be investigated in the classroom using aquaria stocked with pond life and two or three lab periods involving student observations.

Investigating Food Utilization with Caterpillars by Jones is a terrific demonstration of energy input as feeding is transformed into a physical response in the form of growth. It incorporates several skill building activities where students use various techniques and tools to take measurements and collect data. Students then convert their data into tangible results using simple formulas.

Eutrophication and larger environment issues relating to freshwater pollution are investigated in *Demonstrating Eutrophication in a Beaker* by Gill and Markby. This activity can easily be integrated into existing labs, requiring only a few minutes over several labs to make observations and collect data. The follow-up discussion is an ideal introduction to pollution, freshwater systems, energy production, and other topics.

A hands-on activity involving the entire class is the foundation for *Investigating Decomposition with Classroom Compost* by Cronin Jones. Environmental issues, such as solid waste disposal, are explored as nutrient cycles and decomposition are demonstrated. Developing, maintaining, and using a compost pile have practical applications and can be expanded beyond the classroom as students include their family in the learning process.

This is an inquiry laboratory activity that develops fundamental concepts of energy flow through an ecosystem. The investigation, using an aquatic ecosystem as a model, is unique in that there are typically few ecologically oriented activities in commercial biology programs and even fewer that develop the principles of a food web and energy pyramid. The only assumption for this activity is that the number of organisms is directly related to the biomass (and, therefore, energy availability) of that species in the ecosystem. Students may discover the notable exception for zooplankton and some phytoplankton; if they do not, it can be pointed out at the appropriate time.

Investigating Ecosystems Energetics

Based on an original activity by William H. Leonard

Ecological Principles Illustrated

- Energy flow
- Food web

Materials

- reconstituted or fabricated ecosystem in a 10-gallon aquarium
- microscope
- slides
- several long pipets
- live organisms

There are three setup options, depending upon the teaching resources available.

Option 1 – An Artificially Stocked Ecosystem in a Classroom Aquarium

At least one 10-gallon aquarium with a moderate filtering system will contain the aquatic ecosystem. The exact organisms are not critical, but the ecosystem should have balanced biomasses of a variety of primary producers, primary consumers, secondary and tertiary consumers, and decomposers so that approximately a 10-to-1 ratio of numbers of organisms is established with each ascending trophic level in such quantities that student sampling will not deplete their populations. It is recommended that the bottom contain coarse sand to a height of several centimeters and that the water be relatively clear. A light source, such as from a window, is important for producer growth. The ecosystem should have been established several days in order for quantities of algae to be growing on the sides of the glass. Recommended organisms to order are:

1. Producers: Alga cultures (*Ankistrodesmus* sp., *Scenedesmus* sp., etc.) and some motile forms, such as *Chlamydomonas* sp. or Macrophytes, such as *Elodea* sp., can be added to the extent desired. Floating some *Lemma* sp. on top is also recommended.

2. Herbivores: Microcrustaceans, such as *Daphnia* sp. or copepods, at a density of 10 to 20 per liter; 2 to 3 snails per macrophyte strand, plus 10 to 20 snails for the tank at large (fewer if the snails are large). Water scavengers such as midge larvae and water boatmen could be used in place of some of the snails.

3. Carnivores: Approximately 5 minnows or fry of bluegill will maintain a proper balance. Any more will too quickly consume the herbivores. A small tiger salamander is another vertebrate that will feed on zooplankton. If one is added, remove 1 or 2 fish. Dragonfly or damselfly larvae are also good predators, and larger ones will also eat the small fish. Other good predators to use as alternatives (not additionally) are backswimmers, giant water bugs, and dytiscid beetles.

4. Others: A small crayfish or two may be added, as they are showy and fill a variety of niches (carnivores on snails, scavengers, sometimes herbivores). Small bivalves and

many other insects are also possible. It is important to avoid the temptation to add too many large consumers. A balanced ecosystem will appear almost empty compared to home aquaria.

Option 2 – Obtain Organisms from a Local Pond for the Classroom Ecosystem

In some cases, it may be convenient (and inexpensive) to stock the classroom ecosystem with organisms collected at a local pond. The pond environment would provide a much wider variety of organisms than could normally be afforded from a biological supply company. Gaps in the community, particularly representing whole trophic levels, can always be purchased. Using fresh pond samples also has the advantage that students will consider the ecosystem more real than one stocked commercially.

Water samples should be collected from several different depths. Collect representative vegetation also from all depths. Sample the mud on the bottom by using a screen or sieve. More extensive bottom samples can be collected by dragging a scoop sampler (or weighted net with strap iron handles and rigid opening) along the bottom. Use a sweep net at the surface to collect phytoplankton and some major herbivores. All of these efforts likely will yield the following organisms from a typical pond: a wide variety of different kinds of algae, phytoplankton, and zooplankton; water spiders; whirligig beetles; a variety of insect larvae such as stonefly, mayfly, dragonfly, damselfly, dipertans, and caddisfly; snails, leeches; *Planaria;* floating forms such as water fleas and copepods, rotifers, and protozoans; swimmers such as fish and amphibians; and burrowing forms such as annelids and other diptera larvae. After reconstructing the ecosystem, allow the water to settle for several days. In the meantime, check for the organisms needed for the student investigation.

Option 3 – Take the Students to a Natural Pond or Marsh

Probably the most desirable ecosystem study is the natural habitat itself. Most natural ponds will have a lush variety of organisms except in midwinter or late summer. The students should bring equipment to measure the physical environment. If they are to examine the microbiota back in the laboratory, they should bring collecting equipment as well. The same sampling preparatory procedures as in the second option should be followed.

Procedure

1. An introduction to the investigation and Step I on the Student Procedures page (see Figure 1) will take most of one 50-minute period.

2. If students work in groups of two and divide the work, data collection (Steps 2 and 3) will take a full period.

3. The calculations, analysis, and questions in Figure 1 will take another period, part of which can be assigned as homework. A list of references for more information on the related ecological concepts, identification of aquatic organisms, maintenance of a balanced aquatic ecosystem in the classroom, or about this specific teaching strategy follows:

Janus, H. (1966). *Pond Life in the Aquarium.* Princeton, NJ: D. Van Nostrand Company, Inc.

Leonard, W.H. (1980). Using an extended discretion approach for high school biology investigations. *The American Biology Teacher, 42*(6), 338-348.

Leonard, W.H. (1981). Designing an extended discretion laboratory activity. *The American Biology Teacher, 43*(5), 254-266.

Masters, C.O. (1975). *Encyclopedia of Live Foods.* Neptune City, NJ: T.F.H. Publications, Inc.

Pennak, R.W. (1978). *Fresh-Water Invertebrates of the United States.* New York: John Wiley & Sons, Inc.

Wiegert, R.G. (1976). *Ecological Energetics* (Volume 4 of Benchmark Papers in Ecology Series). Stroudsburg, PA: Dowden, Hutchinson and Ross.

Original Source

This activity is based on an exercise by William H. Leonard (1986) titled "A Laboratory Activity for Ecosystem Energetics" in *The American Biology Teacher, 48*(7), 432-434, and is modified and reprinted with permission of the publisher.

ECOSYSTEM ENERGETICS

Introduction

Ecosystems are ecological units of a variety of organisms interacting with each other on a regular basis. A pond, woodland, small section of prairie, and cave are each ecosystems. The African Baobab tree is so large and serves as a habitat for so many other organisms that it is an ecosystem in itself. Ecosystems are relatively independent and self-sustaining because they have producers, consumers, and decomposers.

Goal

Identify some of the major principles dealing with the flow of energy through ecosystems.

Steps

1. Study the definitions of the following terms: ecosystem, biomass, energy pyramid, food chain, food web, producer, primary consumer, secondary consumer, decomposer, trophic level, entropy.

2. Sample an ecosystem systematically to estimate the biomass per volume of ecosystem. Count in your sample representatives from all trophic levels: producers, primary and secondary consumers, scavengers (if any), and decomposers (if possible).

3. Describe the abiotic conditions and surroundings of the ecosystem.

4. Construct a food web and an energy pyramid for the ecosystem under study.

5. Answer the following questions:

   a. What does the food web you constructed represent?

   b. What does the energy pyramid you constructed represent?

   c. How does a food web illustrate the First Law of Thermodynamics?

   d. How does a food pyramid illustrate the Second Law of Thermodynamics?

   e. What does the answer to "d" have to do with the shape of the pyramid?

   f. Is the ecosystem you studied a natural one? Give reasons why it may and may not be natural.

   Optional

6. Measure some of the abiotic conditions of the ecosystem and relate these to the types and abundance of organisms supported.

Resources

A. Materials

   • Aquarium (at least 10 gallons) containing a variety of primary producers and consumers at different trophic levels

continued

FIGURE 1. Student procedures for a study of ecosystem energetics.

- microscope
- slide
- coverslip
- Pasteur pipet
- meter stick
- a general biology textbook

OR

- Actual samples from a natural aquatic ecosystem (such as a pond) either collected on site or brought freshly into the classroom laboratory

B. Definitions to the following terms may be useful. They can be found in most biology textbooks or obtained from your teacher:
- abiotic
- biomass
- community
- ecosystem
- First Law of Thermodynamics
- sample
- Second Law of Thermodynamics
- trophic level
- primary consumers
- secondary consumers
- scavengers
- decomposers

C. Techniques

1. How to sample an ecosystem.

You can first divide your observations into (a) those large organisms you can see without the microscope (macrobiotic community) and (b) those that are too small to see without the microscope (microbiotic community).

Macrobiotic Sampling

Since there will be a few of these organisms, just identify the common name of each organism present and count the number present.

Microbiotic Sampling

A frequent and simple technique is to sort all organisms seen under the microscope into I of 4 groups:

a. Arthropods: insects and crustaceans that have obvious eyes, jointed legs, and generally move rapidly.

b. Worms: multicellular worm-shaped organisms. Most will be colorless roundworms.

c. Zooplankton: single or few-celled organisms lacking pigment but usually quite active.

d. Phytoplankton: single or few celled organisms that contain pigment (usually shades of green) and usually do not move on their own.

You should sample several layers (depths) of the ecosystem, including surface and bottom. It is not necessary to identify the names of organisms. If you do not know the name of an organism, assign a new number or letter to each new one you observe. For example, when encountering several species of zooplankton, they can be named Z1, Z2, Z3, etc. for each differently appearing organism. Phytoplankton can be named PI, P2, etc. Be sure to organize your sampling data by trophic levels so the organisms are represented correctly on the food web and energy pyramid that you will construct later. A recommended structure for your data table is given below. Consider working in groups with other students to divide up the labor by counting the organisms in each sample.

continued

FIGURE 1.

continuation

LEVEL	SAMPLE #		CODE		DESCRIPTION		COUNT
	1						
	2						
	etc.						
	1						
	2						
	etc.						

FIGURE1.

continuation

If you do not have sufficient time to count the organisms in your samples, you may wish to judge the relative numbers in qualitative terms, such as abundant, many, some, few, or none. If you follow this strategy, it is important to apply your interpretation of each of these terms consistently to each sample.

1. How to construct a food web.

   A food web shows the energy relationships of organisms in an ecosystem. If all organisms are not represented, at least all trophic levels should be. Diagrams of sample ecosystems are available in most textbooks. Try to show all possible food interactions for each different organism you sample. The arrows are pointed in the direction of the organism doing the consuming.

2. How to construct an energy pyramid.

   An energy pyramid illustrates the relative amount of food energy present at any given trophic level of an ecosystem. Actual energy available in an ecosystem is nearly impossible to measure directly. However, since food energy is in the bodies of potentially consumable organisms, a good estimate of energy in any population is the total biomass of organisms that look very much alike. An example of an energy pyramid is given in most biology textbooks.

3. How to determine biomass.

   Biomass can be measured accurately by weighing all the organisms in a population. It turns out that the total number of organisms is, in most cases, closely related to the biomass of a given population. One can estimate the energy available in a population at the trophic level relative to other populations by sampling their numbers in a given space and then multiplying that number by the total space occupied by that population.

If you use sampling to determine numbers of a population, be sure to take several samples in different locations and average the samples. Multiply this average times the ratio of total volume occupied by the ecosystem to the volume from which the sample was taken. This will give you a more accurate estimate of the number in the total population in the space in question. Use the following formula when computing the total population from the average in several examples:

$$\text{Total Population} = \text{Average \# in samples} \times \frac{\text{Total volume or area of space}}{\text{Volume or area of space sampled}}$$

When you have computed the total population for each organism of similar appearance in the ecosystem, place these totals into the appropriate level of your constructed pyramid. Then sum all the organisms at each trophic level and compare the relative numbers at each of these levels.

Investigating Food Utilization with Caterpillars

Based on an original activity by Derek H.T. Jones

Energy-flow studies, which enable Gross Production and Assimilation Efficiencies to be calculated, can readily be carried out with caterpillars. The basic investigation can be completed in one week or less. Topics in which these energy-flow investigations are relevant include animal feeding, growth and respiration, ecology (predator-prey relationships and population regulation), and applied biology (the use of efficient animal husbandry to achieve good production).

Students will determine the mass of food consumed by small batches of caterpillars, the mass gained and the waste produced by the batch in this period. The Gross Production Efficiency and Assimilation Efficiency of these caterpillars will also be calculated.

Ecological Principles Illustrated

- Assimilation
- Energy flow
- Energetic efficiencies

Materials

- Cabbage white caterpillars (readily available either from biological suppliers or from infested vegetable plots. Suitable food plants include many species and varieties of the family *Cruciferae* — cabbage, broccoli, sprouts, nasturtium.)
- glass or transparent plastic containers with lids as "vivaria"
- balances
- brushes
- an oven

Students can work in pairs since the vivaria take up little space. Most caterpillars grow rapidly and quite uniformly if provided with adequate food. Caterpillars that have reached about two centimeters long are particularly suitable for the investigations described here.

Procedure

Relevant equations are shown in Table 1.

Basic Method

A filter paper disk is placed in the base of a transparent vivarium about 15 cm in diameter. A weighed lead section is then introduced, together with a pad of cotton wool, dampened with 5 cm³ of water, surrounding the larger cut veins to maintain a water supply and a high relative humidity. Next a batch of weighed caterpillars (say, 5) is added with a brush. A lid that is sufficiently tight to maintain humidity but not completely air-tight is put on the vivarium.

After several days, the caterpillar batch and remaining leaf material are reweighed. The droppings are also carefully transferred with a brush to a weighed crucible, and their mass is found. [Note that the batches of larger caterpillars may require additional weighed leaf portions to be added on one or more occasions (unless larger vivaria and leaf sections are used). A suitable results chart for fresh mass data is shown in Table 2.]

TABLE1. Energetics equations.

$$P = C - W - R$$
$$A = P + R$$
$$A = C - W$$
$$\therefore {}^{*}P + R = C - W$$

where:

P = biomass produced (and would include offspring in long-term studies)

C = biomass consumed

W = biomass of wastes (feces and excreta)

R = biomass respired

A = biomass assimilated (i.e., absorbed and used for numerous metabolic processes)

Energetics efficiencies:

$\dfrac{P}{C}$ x 100 = Gross Production Efficiency

$\dfrac{A}{C}$ x 100 = Assimilation Efficiency

$(\dfrac{P}{A}$ x 100 = Net Production Efficiency)*

* Not used in this study

TABLE1. Energetics equations.

Dry Mass Calculations

For dry mass data, the following procedures are suggested:

1. For estimating the increase in dry caterpillar biomass, the ration of dry to fresh mass is required. A small batch (which suffices for the whole class) is weighed fresh, killed as humanely as possible (e.g., etherized), and then dried in a weighed container. The ratio of dry mass to fresh mass provides a multiplication factor that students can use to calculate the probable dry mass of their experimental batches:

$$\text{fresh biomass produced} \quad \text{x} \quad \frac{\text{dry sample mass } (D)}{\text{fresh sample mass } (F)} \quad = \quad \text{dry mass produced}$$

2. For dry biomass of leaves eaten, a similar procedure is adopted. Leaf portions similar in form and fresh mass to those given to the caterpillars are weighed fresh and then dried and reweighed, the ration being used as a multiplication factor as above:

$$\text{fresh biomass eaten} \quad \text{x} \quad \frac{\text{dry sample mass } (D)}{\text{fresh sample mass } (F_1)} \quad = \quad \text{dry mass produced}$$

TABLE 2.

Example of class results chart for fresh mass (in grams based on a period of 6 days using batches of 5 caterpillars, 2-cm long, fed on cabbages and kept at 18° C).

Batch	1	2	3	4	5
1. (a) Initial biomass of caterpillars	0.28	0.20	0.25	0.22	0.25
(b) Final biomass of caterpillars	0.97	1.09	1.07	0.90	1.02
(c) ∴ biomass gain (P)	0.69	0.89	0.82	0.68	0.77
2. (a) Initial biomass of leaf	14.48	16.00	15.20	15.81	14.92
(b) Final biomass of leaf	8.31	7.80	6.04	6.89	7.81
(c) ∴ biomass consumed (C)	6.17	8.20	9.16	8.92	7.11
3. Control: Leaf biomass change in the absence of caterpillars*					
(a) Initial biomass of control leaf	4.50	6.20	5.10	5.70	4.95
(b) Final biomass of leaf	4.50	6.40	5.15	5.75	4.95
(c) ∴ biomass change	0.00	0.20	0.05	0.05	0.00
4. Gross Production Efficiency i.e., $\frac{P}{C} \times 100$	11.18%	10.85%	8.95%	7.62%	10.82%
5. (a) Biomass of wastes (W)	3.09	3.44	3.40	3.70	3.28
(b) ∴ assimilated biomass (A) $= C - W$	3.08	4.76	5.76	5.29	3.88
6. Assimilation Efficiency (%) i.e., $\frac{A}{C} \times 100$	50%	58%	63%	59%	55%

* Regarded as negligible, so that leaf changes in investigations are almost entirely attributed to consumption by caterpillars. No adjustment to this data was made in light of the control results.

An alternative would be for students to select 2 similar fresh leaf samples at the commencement, using the dry weight of one to represent the starting biomass of food and drying and weighing the remnants of the other at the end. Subtraction provides a direct consumption value.

3. To calculate the dry biomass of wastes, the dried feces, including the contaminated filter paper from the vivarium base, are weighed, and then the mass of a clean dry filter paper is subtracted from the total. Table 3 shows a convenient results chart for dry mass data.

Discussion and Follow-up Work

It is interesting to compare fresh and dry mass results. Class batch averages are shown in Table 4 on the next page. If sufficient records are available, standard deviation of these means can be calculated, as can the statistical agreement between fresh and dry mass values. The results obtained by the students with batches of five 4-week-old caterpillars about 2 cm long, fed on cabbage, and kept at 18° C for 6 days gave good agreement between fresh and

1. Ratio of dry : fresh biomass (one batch used for all class)

For caterpillars:

(a) Fresh mass of batch (F)	=	0.64
(b) Dry mass of this batch (D)	=	0.10
∴ ratio for use as a multiplication factor	=	10/64

For leaves:

(a) Fresh mass of leaf sample (F_1)	=	17.3
(b) Dry mass of this sample (D_1)	=	2.7
∴ ratio for use as multiplication factor	=	27/173

TABLE 3.
Example of class results charts for dry mass (in grams; based on a period of 6 days using batches of 5 caterpillars, 2 cm long, fed on cabbage, and kept at 18° C).

Batch	1	2	3	4	5
2. Estimate of dry biomass of caterpillar tissue produced (P_{dry}) $P_{fresh} \times \dfrac{D}{F}$ i.e., $P_{fresh} \times \dfrac{10}{64}$	0.11	0.14	0.13	0.11	0.12
3. Estimate of dry biomass of leaf tissue consumed (C_{dry}) $C_{fresh} \times \dfrac{D_1}{F_1}$ i.e., $C_{fresh} \times \dfrac{27}{173}$	0.96	1.27	1.42	1.39	1.10
4. Gross Production Efficiency (%) i.e., $\dfrac{P_{dry}}{C_{dry}} \times 100$	11.40%	10.94%	9.01%	7.70%	10.90%
5. (a) Biomass of dry wastes (W_{dry})	0.61	0.58	0.72	0.67	0.54
(b) ∴ Assimilated dry biomass (A_{dry}) i.e., $C_{dry} - W_{dry}$	0.35	0.69	0.70	0.72	0.56
6. Assimilation Efficiency (%) $\dfrac{A_{dry}}{C_{dry}} \times 100$	36%	54%	49%	52%	51%

dry values for Gross Production Efficiency (9.88% and 9.99%, respectively). The Assimilation Efficiency values were less close, being 57.00% and 48.40%, respectively. Thus, whether it would be reliable to dispense with dry mass data is debatable.

Gross Production Efficiency and Assimilation Efficiency values show the effectiveness of food in providing new growth. Here they reveal *Pieris brassicae* as an effective cabbage consumer, even though their herbivorous diet produces much waste. The typical herbivore habit of long periods of continuous feeding enables it to grow rapidly and accounts for the extensive crop damage which the species can inflict.

Further discussion of factors likely to influence the two efficiencies might consider:

• Stage of development of the caterpillars.

TABLE 4.
Comparison
between fresh
and dry mass
batch results.

Batch	Gross Production Efficiency (%)					Assimilation Efficiency (%)				
	1	2	3	4	5	1	2	3	4	5
Fresh mass	11.18	10.85	8.95	7.62	10.82	50	58	63	59	55
	Average = 9.88%					Average = 57.00%				
Dry mass	11.40	10.94	9.01	7.70	10.90	36	54	49	52	51
	Average = 9.99%					Average = 48.40%				

- Environmental conditions affecting caterpillars and leaves (e.g., temperature, humidity, illumination).

- Palatability and digestibility differences of leaves, related to plant variety, species, and age.

- Genetic variation in feeding efficiency between individual caterpillars.

These points suggest the possibility of further investigations into energetics efficiencies:

- *With batches of caterpillars at different stages of development kept under similar conditions.* This could enable graphs to be constructed of rates of consumption, production, and energetics efficiencies against length or age.

- *With batches of caterpillars of similar age kept under different environmental conditions.*

- *With batches of caterpillars of similar age fed on leaves of different age, variety, or species.*

Study of the application of these studies to livestock production might be feasible, perhaps with help from a local chicken farm, experimental farm, agricultural college, or university department. It is hoped the themes suggested above can provide the basis for much realistic project work.

Original Source

This activity is based on an exercise by Derek H.T. Jones (1985) titled "Food Utilization (Energy-Flow) Investigations with *Pieris brassicae* (Large White) Caterpillars" in the *Journal of Biological Education, 19*(1), published by the Institute of Biology in London and is modified and reprinted with permission of the editor.

Demonstrating Eutrophication in a Beaker

Based on an original activity by John Gill and Jane Markby

Eutrophication (the increase in the nutrient status of water with sometimes disastrous consequences to the organisms living in it) is a serious problem associated with the overuse of fertilizer in areas of intensive agriculture. It may also occur as a result of high levels of nutrient-rich effluent (for example, from treated domestic sewage) entering water courses that cannot provide adequate dilution (e.g., when summer flow rates are low).

Ecological Principles Illustrated

- Eutrophication

Materials

- pond water (100 cm^3)
- glass beakers
- Phostrogen

(Note: Phostrogen is manufactured by Phostrogen Ltd., Corwen Clwyd LL21 OEE, but similar products are available at garden centers. The analysis is as follows: NPK 10-10-27 with 1.3% magnesium, 0.4% iron, and 0.02% manganese. A dose rate of approximately 1g Phostrogen in 100 cm^3 water promotes a considerable bloom. A plastic pot label suitably cut down and marked with a loading line makes a good dosing spatula.)

Procedure

1. Pond water is used as the starter culture. Many ponds contain a large proportion of *Chlorella,* a significant number of colonial forms, and the usual collection of diatoms and desmids. Other ponds, with other algal flora, have also been used successfully.

2. Place 100 cm^3 portions of pond water (taken from an open position and deliberately avoiding larger plants and animals) in labeled glass beakers.

3. Leaving one beaker alone as the control beaker, add 0.25 g, 0.5 g, 1.0 g, 1.5 g, and 2 g Phostrogen to 1 each of 5 other beakers.

4. Place the beakers in a growth room under constant illumination of 4500 lux at 25° C.

5. Mark the water level on each beaker and add distilled water to maintain the original volume as evaporation occurs.

Results

"Greening" of the beakers became apparent within 14 days in the growth room conditions. A replicate sample on a laboratory bench in front of a window was not as far advanced and required an additional 3 days to develop to a similar extent.

The population causing the bloom was largely *Chlorella,* which caused a scum on the water surface. There were also large numbers of Euglenoids, diatoms, desmids, and colonial green algae in the free water.

Discussion

At the simplest level, "What happens if fertilizer gets into a river?" can be answered by a demonstration involving 2 beakers or jars, 1 with fertilizer and 1 without (the control beaker). Determining how much fertilizer is needed to cause a reaction to occur raises a more complex question that students can be invited to attempt to solve. The other two important variables — light intensity and temperature — may also be included as the investigation proceeds. The link with photosynthesis may be exploited, and the effect of the type of fertilizer entering the water can be tested. The investigation has a wealth of applications for both general and advanced biology classes.

Eutrophication is mentioned in environmentally conscious texts available to schools. Monger (1988) cites nitrates as the cause of "green pea soup" in which plants grow, die, and decompose. Bacterial decomposition reduces the oxygen level of the water, and the animal life dies. Mackean (1986), in his account of the "human impact on the environment," presents a more comprehensive account in which the contributions of both nitrate and phosphate are included, and the environmental effects of both agriculture and detergent effluent are considered.

Sample Student Questions

1. What would a pond or river be like if this had happened?

2. What time of the year is this likely to happen? (Clue: you are indoors and you needed a bright light.)

Original Source

This activity is based on an original exercise by John Gill and Jane Markby (1991) titled "Eutrophication in a Beaker" in the *Journal of Biological Education, 25*(1), published by the Institute of Biology in London and was modified and reprinted with permission of the editor.

APPENDIX. Sample statement instructions for middle grades (ages 9 to 13 years).

What happens if fertilizer gets into water?

You may have wondered what would happen if fertilizer got into a river or a pond. Read these instructions, then do the experiment as carefully as you can.

1. Get 2 jars. Write your name on both of them. Write POND WATER on one, and POND WATER WITH FERTILIZER on the other.

2. Put a scoop full of fertilizer in the "with fertilizer" jar.

3. Fill both jars up to the neck with pond water.

4. Put both jars in a sunny window or under a bright light.

5. Don't forget to come back to look at your jars every few days.

6. Write down what happens to them. If the water level drops, fill them up again with distilled water.

The following activity will help teachers and their students construct and monitor a classroom compost pile. By completing this activity, students will become familiar with the components necessary for the proper function of a compost pile and will be able to observe the composting process in action. In addition, the class will learn about current and potential markets for finished compost and should be able to describe the benefits of composting as a waste management technique.

Although the entire activity can be completed inside a traditional classroom or laboratory, ideally an active compost pile should be established outside in the schoolyard. The composting process takes time — usually a minimum of three weeks. To complete this exercise, allow two full periods in the beginning for student research, planning, and construction of the compost pile and one full period at the end for discussion of the results. While the compost pile is working, students will need a few minutes to record observations each day.

Investigating Decomposition with Classroom Compost

Based on an original activity by Linda L. Cronin Jones

Ecological Principles Illustrated

- Solid waste disposal
- Decomposition
- Nutrient cycles

Introduction

Composting of organic materials is one of the oldest forms of natural recycling. Without composting and other forms of decomposition, most chemical and organic nutrient cycles would be interrupted, and ecosystems could not continue to function.

When dead leaves fall to the ground in wooded areas, they are broken down and decomposed over time by a combination of physical and biological factors. Eventually, the elements and compounds that were once part of the living leaves are released into the air and soil where they can be used to form new plants or other organisms in the endless cycle of life. Given proper conditions, many of the organic wastes thrown away every day can also be decomposed and contribute to the natural recycling process.

Although most forms of recycling require machines and other types of modern technology, the composting process relies primarily on living organisms to get the job done. To initiate the composting process, organic wastes such as grass clippings, leaves, sewage sludge, and food waste must be combined with microscopic bacteria, fungi, and other decomposers such as earthworms. Given sufficient air and water, the decomposing organisms, especially bacteria, proliferate. These organisms generate a temperature of up to 150° F and literally "cook" the waste. The finished product, called "compost," is an important source of nutrients (such as carbon and nitrogen) for plants. Compost also improves the structure of soil by holding it together yet making it easier for plant roots to penetrate.

The large-scale use of composting as a waste management tool could significantly reduce the volume of solid waste communities sent to landfills and incinerators. Composted yard waste and sewage sludge can be used for soil enhancement and landfill cover and as a top dressing for grassy areas and planted fields. Current major purchasers of compost are state and county road and park departments, landscapers, golf courses, campgrounds, airports, and hay and corn farmers. Other potential purchasers include cemeteries, state and U.S. forests, fruit growers, horse farms, topsoil and bark companies, retail farm and garden suppliers, mining companies, building contractors, and the fertilizer industry. In addition to large-scale commercial uses, individual homeowners can compost their own home food and yard waste and use the finished compost to enhance the growth of their lawns, vegetable gardens, and flower beds.

Materials

- Classroom Compost data sheet (one per class) found on page 152

- wire or screen compost pile or large glass or clear plastic container for indoor compost pile (Wide-mouth, 1-gallon jars or small 1- to 2-gallon plastic aquaria work well.)

- organic yard and food waste (e.g., leaves, grass clippings, wood ash, sawdust, eggshells, fruit, and vegetable waste)

- lawn fertilizer containing nitrogen

- dirt or nonsterile potting soil

- 1 to 2 dozen earthworms

- thermometer

- garden trowel or large kitchen spoon

Procedure

A few days before compost pile construction is scheduled, ask the class to bring in samples of yard and food waste from home. Remind students not to bring in meat scraps, fats, or oils.

Food waste can also be obtained from student lunches. Ideally, the procedure developed by the class should consist of the following steps:

1. Chop the food and yard wastes into small pieces.

2. Alternate layers of soil (1"), organic waste (2"), a sprinkle of fertilizer, and a sprinkle of water.

3. Place a top layer of 1" of soil on the completed pile.

4. Add additional water as needed to make the pile moist but not soggy. (It should feel like a damp sponge.)

5. Add earthworms to the top layer of soil.

6. Place a thermometer into the middle of the pile.

7. Do not seal the compost pile. Air circulation is critical!

Place the completed compost pile in an easily accessible area in the classroom or school-yard and post the Classroom Compost data sheet nearby (See the example following the activity). Have one student record the initial temperature, odor, and texture of the compost pile and list the organic waste materials added to the pile in the appropriate boxes next to "START" on the data sheet.

While the Decomposers Are at Work

Keep the compost pile away from extreme temperatures and direct sunlight. Assign a different student to examine the compost pile and use the data sheet to record data regarding the temperature, odor, texture, and changes observed in the compost pile each day. Once each week (Days 6, 11, and 16), use a garden trowel or large kitchen spoon to gently turn and aerate the compost. On these days, have students make and record their observations before the compost is turned and aerated. Remind students to record the temperature of the compost pile from the same location and depth and at the same time each day. Check the moisture level of the compost pile every few days and add water as needed.

Record the final temperature, odor, and texture of the finished compost product and allow each student to feel, smell, and look at a sample of the finished product. Have students help construct a graph of the compost pile over time and reproduce the completed Classroom Compost data sheet on the chalkboard or overhead.

Discussion

Student understanding may be assessed or class discussion guided with reference to the following questions:

1. Why was it important to record the temperature of the compost pile from the same location and depth and at the same time each day?

2. How did the temperature of the compost pile change over time?

3. Why did the temperature of the compost pile change over time?

4. Were any odors produced during the composting process?

5. Why does compost have an odor?

6. How did the texture of the compost change?

7. What happened to the original organic wastes added to the compost pile?

8. Which materials were broken down and decomposed fastest? Slowest? Why?

Ask students what they could do with the finished compost product. Explain that finished compost is a natural fertilizer and tell students that, in natural settings, especially wooded areas, dead leaves, branches, and other organisms are naturally composted to produce humus, a nutrient-rich soil. Review the current and potential purchasers and uses of composted sewage sludge and plant and yard waste compost.

Finally, ask students what they think happens to organic food and yard wastes when they are buried in landfills. Explain that most landfills are not exposed to air, a critical component of the natural composting process. Without adequate aeration, most decomposing organisms cannot function properly. As a result, organic wastes buried in landfills can take decades to decompose. In addition, without ventilation, methane gas, a natural byproduct of the decomposition process, is trapped in landfills. As methane gas builds up, it expands and has been known to "float" or lift entire landfill layers.

Explain the benefits of composting as a strategy for reducing the volume of waste sent to landfills and recycling the elements and compounds necessary to sustain life.

Other Composting Activities

To extend this exercise, or if the students are interested in investigating composting further, try one of the following activities:

- To test the value of compost as a soil conditioner, have the students in the class design and conduct an experiment comparing the effects of different soil/compost ratios on plant growth.

- To investigate the effect of material size on the rate and effectiveness of decomposition, prepare one compost pile containing large pieces of organic waste and another containing small pieces of organic waste. Observe and compare the characteristics of compost in these two piles over time.

- If materials are available, have small groups of students design and monitor different kinds of compost piles (e.g., one low in nitrogen, one without moisture, one without aeration, one with sterile potting soil, one with a single organic waste ingredient such as banana peels, one without earthworms, etc.). After several weeks, compare the rates and effectiveness of decomposition among the different piles.

- To compare classroom compost and natural compost, collect samples of humus from a wooded area. Have students observe and compare the texture, odor, and color of the natural and the prepared compost and examine the humus for evidence of decomposers (fungi, earthworms, insects, etc.).

For Further Reading

To find out more about composting and the uses of compost, consult the following references:

Bern, R. (1978). *Everyone's Guide to Home Composting.* New York: Van Nostrand and Reinhold.

Johnson, C.E. (1980). The wild world of compost. *National Geographic, 157*(8), 273-284.

McLaughlin, M. (1986). *Earthworms, Dirt & Rotten Leaves: An Exploration in Ecology.* New York: Macmillan.

Rodale, J.I. (1975). *How to Grow Vegetables & Fruits by Organic Method.* Emmaus, PA: Rodale Press.

Original Source

This activity is based on an exercise by Linda L. Cronin Jones (1992) titled "Strike It Rich with Classroom Compost" in *The American Biology Teacher, 54*(7), 420-423, and is modified and reprinted with permission of the publisher.

STRIKING IT RICH WITH COMPOST

Key Component	Function
1. Soil	Contains microorganisms (bacteria) that help decompose organic materials.
2. Organic wastes (e.g., leaves, fruit and vegetable scraps, egg shells, and grass clippings) containing both carbon and nitrogen Meat scraps, fats, and oils inhibit decomposition and their strong odors can attract dogs, rats, raccoons, and other animals. They should not be used in compost piles.	Alternating layers of high-carbon and high-nitrogen wastes creates good environmental conditions for decomposition to occur.
3. Fertilizer containing nitrogen or manure or green grass clippings containing nitrogen	Many of the organisms responsible for decomposition need extra nitrogen for rapid and thorough decomposition.
4. Earthworms	Eat the waste and help break it down; make droppings that enrich the soil; tunnel through and aerate the waste, thus aiding decomposition; eventually die and become part of the compost.
5. Water	Essential component of the decomposition process; too much water can make the compost pile soggy and slow decomposition by reducing needed oxygen.
6. Air	Fungi, bacteria, small insects, and other decomposing organisms require adequate amounts of oxygen to survive and function.
7. Time	Decomposition takes time; aerating the compost pile every few days can speed up decomposition.
8. Heat	Heat is a by-product of the chemical reactions occurring during decomposition; a properly functioning compost pile can reach a temperature of 150° Fahrenheit; these high temperatures help sanitize compost by killing weed seeds, pathogens, and harmful insect larvae.
9. Mass	In order to generate enough heat for optimal decomposition, a compost pile should contain at least one cubic meter of organic material.

CLASSROOM COMPOST

Age of Compost Pile	Temp. (°F)	Odor of Compost	Texture of Compost	Changes in Organic Waste Materials (size, color, etc.)
START (DAY 1)				
DAY 2				
DAY 3				
DAY 4				
DAY 5				
DAY 6 (Aerate)				
DAY 7				
DAY 8				
DAY 9				
DAY 10				
DAY 11 (Aerate)				
DAY 12				
DAY 13				
DAY 14				
DAY 15				
DAY 16 (Aerate)				
DAY 17				
DAY 18				
DAY 19				
DAY 20				
DAY 21				
(Finished compost)				

VI

HUMANS *Impacting the Environment*

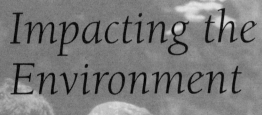

VII HUMANS: IMPACTING THE ENVIRONMENT

An awareness of how humans influence the environment did not begin with the first Earth Day in the 1970s. For instance, smoke pollution in the Los Angeles area had been known for a very long time. Native American tribes residing near the site of what are now the famous La Brea Tar Pits called the region "The Valley of the Smoke." After World War II, Los Angeles grew, and the city was plagued with a black haze that often obscured the skyline and inflicted respiratory inflammation. It was recognized that something was causing the death of the crops and accelerating the decay of rubber and plastic products (Air Quality Management District, 1997).

Early attempts to alleviate the problem involved removing particulate matter from the air. Scientists and engineers assumed that the health and agricultural problems resulted from pollution that could be seen floating in the sky. Even after the sky cleared up, plants kept dying or were subject to mutations. Rubber tires and plastic toys continued to crumble. A.J. Haagen Smit, a Dutch organic chemist working at the California Institute of Technology, identified the culprit as *ozone*. Ozone is created when certain chemical reactions are fueled by the energy of the sun. This gave rise to the term photochemical smog (Turco, 1997).

Recently, there have been many investigations of how industrial activity influences the environment. The activities contained in the following section examine how the burning of sulfur-rich fuel sources contributes to chemical changes in soil and water. In many instances, the emissions of one country will have an adverse environmental impact in a region sometimes thousands of kilometers away from the source. Gaseous pollutants pose one kind of threat, but when they dissolve in water, a whole new host of problems arises. Oxides of sulfur, for example, will form acidic solutions with a low pH when dissolved in water. Smith discussed the phenomenon (which he called *acid rain*) as early as 1872 in the book *Air and Rain*.

Lowering the pH of a system can kill or severely damage living things accustomed to specific life conditions. Exposure to heavy metals, like lead or cadmium, may cause adverse changes to the life process of an organism. One substance that has been largely ignored by the public is carbon dioxide pollution. Automobiles operating in the Los Angeles area are responsible for releasing nearly five million kilograms of carbon dioxide into the air every day. Discussion in many scientific circles suggests that an excess of carbon dioxide in the atmosphere may lead to long-term climatic changes on the Earth. Observing the rapid shrinking of glaciers at the end of the 19th century, Arrhenius attributed gases released in Western Europe to changes in the environment and in 1896, he coined the term "Greenhouse Effect."

The activities in this section provide insight into how sources of industrial pollution can directly or indirectly affect organisms. Through these activities students can explore and measure the impact of acid rain on seed germination, investigate how pH influences fast-growing plants, and test for pollutants using onion root tips. Other strategies assist students in making wise environmental decisions through a land use analysis and engage them with simulations of the mythical lands of "Islandica" and "Meridionalis."

An important aspect of the acid precipitation problem is the water incorporation of oxides produced by combustion and subsequent acid formation. The basic chemistry of this process is given below:

$$S_{(S)} + O_{2(g)} \rightarrow SO_{2(g)}$$

$$SO_{2(g)} + H_2O_{(1)} \rightarrow H_2SO_{3(aq)} \rightarrow 2H^+_{(aq)} + SO^2_{3(aq)}$$

sulfurous acid

One step that occurs in the atmosphere, not represented by the demonstration, is the oxidation of the sulfur from the plus four to a plus six oxidation state. Whether this occurs in the gaseous state ($SO_2 + 1/2O_2 \rightarrow SO_3$) or after dissolution ($SO_3^2 + 1/2O_2 \rightarrow SO_4^2$) is not clear. In any case, it should be mentioned that sulfuric (and not sulfurous) acid actually occurs in acid precipitation.

In the discussion, point out the sources of sulfur dioxide such as those from the burning of sulfur: volcanoes, power plants, industry, metal smelting, and transportation. Make the point that the gases (SO_2 or SO_3) can travel long distances in clouds before and after dissolving in water.

Investigating the Effects of Acid Rain on Seg Germination

Based on an original activity by Eric Johnson, Rodger Bybee, Edward Engroff, Elizabeth Gronen, Stuart Grubb, Mark Hibbs, Benjamin McLuckie, Amy Sager, and Jan Woodwell

Ecological Principles Illustrated

• Impact of acid rain

Introduction

Students investigate the effects of acid rain on seed germination by conducting an experiment with bean seeds, or locally available seed, under varying pH conditions. The estimated time for this activity is one class period to organize groups and set up the experiment. Then, take a few minutes at the start of every other class (for approximately 2 weeks) to water and measure seed growth and to record data on individual and class groups. Finally, there should be a class period to summarize results and prepare reports.

The ability of a plant to germinate depends on breaking dormancy, which includes:

• The softening of the protective seed coat.

• The chemical change of starch to usable sugars.

• The stimulation of growth of the young plant.

Just like people, plant seeds depend on proper conditions, such as temperature, light, and moisture to germinate, grow, and reproduce. Acid rain, however, has the potential to bring about an imbalance of these conditions necessary for seed germination.

Major concepts to keep in mind while performing this activity are:

• Seed germination is dependent upon proper conditions of pH.

• Increased acidity due to acid rain may inhibit seed germination and plant growth.

Materials

- petri dish
- 4 bean seeds (preferably seeds grown locally, e.g., alfalfa, pea, bean, etc.)
- water solutions ranging in pH from 2 to 7 (boiling will be necessary to drive off CO_2 and raise pH to 7)
- rainwater or distilled water
- absorbent paper towels
- transparent metric ruler
- graph paper
- colored chalk or magic markers

Procedure

Preparation of the Bean Seed

1. Assign each student a pH solution to "water" their bean seeds. A couple of students should be assigned distilled or rainwater for a control. The class as a whole should represent increments on a pH scale ranging from 2 to 7.

2. Cut 4 paper disks the size of a petri dish from the absorbent paper towel.

3. Dampen the paper disks with appropriate pH or rainwater solution.

4. Place the 2 disks at the bottom of the petri dish.

5. Measure the seeds and average them.

6. Arrange seeds in the petri dish and cover with the 2 remaining paper disks.

7. Replace the lid on the petri dish and label it with the student's name.

8. Each student should hypothesize in writing what they believe will be the ideal pH.

Preparation of Graph

1. Obtain a piece of 8" x 11" graph paper.

2. Set up the graph as follows:

   horizontal axis – age of seed in days

   vertical axis – length of seed in mm

Procedure for Alternate Days

The students will be taking measurements of seed growth and recording data on individual and class graphs.

1. Taking measurements and plotting the data on individual graphs:

   (a) Remove the lid from the petri dish.

   (b) Sketch the shapes of the 4 seeds. Note the color of the seeds.

   (c) Use a transparent ruler to measure the straight length of the seeds.

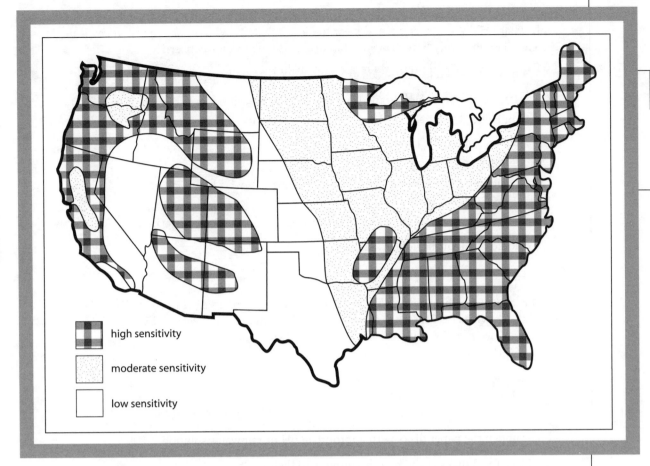

FIGURE 1.
Areas of the United States sensitive to acid rain.

high sensitivity

moderate sensitivity

low sensitivity

(d) Take the average straight line length increase and plot it on the graph. (It is important to plot the increase of seed growth because seeds are different lengths before germination takes place.)

(e) Make sure the paper towel is still moist. If not, add more pH solution (be sure pH solutions are not mixed).

(f) Replace the lid on the petri dish.

2. Class graph: Constructed on the chalkboard or on a large piece of white construction paper attached to the wall or the chalkboard and saved throughout the experiment. (The graph should use the same layout as the individual graphs.)

(a) Assign each pH a particular color.

(b) More than one student may be experimenting with the same pH solution. These students should average their results of seed length.

(c) Have one student representing each pH record data on the board using a code color that represents pH used. (Example: a pH of 3 is represented by the color green; a pH of 7 is represented by the color purple.)

(d) After a few recordings have been plotted, students should draw a line connecting points of the same pH.

Questions, Discussion, and Extension

Have the class gather around the completed class graph. What appears to be the optimal pH solution for successful seed germination and growth? The least ideal? How does the local rainwater used compare to the other pH solutions used? From the data expressed on the class graph, what pH does the rainwater appear to have? (Test it!) What impact on local crops might an increased rain acidity have? Do you think there is a reason for concern?

Each student should prepare a report that includes:

- Brief description and purpose of the experiment.

- Data collected, individual graphs, and seed drawings.

- Analysis of individual class results: (a) Ideal pH (b) Least favorable pH (c) Comparison of rainwater to other pH solutions.

Discussion questions: What impact of local crops might an increased acidity have? Do you think there is a reason for concern?

Provide a concrete example of how acid rain and its effect on seed germination could have an effect on food crops grown in the nearest agricultural area.

Original Source

This activity has been adapted from an original activity by Eric Johnson et al. (1983) titled "Acid Rain Activities for Science Teachers" in *The American Biology Teacher,* 45(4), 228-239, and has been modified and reprinted with permission of the publisher.

This activity is an investigation of the effects of dilute sulfuric acid solutions on the growth of seedlings. The simple experiment requires only limited apparatus and yet provides striking results in a short period of time.

Acid Rain in the Classroom: A Student Research Project

Based on an original activity by Garrie Fleet, Crispin Jones, and Darren Petter

Ecological Principles Illustrated

- Effects of pollution

Introduction

Acid rain is a matter of great concern in North America and Western Europe. Research already carried out indicates that plants, whole forests, and even animals such as fish could be at great risk. Acidity in rain is chiefly caused by the input of pollutant gases into clouds and rain, including gases such as sulfur dioxide, nitrogen dioxide, and sulfates and nitrates derived from these gases. The following project seeks to discover the effect of a component of acid rain on a small and quick-growing plant. It also investigates the relationship between the acid concentration and the effects it causes.

Materials

- any seedling that germinates quickly and grows reliably in a petri dish
- petri dishes
- sulfuric acid solution
- metric ruler (mm)
- filter paper discs to fit into petri dishes
- incubator
- hydrogen peroxide
- pH paper

Procedure

A. Identifying the Most Interesting and Informative Range of Acid Concentrations

Sow approximately 100 cress seeds on cotton wool in petri dishes previously soaked in a 1.0 mol dm-3, 10^{-1} mol dm^{-3}, 10^{-2} mol dm^{-3}, and so on to 10^{-4} mol dm^{-3} sulfuric acid solution. Observe the seeds twice daily for 1 week and note germination and growth. From this experiment, it is apparent that, in acid concentrations of 1 and 10^{-1} mol dm^{-3}, no growth occurred. Some germination appears to have begun in the 10^{-2} mol dm^{-3} dish, and the dilutions from 10^{-3} down appear to be growing normally. With these results in mind, it seems wise to concentrate on the range of acid concentrations from 10^{-1} to 10^{-3} mol dm^{-3}, as this was the range in which most changes in response appear to occur.

B. Investigating the Germination and Growth of Cress Seedlings in Acid Concentrations from 10^{-1} to 10^{-3} mol dm^{-3}

Syringe 2 cm^3 of sulfuric acid solutions of 0.1, 0.09, 0.08 mol dm^{-3} and so on to 0.001 mol dm^{-3} onto filter paper discs in 90-mm diameter plastic petri dishes. Evenly space out 10 cress seeds on each filter paper and label each one on the lid. Incubate the dishes in an illuminated incubator (to avoid etiolation) at 25° C. Examine the dishes daily and measure and record germination and root and shoot outgrowth. Weigh the dishes and add distilled water to replace the water lost through evaporation. While this method does not take into account the water incorporated into the seedling, it is the only practical way of accounting for evaporation.

C. Replicating the Experiment

Repeat the experiment with 3 dishes used at each concentration of acid. One dish contains no seeds, the second surface-sterilized seeds (10 seconds in 20 volume hydrogen peroxide immediately prior to sowing upon autoclaved filter paper in a sterile dish), and the third

TABLE 1. Growth of cress seedlings in acid solution.

Acid Concentration (mol dm^{-3})	Cracking of Tests	Presence of Mucilage	Seedlings Damping-off	Root Growth Mean Length (mm) After[2]			Shoot Growth Mean Length (mm) After[2]		
				21 hrs.	41 hrs.	65 hrs.	21 hrs.	41 hrs.	65 hrs.
Control 0	+	+	-	4.7(0.25)	20.8(1.29)	55.2(2.50)	0.4(0.29)	12.3(0.49)	25.2(1.40)
1 X 10^{-3}	+	+	-	3.8(0.28)	20.9(1.36)	63.4(7.89)	0.9(0.26)	11.3(0.58)	18.4(0.67)
2 x 10^{-3}	+	+	-	3.2(0.37)	15.4(1.60)	51.0(6.36)	0.5(0.21)	13.0(0.63)	19.4(l.16)
3 x 10^{-3}	+	+	-	1.7(0.38)	3.1(0.66)	6.5(2.65)	0.8(0.34)	6.3(0.81)	9.5(0.71)
4 x 10^{-3}	+	+	+	1.6(0.21)	2.8(0.19)	2.0(0.28)	0.3(0.15)	3.9(1.26)	4.6(1.96)
5 x 10^{-3}	+	+	+	0.6(0.55)	1.9(0.22)	2.0(0)	0 (0)	1.2(0.77)	0 (0)
6 x 10^{-3}	+	+	+	0.7(0.15)	2.2(0.27)	2.8(0.33)	0 (0)	0.3(0.28)	0.8(0.18)
7 x 10^{-3}	+	+	+	0.6(0.25)	2.6(0.57)	1.5(0.35)	0 (0)	0.4(0.38)	0.5(0.35)
8 X 10^{-3}	+	+	+	0.8(0.19)	1.7(0.38)	1.3(0.22)	0 (0)	0.3(0.28)	0.3(0.22)
9 X 10^{-3}	+	+	+	0.7(0.15)	1.2(0.13)	1.3(0.45)	0 (0)	0 (0)	0 (0)
1 X 10^{-2}	+	+	+	0.3(0.15)	0.9(0.17)	1.0(0.20)	0 (0)	0 (0)	0 (0)
2 x 10^{-2}	+	+	-	0.4(0.16)	0.8(0.13)	1.0(0)	0 (0)	0 (0)	0 (0)
3 x 10^{-2}	+	+	-	0.4(0.15)	1.0(0)	1.0(0)	0 (0)	0 (0)	0 (0)
4 x 10^{-2}	+	+	-	0.4(0.15)	0.8(0.13)	0.0(0.13)	0 (0)	0 (0)	0 (0)
5 x 10^{-2}	+	+	-	0.4(0.15)	0.7(0.14)	0.7(0.14)	0 (0)	0 (0)	0 (0)
6 x 10^{-2}	+	+	-	0.3(0.15)	0.7(0.13)	0.8(0.13)	0 (0)	0 (0)	0 (0)
7 x 10^{-2}	+	+	-	0.3(0.15)	0.6(0.15)	0.7(0.15)	0 (0)	0 (0)	0 (0)
8 X 10^{-2}	+	+	-	0 (0)	0.2(0.10)	0.3(0.10)	0 (0)	0 0)	0 (0)
9 x 10^{-2}	+	+	-	0 (0)	0.1(0.06)	0.1(0.06)	0 (0)	0 (0)	0 (0)
1 x 10^{-1}	+	+	-	0 (0)	0 (0)	0 (0)	0 (0)	0 (0)	0 (0)

Note: While there is no fungal growth on the sterilized seeds after 3 days, by Day 4 there was a degree of growth occurring in the same concentration range as the unsterilized seeds. It is presumed that disturbance of the lids allowed contamination to occur.

unsterilized seeds as described in the previous paragraph (B.). Estimate the pH of these dishes using a minimum quantity of Whatman Universal Indicator paper. Also record the presence of fungus on the seeds over a period of 4 days.

Analysis

The results of these experiments are presented in Tables 1 and 2 and Figures 1 and 2. Acid concentrations above 0.09 mol dm^{-3} were found to be lethal to the seeds; no outgrowth of

Acid Concentration (mol dm^{-3})	No Seeds pH	Sterilized Seeds pH	Fungus	Unsterilized Seeds pH	Fungus
Control 0	6	6	-	6	-
1 X 10^{-3}	4	6	-	6	-
2 x 10^{-3}	4	6	-	6	-
3 x 10^{-3}	4	4	-	5	-
4 x 10^{-3}	3	4	-	5	+
5 x 10^{-3}	3	4	-	3	+
6 x 10^{-3}	2	4	-	3	+
7 x 10^{-3}	1	3	-	2	+
8 x 10^{-3}	1	3	-	2	+
9 X 10^{-3}	1	3	-	2	+
1 X 10^{-2}	1	2	-	2	+
2 x 10^{-2}	1	2	-	2	+
3 x 10^{-2}	1	1	-	1	-
4 x 10^{-2}	1	1	-	1	-
5 x 10^{-2}	1	1	-	1	-
6 x 10^{-2}	1	1	-	1	-
7 x 10^{-2}	1	1	-	1	-
8 X 10^{-2}	1	1	-	1	-
9 X 10^{-2}	1	1	-	1	-
1 X 10^{-1}	1	1	-	1	-

Note: While there is no fungal growth on the sterilized seeds after 3 days, by Day 4 there was a degree of growth occurring in the same concentration range as on the unsterilized seeds. It is presumed that disturbance of the lids allowed contamination to occur.

TABLE 2.

pH and fungal growth on cress seeds after 3 days in 3 replicate dishes of acid solution.

radicles or plumules occurred in acid solutions of these strengths. From 0.09 to 0.02 mol dm^{-3}, root emergence occurred, but the resulting root did not extend beyond a mean of 1.0 mm. From 0.01 to 0.004 mol dm^{-3}, the growth that occurred rapidly ceased.

There was also fungal growth in these dishes. No shoots grew in acid concentrations above 0.008 mol dm^{-3}; below this, growth was very reduced and was usually rapidly terminated

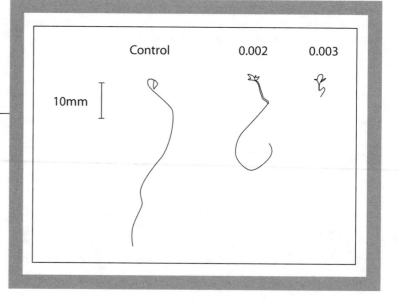

FIGURE 1. Typical cress seedlings after 100 hours at 25° C in different concentrations of sulfuric acid (mol dm⁻³).

and accompanied by fungus. In 0.004 mol dm⁻³ acid solution, growth occurred relatively rapidly, with the shoot growth exceeding the root. Fungal spoilage greatly affected the developing seedlings. The 0.003 mol dm⁻³ solution caused over 50% reduction in shoot growth and nearly 90% reduction in the growth of the roots. The 0.002 and 0.001 mol dm⁻³ solutions produced results not significantly different from the control.

The repeated experiment (C) gave a further insight into the relationship between acid concentration and plant growth. Records of pH in the dishes, although crude, indicated a rise in pH over a 3-day period. This rise was substantially higher in the dishes containing seed than in those that did not. One can only guess at the processes occurring in the dish but wonder whether the acid is effectively buffered or neutralized by proteins present within the seeds. The differences between the level of fungal growth on the sterilized and unsterilized seeds was marked, but both batches ceased to grow in a similar manner as acid concentration rose. It would therefore appear that the fungus attacked the plants after they had ceased growing, and not the other way around.

Discussion

The effect of very dilute sulfuric acid solutions upon the growth of cress seedlings is catastrophic. Even 0.003 mol dm⁻³ solutions (a dose rate of 1.96×10^{-3} grams of sulfuric acid per seedling, or a ratio of $1:7.54 \times 10^{6}$ grams of acid per gram of dry seed) cause a marked decrease in growth. A more subtle effect also occurred in acids of increased strength where the effect was not direct; the seedlings began to grow but then rapidly died.

The place of the fungus in the scene was made clearer by the repeated experiment (C). It was evident that the fungus attacked plants after the acid had caused growth to cease.

Acid rain surveys are usually focused on the pH effect of atmospheric discharges. While the less concentrated acid solutions, when applied, all had pH values of 4 or less, it was clearly noticeable that a rise of pH occurred even in the absence of living tissue. With living tissue, the rise was much more rapid. Although our pH estimates are crude, it is nevertheless clear that a more direct relationship occurs between acid concentration and plant growth than between pH and plant growth and that pH is rapidly altered by contact with nonliving material and very rapidly modified by contact with living tissue. Possibly, an estimation of total acidity, rather than pH, would be of more value in predicting the deleterious effects of acid rain upon the growth of plants.

For Further Reading

Fowler, D., Cape, J.N., Leith, I.D., Paterson, I.S., Kinnaird, J.W. & Nicholson, I.A. (1982). Acidifying influences of air pollutants and acid rain. In *The Institute of Terrestrial Ecology Annual Report.*

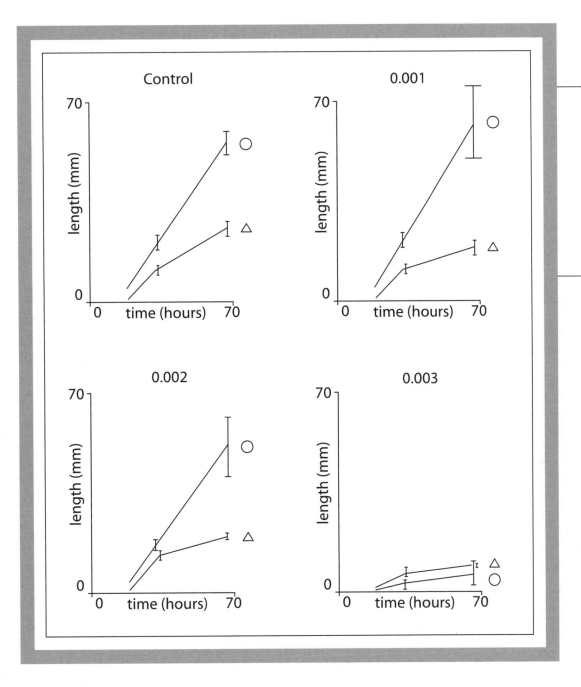

FIGURE 2. Effect of different concentrations of sulfuric acid (mol dm⁻³) on the growth of cress roots (O) and shoots (△). Standard errors are indicated by I (omitted from the 21-hour results for the sake of clarity).

Acknowledgments

The authors are grateful to Margaret Badcock for her assistance in the preparation of apparatus and chemicals, to Peggy Rawlins and Valerie Kay for the typing, and to Dr. John Gill for his advice and assistance. The work was supported by a grant from the Department of Trade and Industry's Industry Education Unit.

Original Source

This activity is based on an exercise by Garrie Fleet, Crispin Jones, and Darren Petter (1987) titled "Acid Rain in the Classroom: A Student Research Project" in the *Journal of Biological Education, 21*(3), 156-158, published by the Institute of Biology in London and has been modified and reprinted with permission of the editor.

The Allium test is easily conducted with inexpensive and readily available equipment. It can be adapted for use at both the high school and college level. The test uses macro and micro observations of onion root tips to demonstrate mutagenic and other toxic effects of various contaminants. Results are obtained in less than a week and may often be extrapolated to human cell systems.

Ecological Principles Illustrated

- Measuring the effect of pollution

Introduction

Contamination of the environment by carcinogenic and other toxic chemicals is an ongoing concern. A simple but reliable test, first introduced 50 years ago, may be used both by professional researchers and biology students to identify toxic environmental contaminants. This test, called the Allium test, was initially used by Levan (1938) to study the effects of colchicine on chromosomes from *Allium cepa,* the common onion. A modification of the Allium test by Fiskesjo (1985, 1988) permits monitoring of an array of environmental pollutants found in nature.

In a report compiled for the Environmental Protection Agency, the Allium test was described as excellent for assay of chromosome aberrations following exposure to certain chemicals. It was recommended that this test be routinely used for that purpose (Grant, 1982). This activity describes the procedures used to conduct several versions of this test, a versatile tool for the laboratory component of a variety of biology courses.

Materials

- a minimum of 20 (10 experimental, 10 control) fresh, unsprouted, mold-free, young onion bulbs of approximately equal size for each series of tests. Small white bulbs between 1.5 and 2.0 cm in diameter, weighing 10 to 20 grams, are recommended, but a variety of sizes can be used with success. Avoid commercial onion bulbs that may have been exposed to a growth inhibitor to prevent sprouting during storage. These may produce poor and uneven root growth.

- 1 test tube or small jar for each bulb tested. The base of the onion should just fit over the top of the tube.

- toxic solutions. Potentially toxic solutions may be obtained from streams adjacent to chemical and/or pharmaceutical factories. Precautions should be taken to avoid skin contact with the material. Alternatively, water-soluble chemicals may be used from available supplies. Sodium chloride solutions yield satisfactory results in stunting root growth. Several dilutions of the chemical should be tested. For lipid-soluble chemicals, use the specific lipid solvent as a control. When acidic or alkaline solutions are tested, a buffer control may be necessary.

- razor blades or knives

- microscopes

- slides and coverslips

- 70% ethanol

- colchicine (0.1 aqueous solution)

- refrigerator

- HCl (5N)

- Pasteur pipets

- 3-liter Erlenmeyer flask
- Bunsen burner or heat pad
- basic fuchsin (4 g stain)
- Buchner funnel under vacuum
- #1 filter paper

- potassium metabisulfite (12 g)
- decoloring charcoal (3 g)
- bibulous paper
- acetic acid

Procedures

Before placing the bulbs on the tubes or jars, remove the loose outer scales and cut off a 2-mm slice from the base to expose the root primordia. Too thick a slice will remove the primordia completely and roots will not grow. The bulbs are placed with their bases in the test solution, in dark or in dim light at room temperature. While not absolutely essential, changing the solutions daily will help eliminate bacterial or fungal contamination, thus contributing to the accuracy of the test. Daily observations of water levels should be made for 5 days, at which time the experiment is usually complete.

Another form of the Allium test involves starting root growth in pure water. Specific treatments are begun when the roots are between 1 to 2 cm in length. This was, in fact, the original version of the test (Fiskesjo, 1985). An advantage of this method is that nonsprouting bulbs can be replaced. Accordingly, several additional bulbs should be added to each series. Irrespective of the method used, liquid levels in the tubes should be checked periodically, and the appropriate liquid replaced as needed.

Macroscopic Procedures

The simplest form of the Allium test is to determine mean root length in a root bundle for each bulb by measuring root lengths of experimental and control bulbs on Day 5. In procedures where different concentrations of chemicals are used as the test solutions, the mean root length for each bulb could be plotted as a percent of the control on the ordinate against treatment concentrations on the abscissa. From this curve, the effect concentration (EC) may be determined. For example, EC_{10} and EC_{50} represent the effect concentration causing 10% or 50%, respectively, of growth reduction compared to controls. EC_{50} could be used as a standard analogous to LD_{50} (lethal dose) in animal toxicology studies.

Although these relative values are reliable, other measurements would improve accuracy. Each root could be removed from each bulb and measured and/or weighed separately. The disadvantage of this procedure would be termination of the experiment. Other macroscopic parameters include measurement of shoot growth, assessment of root tip hardness, changes of root tip, swelling of root tip, and bending of roots or root tips.

Data from an experiment using distilled water and a 1% sodium chloride solution are presented in Table 1. Statistically significant differences in both number of roots and average length of roots are always found under these experimental conditions.

Microscopic Procedures

Fixation and Staining

For standardization purposes, root tips are removed on Day 2, regardless of length. One root tip from each bulb is used to prepare each slide. If necessary, root tips may be stored in 70% ethanol.

Preparations may be fixed immediately or pretreated prior to fixation with colchicine. Colchicine arrests chromosomes in metaphase, permitting scoring of chromosome interchanges and deletions. To do this, expose specimens to a 0.1% aqueous solution of colchicine for 1 to 2 hours at 20° C.

Prior to staining, pour off the 70% ethanol and replace it with 5N HCl for 15 minutes at 20° C. Then pour off the acid and wash roots 3 times in distilled water for 1 minute each wash. Add enough water to cover the roots. Remove water by means of a Pasteur pipet. The roots are now ready for staining with Feulgen reagent.

Preparation of Feulgen Reagent

The Feulgen reaction is an aldehyde-specific reaction based on formation of a purple-colored compound when aldehydes react with basic fuchsin-sulfuric acid. DNA gives this reaction after removal of its purine bases by acid hydrolysis. Accordingly, the Feulgen staining technique is used to stain nuclei and provides greater contrast than orecin. On the other hand, the orecin technique is rapid and effective and is especially advantageous when preparing many slides (Fiskesjo, 1985). [For orecin staining, squash root tips in 2% orecin in 45% acetic acid after fixation.]

Feulgen reagent is prepared as follows:

1. Place 1 liter of water in a 3-liter Erlenmeyer flask and bring to a boil.

2. To the boiling water, slowly add 4 grams of basic fuchsin, shake well, and allow suspension to cool to 50° C.

3. Filter through the Buchner funnel under vacuum through #1 filter paper.

MEAN ROOT NUMBER AND LENGTH

In Distilled Water		In 1% Sodium Chloride	
Number	Length (mms)	Number	Length (mms)
35	18.2	10	1.7
35	20.0	13	1.5
35	2.6	29	1.8
26	7.8	19	2.4
36	13.3	38	1.8
33	14.2	33	2.9
46	13.4	8	1.8
35	8.4	16	1.9
35	7.8	20	2.2
39	17.0	38	2.8
x̄ 35.5	12.3	x̄ 22.4	2.1
s 4.7	5.5	s 11.3	0.5

t = difference between means for number of roots 3.355

p = 0.01

t = difference between means for length of roots = 5.841

p = 0.001

TABLE 1. Number and mean length of onion roots after 4 days in distilled water and in 1% sodium chloride solution.

4. Add 120 ml of 1N HCl, then add 12 grams of potassium metabisulfite ($K_2S_2O_5$) and allow the solution to bleach in the dark for 24 hours.

5. Add 3 grams of decoloring charcoal (carbon) to the filtrate and shake well for one minute.

6. Filter rapidly through #1 filter paper under vacuum. Do not change filter paper.

7. Store filtrate in a dark bottle in the refrigerator.

The reagent should be clear to be effective. Avoid contact with skin and clothing to prevent staining.

Add enough Feulgen reagent to cover the roots. Leave roots in the reagent for at least 1 hour at room temperature; they should be covered and in the dark. Reagent is removed by means of a Pasteur pipet.

Slide Preparation

Place root on a slide using forceps and cut off approximately 2 mm of the terminal meristem. This should be stained a pink color. Use a glass squashing rod to tap the root tip until a pink smear is produced. Then add a drop of 45% acetic acid and cover with a coverslip.

Place the slide between 2 sheets of bibulous paper and press down to blot. Examine under 430X. If preparation begins to dry out, add a drop of acetic acid to edge of coverslip and allow it to diffuse underneath. Determine the mitotic index by observing 1000 cells. The mitotic index (MI) is the number of cells undergoing mitosis per 1000 cells. MI of the experimental group is compared to MI of the controls.

Permanent preparations may be made by first attaching the cells to the slide by use of an adhesive such as Knox™ gelatin (5 grams per liter warm water with phenol as a preservative). Dehydrate by using a series (15%, 30%, 60%, 95%, absolute) of ethanol and xylol. The coverslip is sealed with Canada balsam, applied with the wooden end of a cotton swab.

Applications

The Allium test has proven useful in screening a wide variety of environmental contaminants for toxic effects (Grant, 1982; Fiskesjo, 1988). Introductory biology, ecology, or genetics students can exploit it for this purpose for individual or group research projects. The test can be adapted by instructors to demonstrate the effect of specific chemicals on macroscopic and microscopic parameters such as root growth and chromosome abnormalities, respectively.

The Allium test could be used as a focal point for discussion of adverse effects of various chemicals. It has been asserted recently that up to nine-tenths of all human cancers may be induced by environmental agents (Barfknecht & Naismith, 1988). There are currently some 60,000 synthetic chemicals in daily use; between 1000 and 2000 new chemicals are introduced into the environment annually (International Commission for Protection Against Environmental Mutagens and Carcinogens, 1983). These manufactured compounds appear in pharmaceuticals, pesticides, food additives, cosmetics, industrial chemicals, and many other products.

Among these chemicals are potential human carcinogens and other potentially harmful substances. These can be identified by screening procedures using laboratory animals. However, these tests require up to three years and cost up to one-half million dollars for each chemical screened (Weisburger & Williams, 1981). Consequently, not more than one-third of the new chemicals produced each year can be scrutinized in this way.

Twenty-five years ago, Bruce Ames and his colleagues at the University of California at Berkeley developed a short-term, relatively inexpensive test that bears his name (Ames et al., 1973). In the Ames test, mutations induced in a mutant strain of *Salmonella typhimurium* permit its growth in a histidine-free medium. Roughly 90% of the carcinogens so tested are mutagenic (McCann, Choi & Yamasaki, 1975).

Success of the Ames test led to the development of dozens of other short-term mutagen assays, most of which test for gene mutations or for chromosome aberrations. Chemicals testing positive for gene mutations are called "mutagens," and those testing positive for chromosome aberrations are called "clastogens." As with ionizing radiation, most chemical carcinogens cause both types of abnormality. Other approaches to carcinogen screening include attention to the molecular structure of the compounds in question (Weisburger & Williams, 1981).

The Allium test can be used to detect abnormal chromosomal changes and alterations in root growth (Fiskesjo, 1985). It can thus be employed to assess the deleterious effects of a variety of environmental or laboratory chemicals. The rationale for extrapolating results of the Allium test to human cells is supported by a review of pesticide studies showing a high correlation between frequency of chromosomal abnormalities in plants and animals (Grant, 1978). More recently, agreement between the Allium test and mammalian cell assays was shown to be approximately 70% for 14 chemicals (Grant, 1978). Weak damage indicated by the Allium test may be indicative of severe damage in mammalian cell test systems (Fiskesjo, 1981).

To conclude, the Allium test has several advantages as a laboratory procedure for detecting toxic effects of various chemicals. The bulbs are available year round, and other materials required are readily obtained and inexpensive. Also, with this system, a large number of root tips are produced in a short period of time. Chromosomes average 10 μm in length, allowing for easy detection of aberrations. The test works exceptionally well with improvised equipment; yet it can be refined for sophisticated studies. For example, pH and temperature can be controlled, buffers can be used, solutions can be sterilized, distilled water can be substituted for tap water, roots can be weighed on an analytical balance, chromosome studies can be conducted, and results can be analyzed statistically.

The Allium test's simplicity encourages its use at the junior high and high school levels. Its accuracy commends its use by undergraduates in introductory biology, ecology, and genetics laboratories.

Acknowledgments

The authors wish to thank their colleagues from Manhattan College, particularly Sr. Francis Cardillo of the Tissue Culture Laboratory and William Tramontano of the Plant Morphogenesis Laboratory for suggestions concerning microscopic methodology.

Original Source

This activity is based on an original exercise by Barry S. Kendler and Helen G. Koritz (1990) titled "Using the Allium Test to Detect Environmental Pollutants" in *The American Biology Teacher*, 52(6), 372-375, and is modified and reprinted with permission of the publisher.

Predicting the Biological Impact of Global Warming

Based on an original activity by Jane M. Beiswenger and Carol A. Brewer

The following exercise enlists students and teachers as local experts to predict the effect warmer temperatures will have on agricultural and natural ecosystems with which they are familiar. In pursuing the activities, the students will gain an understanding of the "greenhouse effect," an appreciation of how climatic change might impact at least one agricultural system and one natural ecosystem, and an ability to identify factors that determine which organisms occur together naturally. These activities can be adapted to different instructional levels and to different geographical regions.

For those who live within an agricultural region, in mountainous terrain, or near an ecotone, the best approach to this activity is to incorporate one or more field trips. A visit to a local farm can be followed by a discussion of how dependent local crops are on irrigation, fertilizers, pesticides, or other factors. For a natural ecosystem, students determine how the dominant plants and animals change with elevation, soil moisture, or other types of environmental gradients. Although the examples herein deal with corn production and a nature reserve, many types of agricultural and natural landscapes can be considered.

Ecological Principles Illustrated

- Greenhouse effect
- Biological effects of temperature

Introduction

A measured rise in the carbon dioxide content of the atmosphere is expected to have a significant impact on the Earth's climate and biota. Within the next 50 years, the average global temperature is predicted to rise from 0.8° F to 2.5° F (1.5° C to 4.5° C) (Jager, 1988; Houghton et al., 1990, as cited by Ojima et al., 1991) due to the phenomenon called the "greenhouse effect." That is, while carbon dioxide and other atmospheric gases readily permit shorter solar wavelengths to penetrate to the Earth, they trap longer re-radiated wavelengths from the Earth, causing atmospheric temperature to rise. Presently, teams of scientists are working on complicated computer models to predict changes in global temperature and precipitation (Bolin et al., 1986; Ojima et al., 1991). Articles discussing the impacts of changes in temperature and precipitation on global and regional scales are frequent in the popular press (Nash, 1987; Pain, 1988; Revkin, 1988; Adler & Hager, 1988).

Materials

- photocopies of the two laboratory exercises contained in this activity

Procedure

Before conducting one or both of the activities, gather background information through a previous exercise, a slide show, readings, and class discussions. These should include explanations of:

1. The role of carbon dioxide in the atmosphere.

2. Keeling's measured increases in carbon dioxide in the atmosphere at the Mauna Loa observatory (Abrahamson, 1989).

3. Temperature trends from the past 100 years and predictions of future trends (Moomaw, 1989).

4. The potential for increasing loads of atmospheric particulates to actually decrease global temperature.

An Agricultural Ecosystem: The Corn Belt

The *World Atlas of Agriculture* (1969) identifies principal regions of production for a variety of crops. "Corn Belt" states (Iowa, Missouri, Illinois, Indiana, Ohio) are defined as those in which a large part of the state's economy is dependent on corn.

To begin this exercise, the students examine maps (see Figures 1A and 1B) that identify Corn Belt states and temperature contours in the region. They are asked to predict where corn

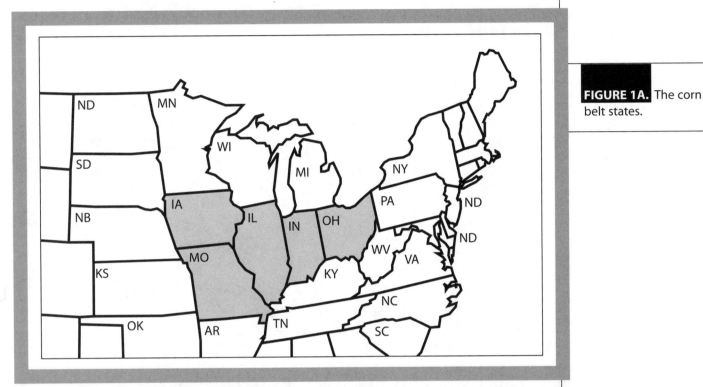

FIGURE 1A. The corn belt states.

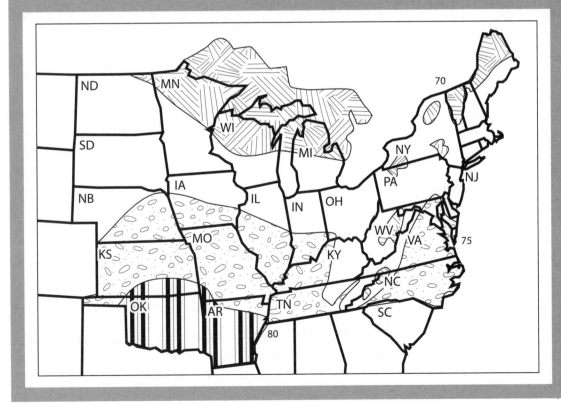

FIGURE 1B. Temperature contours.

would likely be cultivated if the annual temperature were to increase 5 degrees and to mark this change on the "corn belt" map.

Next, students examine a map (see Figure 1C) showing precipitation contours and are asked to reconsider the range sufficient for cultivating corn. After studying precipitation and temperature data, students consider three alternative scenarios: one in which precipitation did not change, a second in which precipitation increased, and a third in which it decreased. It is

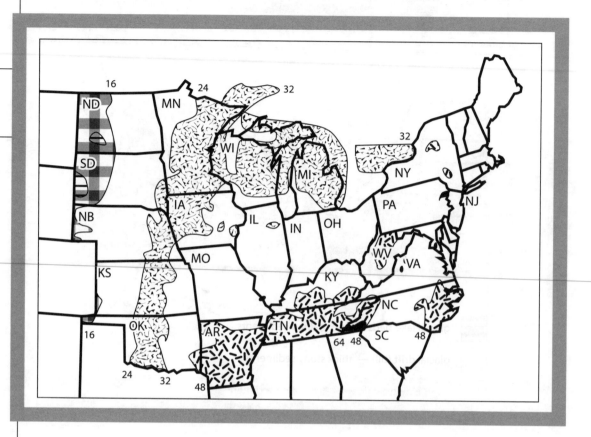

instructive at this point to show students some predictions concerning decreased precipitation for mid-continental locations (Manabe & Wetherald, 1986) or a map drawn from data for a previous time of increased temperature, such as the mid-Holocene altithermal that occurred a few thousand years ago (Manabe & Wetherald, 1986).

Lastly, they consider their predicted "Corn Belt" shift with respect to soil types (Figure 1D). During a concluding discussion, students comment on how the Corn Belt in North America may shift as a function of changing temperatures and precipitation and whether such shifts are possible on existing regional soils. Additional factors such as irrigation potential, treatability of the soil to increase fertility, and the possibility of encountering new pests are topics that may also be incorporated in the discussion.

A Natural Ecosystem: A Nature Reserve

This exercise, inspired by Peters and Darling's 1985 article, deals with a fictitious nature reserve called "Islandica." The reserve is completely surrounded by industry or farmland (Figure 2). Thus, the potential for immigration is extremely low. Degrees of shading indicate different vegetation zones at different elevations. Figure 3 on page 175 illustrates the dominant plants and animals on the reserve, and Table 1 lists the climatic parameters, soil types, dominant species, and migration rates relevant to each zone. If the activity is combined with a field investigation, students can create their own "reserve" and fill in a corresponding chart with their own data. To do this, students will need to estimate migration rates for each species they list.

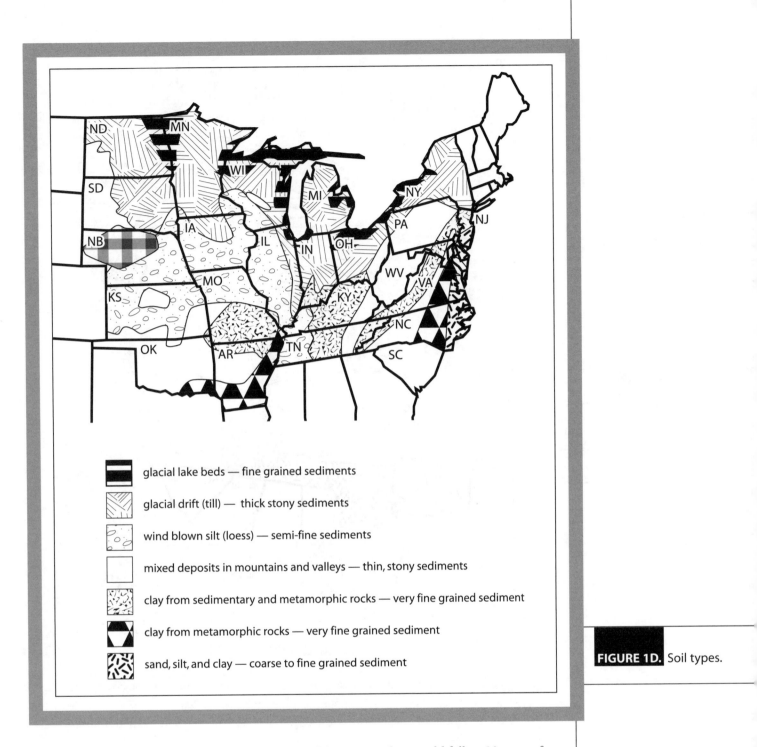

FIGURE 1D. Soil types.

The student's task is to predict the vegetation of the reserve that would follow 10 years of increase in temperature (+0.5° Fahrenheit per year) and decrease in precipitation (-0.5 inches per year). For more advanced students, additional procedural steps may not need to be discussed in detail. For less experienced students, the following approach works well.

First, the students are asked to change the temperature and precipitation values appropriately and determine new regimes for each variable. For each new combination of temperature and precipitation, students identify species that could tolerate the new conditions.

Suggest that they check migration rates to determine if each species could have reached the new location within the 10-year period. Finally, students check a list of "supplemental information" (Table 1) for any special factors restricting potential ranges of each species. If

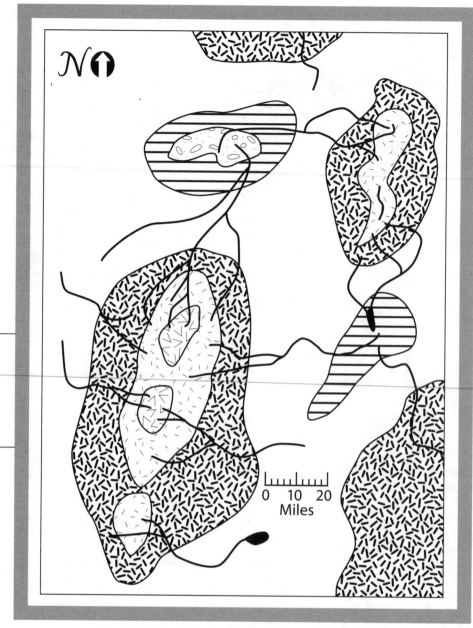

FIGURE 2. "Islandica," a fictitious nature reserve. Shading
patterns indicate different vegetational zones that are identified
in Table 1.

class data are used, students need to determine whether there are likely to be any special factors restricting the potential ranges for species under consideration.

The following questions may be used to guide the students as they begin and to prepare
them for a follow-up discussion.

1. Will the animal species move to a higher or lower elevation or remain at the same elevation as the climate warms?

2. Will all of the species in a vegetational zone move together? Explain your reasoning.

3. Which is more logical to determine first — the ranges for plants or for animals?

At the end of the exercise, these questions might be useful:

1. Which species disappeared and why?

2. What did you predict would grow in the lowest elevational zone following climate
   warming?

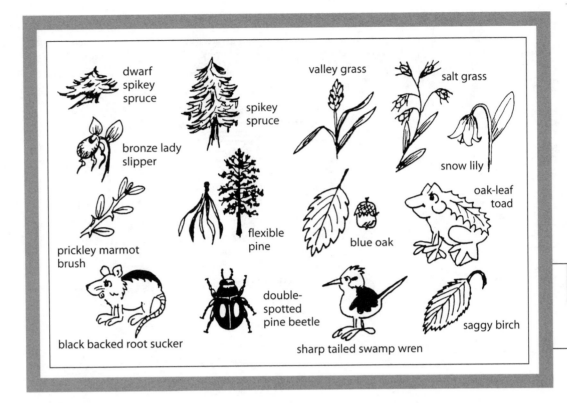

3. Which species will have their presence or absence determined by factors other than climate?

In a summary discussion or report, students should be able to describe how temperature, precipitation, and soil type interact to determine species distributions. They should also understand that migration rates, however difficult to ascertain, are also critical. The presence or absence of another species, as well as microenvironmental factors, may be important. When considering a mountainous environment, such as the Islandica example, students may discover other regulating factors, such as slope, aspect, ultraviolet radiation, and the rate of snow melt. They should also realize that distributions of organisms are dependent upon a complex network of variables and that, in most cases, each species reacts to its own unique set of environmental factors.

Conclusion

Citizens should have an appreciation for current environmental problems, their causes, probable consequences, and possible solutions. Biology teachers are in a unique position to discuss these problems and to help their students learn about them with laboratory activities. Through the activities presented here, students will gain an understanding of the expected biological consequences of global warming resulting from carbon dioxide accumulation in the atmosphere.

Original Source

This activity is based on an original exercise by Jane M. Beiswenger and Carol A. Brewer (1993) titled "Predicting Biological Response to Global Warming: A Laboratory Activity to Promote Discussion" in *The American Biology Teacher,* 55(4),222-226, and is modified and reprinted with permission from the publisher.

Zone	Elevation (feet)	Annual Average Temp (°F)	Annual Average Precip. (in.)	Soil	Dominant Species	Migration Rate Miles/Year
	above 13,000	10-15	40 or more	rocky granitisol	partly snow covered dwarf spikey spruce	1.0
					snow lily	0.01
	10-12,000	16-19	30-39	fine grained forisol	spikey spruce (11,500-12,000 ft. only)	1.0
					flexible pine	0.5
					double-spotted-pine beetle	10.0
					bronze lady slipper (10,000-11,500 ft. only)	0.01
	8-10,000	20-29	25-29	sandy forisol	flexible pine	0.5
	6-8,000	30-39	15-24	aggrisol	prickley marmot brush	1.0
					black backed root sucker	15.0
					valley grass	3.0
	4-6,000	40-42	10-14	alkasol	valley grass	3.0
					salt grass	2.0
					blue oak (riparian)	0.001
					oak-leaf toad	5.0
	below 4,000	43-45	less than 10	sogisol	saggy birch	0.1
					sharp-tailed-swamp wren	100s

TABLE 1. The Islandica Nature Reserve. Vegetational zones identified by shading patterns. Temperature ranges, precipitation ranges, and dominant species are listed for each zone. Migration rates are given for each species.

Supplemental Information

1. Flexible pine requires a forisol.

2. The black-backed root sucker is a vole that depends on marmot brush for food.

3. The oak-leaf toad is an endangered species that requires blue oak for cover.

4. Blue oak is a riparian species (grows along rivers or streams only).

5. Saggy birch depends on ground water or flooded terrain.

6. Salt grass requires alkasol.

7. The double-spotted beetle requires the joint occurrence of pine and spruce.

The purpose of the following exercise is to provide students with an opportunity to explore environmental issues of land use utilizing data and information in Soil Survey Manuals in conjunction with a physical topographical model that they assemble. This role-playing exercise invites students to make decisions on land use activities, requiring them to deal with a range of ecological and environmental issues. The exercise is broad in scope, exposing students to geological, mathematical, biological, and historical concepts. The exercise is most appropriate for students in the high school and lower division college age groups.

Ecological Principles Illustrated

- Land use

- Soil characteristics

Materials

- Soil Survey Manuals

- soil cores of site

- topographic maps

- plywood (based for model)

- 3/4" Styrofoam™ or similar

- rulers

- model trees, houses, etc. (or have students make them)

Time Required for the Exercise

- Constructing the model: 4 to 5 hours (can be an out-of-class assignment)

- Review of soil properties and Soil Survey Manuals: 2 to 3 hours, depending on student understanding of topic

- Land use exercises: 1 to 2 hours for each exercise

Soil Survey Manuals

Soil Survey Manuals (SSM) are publications of the United States Department of Agriculture and the Soil Conservation Service in cooperation with state agricultural agencies. The publications are available free of charge from local Soil Conservation Service offices in each county (most surveys are of single counties; however, some include two counties). Teachers should review with students what is contained in the surveys, particularly how soils are named, the properties of soils, soil formation, and special characteristics. An excellent text for background information on soils is *The Nature and Properties of Soils* (Brady, 1996). Students who have a strong background in the chemical, physical, and biological properties of soils will more readily interpret the data; however, with some instruction on soil characteristics (as described by Brower et al., 1990), students without this background can also use the surveys. Instructors should make a special effort to show how to make use of the Soil Survey Manuals and, particularly, how the aerial maps can be used.

In this exercise, the SSMs serve as guides and references for students in making decisions about land use activities. Specific use is made of the manual's aerial photographs, the descriptions of the soil complex, tables on tree growth, crop yield, suitability indexes, and slope.

Procedures

Selecting a Study Site

Although students will be making use of a model, it is helpful for them to visit the actual site that is to be modeled. This is particularly important if you select a site with which students are not familiar. An interesting approach is to select the school site as the site to study. It is best to pick a site that has some substantial differences in slope and suitable waterways for drinking water and wastewater discharge. Soil cores brought from the site for the model are useful to point out features of soils as described in the SSMs.

Constructing the Site Model

It is possible to conduct the exercise with a paper map of the area; however, a three-dimensional topographical model has the advantage of providing students with a clearer view of topography and its relation to various activities. Once a site is selected, obtain a topographic map of the location from the US Geological Survey at 1-800-USA-MAPS. It is a good exercise for students to actually construct the model. If they do so, you may need to explain the concept of topographic maps and see how they are interpreted. A small pamphlet on reading and interpreting topographic maps will be included with your map; however, a simple review of how topographic maps are constructed can be found in the Boy Scout booklet *Surveying,* a Merit Badge Book, available from the Boy Scouts of America, PO Box 909, Pineville, NC 28134-0909.

Specific Instructions

1. Enlarge the topographic map in sections by 800% on a copier. Later in the exercise, you will be using Monopoly™ pieces for houses, and this is a suitable scale.

2. Piece the enlarged map together with tape and determine the size of the model with which you want to work. My model is a square yard which represents about 450 acres. Cut a piece of solid board, such as plywood, to the size you have chosen.

3. Locate the highest major contours on the map, trace them in a particular color, and cut them out. Note that the major contour lines represent 50 feet in height. Since the contour maps are in standard units of feet, I use that designation throughout — although you may wish to convert to metric.

4. Place the cutouts on a piece of 3/4-inch thick Styrofoam™ or some other light and rigid material, then trace and cut out the Styrofoam™.

5. Find the next highest contour, trace it in color, cut it out, and then transfer to Styrofoam™ and cut it out. Place this piece under the highest point. When you reach the lowest contour, place this Styrofoam™ cutout on the piece of plywood. The plywood base serves as the low point in the model.

6. Stack and glue the foam cutouts together according to the map, being particularly careful to place the 50-foot contour spaces according to their position on the topographical map.

7. Blend in the contours with clay using a single color. Use the topographical map's 10-foot "minor" contours to guide in filling in the clay.

8. Designate streams and other bodies of water with blue clay. At this point your model should conform to the contour map.

9. Place a standard scale marker on the model (3/4 inches = 100 feet) and indicate North.

10. Have the students calculate the area (acres or hectares) that the model represents.

Vegetation Placement

The exercise might start by having the students place trees on the model based on information provided in the SSM chart on woodland management. This step assumes a "presettlement" climax forest condition and represents how the vegetation in the area might have appeared to European settlers. Trees can be represented by a variety of items: cocktail toothpicks work well, with the different colors representing different species; moss also gives a "forested look," although species differentiation is a bit more difficult. Students should understand why a particular species grows preferentially in a particular area (e.g., river bottoms have particular species). This is a good point at which to discuss the concept of forest succession and climax. For example, the instructor could indicate changes that might have occurred if a tornado or fire had destroyed a section.

With the forest model set up, several exercises can be pursued.

Exercise A. Woodland Management

1. With the entire model designated as a rural, forested area, have groups of students act as "owners" of appropriate sections of the model. I assign four different groups to the model, with each group having a different timber harvesting perspective ranging from a complete harvest to a selective cut that removes only 5% every two years. Students use the Soil Survey Manuals to determine the amount of timber present (board feet) and the species present based on soil types. This requires some conversions on the students' part — they must determine the acreage and species composition in each area. A drawing compass will help students determine acreage on the model.

2. After the teacher gives instructions concerning the degree of timber harvest, students should develop a plan to determine what timber should be cut. By instruction, some groups should pay particular attention to the severity of slopes and protection of streams. Many states have a "standoff" distance of 30 feet or more to avoid erosion (part of a "best management practice"). Students should be aware of the option of growing pine trees for pulp in 20-year rotations or hardwoods and pines for lumber in rotations of 40 years or longer.

3. Assign a particular technique to be used in the harvest, either clearcut or selective cut. Each group will need to determine the length of logging roads that would be required because roads cost money to construct and reduce the amount of productive land. In addition, students need to determine the number of streams to be crossed, because this creates an erosion hazard and bridges are costly.

4. It is important for students to determine the profit that is made from timbering the areas designated. Contact local foresters or county agents for current prices for standing timber. Have students compare the profit in different management systems.

5. Follow this exercise with a discussion of erosion, stream quality, and aesthetics. Ask students which management system is most sustainable.

Extensions

A) As an exercise involving the Endangered Species Act, have students assume that a red-cockaded woodpecker nest is located at a particular site. U.S. law states that a minimum of 60 acres must be left undisturbed. Have students calculate the effect that the loss of timber has on the yield from the timbering.

B) A good follow-up to the exercise is to have students comment on the management system that they would like to see implemented on National Forest lands.

Exercise B. Agricultural Management

For this exercise, some familiarity with growing crops is necessary. Therefore, the instructor may wish to define terms such as row crops, cover crops, soil banks, etc. Students with a familiarity in this area can be called upon to lead others.

1. Have the students identify the best soils that they would choose for farmland and clear it on the model. Ask students why particular soils (areas) were selected and what, if any, risks are associated with their choices (i.e., flooding, erosion). The instructor may want to try this aspect of the exercise with and without making the SSMs available to the students to demonstrate soil differences in suitability for farming.

2. Have students identify the best locations to plant the crops and calculate yields (see the SSM table on estimated acre yields) and potential price that would be received. Local county agents can supply crop price information as well as other information on costs and prices. Students should determine the relative suitability of each farmed area.

3. Have students identify where row crops are unsuited and determine the soil management practice, strip cropping, terracing, etc. that they would employ on these areas. Students who have an understanding of the Conservation Reserve Program can identify land suitable for this program and assess the financial and soil conservation benefits.

4. Have students explain the watershed that is defined by the topography. If there are several farms in the watershed, the students should discuss what activities on each "farm" might have impacts on other areas.

Exercise C. Land Development

This component of the exercise is the most variable and involves concepts that may not be familiar to all students but that can be learned quickly. I like students to develop the land in at least two ways: one way similar to the fashion we have historically developed (sprawl and expand), and a second way with land use planning concepts in mind.

Begin the exercise by returning to the model with the climax forest vegetation as indicated in the SSM chart on woodlands. Ask students how animals and native peoples might have affected the land (paths, roads, settlements, fires) and how settlers brought about change. If you have selected the school area as the model, historical information, settlements, mills, mines, etc. in the area can be discussed. Again, emphasize the importance of how particular soils, and therefore regions, were used for particular purposes such as timber, cropland, and settlements. Students should understand that cities prior to the industrial revolution had their workforce living in the city, but with development of a strong industrial base and relatively cheap transportation, the spread to the rural areas began.

At this point, several options of land development can be pursued. Two options are listed on pages 181 and 182.

Classic Development

The "town" consists of a small "downtown area" and three subdivisions. One subdivision has septic tanks; the others have sewer systems. Two roads intersect in the town. Assign student groups roles as residential, commercial, and industrial developers. One or two students should be assigned the role of directors of government and will determine location of structures (marked by *). Allow groups to work independently and without SSMs.

To construct the town and surrounding settlement area, the following buildings and features are recommended:

- 50 single family units (such as green Monopoly™ houses) for family residences
- 25 apartment buildings (such as red Monopoly™ houses)
- 2 grocery stores
- a "quick stop" convenience store
- a city hall with fire/police/library
- 1 hardware store
- a 20-acre park/recreation area (lake)
- 4 small farms of approximately 50 acres each (each farm has 1/2 in timber)
- a small cottage business where dresses are made and sold
- a small business that manufactures furniture from local hardwood
- a small business that manufactures wiring components
- a bank
- a small school*
- 2 highways (audiotape makes a good "road")
- 3 churches
- 1 farm supply store
- 2 service stations
- a water treatment plant*
- a sewage treatment plant*

*You might use either clay models or small blocks of wood for these structures.

After students have developed the area, evaluate their work, using the SSM to determine suitable uses for the land. Particular things to be aware of include:

- Development and farming in floodplains. Floodplains can be risky areas to develop, although they can be used for recreation.
- Houses or roads on unsuited soils. See tables in SSM for suitability.
- Farms on poorly suited soils, both in terms of crop yield and erosion potential.
- Improper placement of water and waste treatment facilities. Waste treatment discharge should be downstream from intake. Are houses located nearby the waste treatment facility?

- Do areas with septic tanks have soils with septic limitations?

Additional questions for students to consider:

- Are residents happy with their "neighbors"? (For instance, how would people generally feel about having a gas station next to houses, etc.)

- How does one travel from housing to bank, school, etc.? Is driving required? What environmental costs are involved?

- Do wildlife have adequate areas to survive? Are forested areas for wildlife chopped into islands?

- Do the town or the developments have trees or a park or any other connection to nature?

You may wish to take a picture of the development or make a video of the arrangement for comparison to the next section.

The Planned Community

Start this section with a review of land use planning. Some suggested references for topics in land use planning are: zoning and land use (ReVelle & ReVelle, 1988), wildlife corridors (Adams & Dove, 1989; Harris & Gallagher, 1989), urban forestry (Sampson, 1989; Ebenreck, 1989), community behavior and planning (Gardner & Stern, 1996). It is particularly useful to point out concepts such as the use of commons, cluster zoning, reliance on highways as sole transportation, and wildlife corridors before the group begins the exercise. Students can stay in assigned groups, but this time they must use soil surveys to determine the suitability of the soils for proposed projects and try to incorporate the above-mentioned concepts. Furthermore, all plans must be fully discussed by the groups before action is taken. An arbitrator, perhaps the teacher, can be appointed.

Changes in planning for this development are:

- 50 single housing units on 50 acres arranged in "cluster housing" with small front yards with a "green" space of about 20 acres

- 25 apartment buildings in two developments with a similar cluster and 7 acres of green space

- Maximized pedestrian accessibility and reduced automobile dependency by locating houses near school, churches, and businesses

- Trees provided in the village

- The recreation area and farms designed so that a "wildlife corridor" exists for the movement of animals.

Discuss with students any advantages or disadvantages to this arrangement. Ask students how they would respond to a "Regulatory Board" which would monitor their actions or impose restrictions. Focus on energy use, quality of life, and overall impact on the environment.

Conclusions

Using Soil Survey Manuals to teach land use concepts has the benefit of introducing soil surveys as a tool with scientific validity to determine the suitability and consequences of particular land use activities. Students use historical, geological, mathematical, and biological information in completing this exercise. Role-playing assignments encourage students to make judgments and decisions on current issues and to base those decisions on ecological concepts and information provided in the Soil Survey Manuals. Student comments were positive about the experience, with most students interested in community planning and with less interest in the agricultural management exercise. This exercise can be "personalized" if local issues such as zoning laws, new developments, or National Forest policies are being debated.

Original Source

This activity has been adapted from an original by John C. Inman (1998) titled "Soil Survey Manuals and 3-D Models: Tools for Teaching Concepts of Land Use in Environmental Science" and appeared in *The American Biology Teacher, 61*(9), 684-687. It has been reprinted and modified with permission of the publisher.

Biodiversity and Human Ecology: The Meridionalis Simulation

Based on an original activity by Neil Snow and Jane M. Beiswenger

The destruction of tropical forests has been widely reported in the scientific and popular media in recent years. The problem has been documented from many perspectives: the preservation of biodiversity (Myers, 1984; Raven, 1990), the human desire to associate with biodiversity (Kellert & Wilson, 1993), the ethnobotanical use of plants (Plotkin, 1993), the resource needs of an expanding human population (Raven et al., 1993), and others.

This exercise based on the fictional Republic of Meridionalis is designed to encourage students to review and debate situations requiring the simultaneous consideration of many factors and engage in authentic environmental decision making with respect to three fictitious land use scenarios. The specific goals of the exercise are to expose students to the benefits of collective thinking and discussion, to increase their appreciation for the difficulties faced by land use managers and politicians, and to further enhance their understanding of tropical forest destruction and its consequences.

Ecological Principles Illustrated

- Biodiversity
- Human ecology
- Tropical forest loss
- Land use issues
- Environmental decision making

Materials

- Meridionalis fact sheet
- map of the Country of Meridionalis (Figure 1)
- solution scenarios

Overview

When a basic concern for the continued viability of organisms emerges in people or communities, national parks or nature reserves are frequently seen as an easy way to preserve biodiversity. However, the creation of parks and reserves does not occur in a political and social vacuum. In reality, land management issues are complex and require the simultaneous consideration of many factors, both human and nonhuman. It is important for students to realize that issues of *any* kind are best considered from multiple perspectives.

The exercise centers on a fictitious southern hemisphere country named the Republic of Meridionalis (Figure 1). Working in threes, students assume the role of foreign consultants to the President of Meridionalis. Students read about the demography of Meridionalis and discuss among themselves three different land use proposals. For each proposal, the students can approve of the proposal, tentatively approve but require alterations in the proposal, or reject the proposal outright. Each student in each group gives part of a short verbal report to the entire class that summarizes their group's recommendations and the factors the group considered in making its decision. All students thus have the opportunity to participate equally.

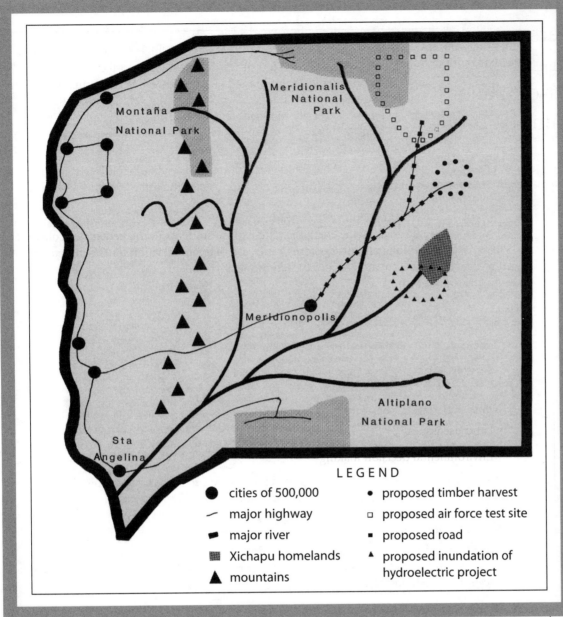

Map labels:

Montaña National Park

Meridionalis National Park

Meridionopolis

Altiplano National Park

Sta Angelina

LEGEND

- cities of 500,000
- major highway
- major river
- Xichapu homelands
- mountains
- proposed timber harvest
- proposed air force test site
- proposed road
- proposed inundation of hydroelectric project

Prior to using this interactive exercise, we recommend that you introduce your students to some of the biological aspects of tropical forests and their loss using a combination of readings, lectures, and videos. The more angles from which tropical land use alteration can be approached, the better your students will be prepared to think about the numerous interrelated issues. It has proved useful to precede the exercise with discussion and videos depicting biodiversity and agriculture in the tropics. On occasion, a biome identification activity, in which climatograms are constructed from temperature and precipitation data, is completed in a prior laboratory period; the rain forest is then used as an example biome.

Students rarely choose any of the proposed projects! They modify them, suggest combinations, or develop entirely new proposals. The students are asked to consider moral, legal, aesthetic, economic, and health and safety impacts; and they have been sensitive to these issues as well as those of biodiversity and preservation.

You may wish to facilitate the discussions by doing the following:

1. Listen carefully to the viewpoints of others.

2. Question other groups as to *why* they arrive at their decision.

3. Resolve conflicts by negotiating solutions that represent the interests of all parties.

Following the initial presentation of proposals, you may wish to have your students reconsider the proposals from different perspectives. For example, would a recommendation have been different if they had been raised as citizens of Meridionalis:

1. On a wealthy ranch?

2. As university-educated members of the Xichapu tribe?

3. As migratory farmworkers along the coast?

Finally, it may be instructive to the students if the class discussed what factors might repeatedly recur when biodiversity and human ecology issues were in conflict.

Specific Instructions to Students

As a team of consultants, evaluate each of the following land use proposals and present your recommendations to the President. Each proposal can:

1. Be approved as it stands.

2. Be tentatively approved, but only with changes suggested by your team.

3. Be rejected, indicating the reasons for the rejection.

Project Number One

The city of Meridionopolis is growing rapidly and has almost 2 million residents. City planners claim that within five years there will be a severe shortage of electricity. They are requesting a loan from the government to permit the construction of a hydroelectric project northeast of Meridionopolis.

The planners claim the project will provide much-needed jobs in the region and will prevent a projected electricity shortage. The planners have stressed to the President that hydroelectric energy is clean and renewable, does not pollute the air, nor contribute to nuclear waste disposal problems.

The planners admit that the project would flood 30% of the homelands of the Xichapu tribe, but contend that the region claimed by the tribe is much larger than what has historically been occupied as a homeland. The loan request is for 350 million dollars (US).

Project Number Two

The city of Meridionopolis is requesting a loan from the International Development Bank to construct a road through virgin rain forest from Meridionopolis so that a region in the northeast can be harvested for its tropical hardwood timber. The proposed area of timber harvest constitutes about 6% of the remaining virgin tropical forest in the country.

The city argues that the international market, particularly the Far East, is very strong for tropical hardwoods, and that there are no economic indicators that the market will change in the future. Since the government needs new sources of foreign exchange to help pay off old international loans, the city argues that the exportation of timber would help generate revenues to help pay off these loans (many of which are already in default).

The city proposes to clearcut 60% of the forest, leave 15% standing for erosion and watershed protection, and selectively harvest the remaining 25%. The loan is for 15 million dollars (US).

Project Number Three

The nation's only Air Force test site is located on the west slope of the Cordillera Occidental (mountain range), about 15 miles west of Montaña National Park. Researchers and tourists in the park complain constantly about the intolerable noise of low-flying military aircraft, as do residents of the three northernmost coastal cities.

The government does not want to lose the foreign exchange that is generated by the tourists and international researchers in the park. The Air Force has recommended to the President that money be allocated in the next fiscal budget for the relocation of the test site.

The proposed test site is in the northeastern portion of Meridionalis, an area that is almost exclusively virgin tropical rain forest. The proposal itself is for money to build an access road into the area, as well as two large airstrips, office buildings, and residential quarters.

The proposal acknowledges that the new test flight region would include the eastern part of Meridionalis National Park, but argues that few tourists and researchers are in that part of the park, and thus would not hear the majority of training maneuvers. In addition, this part of Meridionalis harbors numerous (illegal) coca plantations, where coca is grown for export for conversion into cocaine and crack. The Air Force knows the President is committed to decreasing coca exports, and states that their presence in the region would instill sufficient fear in some growers to cause them to abandon their fields. The proposal stresses that the total land area taken by the construction of new infrastructure and roadways would represent less than 0.5% of the existing rain forest in Meridionalis. The money requested to fund this proposal is 200 million dollars (US).

Acknowledgments

We thank Dr. E. Ribbens for testing this exercise and for comments stemming from its use. We are indebted to Keats Smith of the Flora of North American Office, Missouri Botanical Garden, for assistance with the preparation of the figure.

Original Source

This activity has been adapted from an original by Neil Snow and Jane M . Beiswenger (1997) titled "Biodiversity and Human Ecology: Analysis and Resolution of a Fictitious Conflict" and appeared in *The American Biology Teacher*, 59(6), 344-348. It has been reprinted and modified with permission of the publisher.

Fact Sheet: A Portrait of the Country of Meridionalis

Meridionalis is a fictitious country in the southern hemisphere. A description of the country, its government, economic base, demographics, natural heritage, and biodiversity is provided below. Your team of three has been hired by the President of Meridionalis as outside, non-partisan consultants to evaluate three land use proposals and to make recommendations.

A) Size

135,000 square miles (about 1.5 times the size of Colorado)

B) Government

Semi-democratic. The President can serve two

five-year terms, and leads an Upper and Lower Parliament.

C) Economy

Historically, the sources of income have been:

1. Mining of silver, copper, zinc, and guano (primary economic source)

2. Coffee in the foothills region of the mountains (primary)

3. Bananas and pineapples in the south central and coastal regions (primary)

4. Cattle ranching in the altiplano region (primary)

5. Coca leaves (illegal, but lucrative, and considered primary).

6. Tourism featuring beaches mostly, but increasing numbers of foreigners visit the three national parks (secondary)

7. Hardwoods including teak, mahogany, pernambuco, and others (secondary)

8. Sugar cane in the foothills and coastal regions (secondary).

Meridionalis has lost foreign revenues recently because of several recent bad crops of coffee, an exhaustion of the guano supply, and low international prices for copper and silver. The previous three presidential administrations mismanaged international loans intended for development. Meridionalis owes its lenders 45 billion dollars (US), but can barely meet interest payments on the loans. Inflation has averaged 35% over the last five years.

Austerity measures, including sharp cuts in public assistance programs, were introduced by the current and popular President, who is in the fourth year of his first term. Public support for the austerity programs has slipped dramatically; people want increased wages to counteract their loss of purchasing power.

D) Demographics of Meridionalis

Meridionalis has a population of 9 million people, most living along the crowded, lowland west coast. Meridionalis has a high birth rate: 3.1 births per thousand each year. Forty percent of the population is under 15 years of age. The population is expected to double in 40 years if birth rates remain unchanged. More than 85% of the population is of one religious denomination, but the church opposes artificial means of birth control. When interviewed anonymously, 75% of the women indicated they would use birth control options if they were more widely available. The President is on record as being opposed to abortion.

Many people in the cities have lost jobs due to high interest rates, cancellation of government projects, and austerity programs. The government faces rising crime rates in the coastal cities, and sees voluntary relocation of people to the rain forests as a way to reduce population pressures along the coast. The government will give free title to 100 hectares of land in the rain forest, provided the settler occupies the land for five years continuously and, in the words of the law, "improves" the land. In the last five years, more than 200,000 people have settled into the rain forest that adjoins the major highways. Experts agree that unless a concerted effort is made to halt the influx of settlers into the rain forest, little rain forest will remain in Meridionalis within 20 years.

E) The Natural Heritage of Meridionalis

Meridionalis consists of four major regions: the Coastal Plain (highly populated, little original vegetation remains); the Cordillera Occidental, a mountain range that runs north-south; the Altiplano ("high plains") region of the southeast; and the Interior Lowlands, which consist of mostly undisturbed tropical rain forests (roughly two-thirds of the country).

The mountains support a population of traditional agriculturalists. Although poor, these people are happy with their lives and request little from the government. About half the original vegetation remains in the mountains.

The altiplano region consists of savanna vegetation. Since the 18th century, it has been occupied by cattle ranchers (excluding Altiplano National Park). Ninety percent of the altiplano is used for cattle ranching. Only 20% of the land, however, is considered overgrazed or in poor condition.

The Interior Lowlands are accessible only from the north (via Meridionalis National Park) and the center, from Meridionopolis. The rain forests harbor numerous native tribes, many of which have been nearly eradicated or absorbed by increasing contact with 20th century culture. The largest tribe is the Xichapu, which resents increasing encroachment on its homelands. The constitution of Meridionalis states, in vague language, "efforts must be made to preserve the integrity of the indigenous peoples." Oil companies believe there is oil beneath portions of the rain forest, although it is a poor grade of oil. Most of the southern and central parts of the rain forest have been cleared. This is believed to be due primarily to access from the major highways between Meridionopolis and Santa Angelina, enabling illegal squatters to enter the forest, where they practice slash-and-burn agriculture.

Meridionalis has three national parks. Montaña National Park is the oldest. Not only does it draw many tourists for its natural beauty and artifacts from ancient cultures, it has been a magnet for research in tropical biology for 30 years. The park generates several million dollars a year by providing services to foreign and domestic researchers and tourists. Altiplano National Park consists mostly of beautiful red sandstone formations, similar to those found in portions of Australia and the southwestern United States. It harbors relatively low levels of biodiversity (compared to the rain forest and mountains), but this biodiversity is in general not threatened with extinction.

Meridionalis National Park was formed only 10 years ago, largely due to international pressure to protect the region, which is extraordinarily diverse biologically. However, little money has been appropriated by the government to manage the park and enforce its boundaries. As a result, immigrants from crowded cities are moving in from the northern highway and (illegally) clearing land for slash-and-burn agriculture. The government is under severe criticism from international and domestic groups to safeguard the park's biodiversity, as was originally intended.

F) Biological Diversity of Meridionalis

The biodiversity of Meridionalis is very rich. It is known to have 9000 species of plants. Although in its infancy, a joint venture between Meridionalis National University, MeridioTech Pharmaceutical, and the Meridionopolis Natural History Survey is dedicated to intensively surveying the nation's plants and animals by the year 2005. Experts predict that an additional 500 to 700 species of plants, previously unknown to science, will be discovered from the rain forest region. Biologists travel to northeast Meridionalis from throughout the world to study frogs, moths, and ants, which are particularly species-rich in this area. The Meridionalis Institutes of Health knows of at least five native plant species that have clinically demonstrated potential as cures to ovarian cancer.

Appendices

Appendix A | The NABT Animal Use Statement

The Use of Animals in Biology Education

The National Association of Biology Teachers (NABT) believes that the study of organisms, including nonhuman animals, is essential to the understanding of life on Earth. NABT recommends the prudent and responsible use of animals in the life science classroom. NABT believes that biology teachers should foster a respect for life. Biology teachers also should teach about the interrelationship and interdependency of all things.

Classroom experiences that involve nonhuman animals range from observation to dissection. NABT supports these experiences so long as they are conducted within the long established guidelines of proper care and use of animals, as developed by the scientific and educational community.

As with any instructional activity, the use of nonhuman animals in the biology classroom must have sound educational objectives. Any use of animals, whether for observation or dissection, must convey substantive knowledge of biology. NABT believes that biology teachers are in the best position to make this determination for their students.

NABT acknowledges that no alternative can substitute for the actual experiences of dissection or other use of animals and urges teachers to be aware of the limitations of alternatives. When the teacher determines that the most effective means to meet the objectives of the class do not require dissection, NABT accepts the use of alternatives to dissection, including models and the various forms of multimedia. The Association encourages teachers to be sensitive to substantive student objections to dissection and to consider providing appropriate lessons for those students where necessary.

To implement this policy, NABT endorses and adopts the "Principles and Guidelines for the Use of Animals in Precollege Education" of the Institute of Laboratory Animals Resources (National Research Council). Copies of the "Principles and Guidelines" may be obtained from NABT or the ILAR (2101 Constitution Avenue, NW, Washington, DC 20418; 202/334-2590).

Adopted by the NABT Board of Directors in October 1995

This policy supersedes and replaces all previous NABT statements regarding animals in biology education.

Ecological Glossary

Prepared by Deb Stone

abiotic – nonliving components of an ecosystem.

acclimation – physiological adjustment by an organism to environmental change.

acid rain – highly acidic precipitation that results from the release of oxides of sulfur and nitrogen into the air from burning fossil fuels.

adaptation – an inherited trait that increases an organism's chance of survival and reproduction in a certain environment.

aerate – to be open to air with oxygen.

aerobe – an organism that requires oxygen to survive.

anaerobe – an organism that does not require oxygen to survive.

anemometer – instrument that measures wind speed.

anthocyanin – a red pigment of many plants.

Assimilation Efficiency – the efficiency by which animals convert the food they ingest into energy for growth and reproduction.

benthic – bottom of a body of water.

biodiversity – term used to indicate the number and diversity of species on Earth.

biogeography – a science that deals with the geographical distribution of animals and plants.

biological oxygen – the amount of oxygen needed by microorganisms to decompose waste.

biomass – organic matter in plants or plant products.

biome – region with a distinctive climate and organisms that contains many separate but similar ecosystems.

biota – the sum total of living organisms in a region.

Buchner funnel – a large funnel used to separate out animals living in leaf litter. The leaf litter, retained by a screen, is placed in the funnel, and the funnel is placed tip down in a vial of preservative. When heat, usually from a lamp, is applied to the leaf litter, the animals will crawl down through the screen and fall into the preservative.

canopy – in a forest, the covering of tall trees whose intertwining branches absorb a great amount of sunlight and shade the area beneath.

carcinogenic – cancer causing.

chaparral – a biome with mild, moist summers and hot, dry summers; vegetation is characterized by small-leaved evergreen shrubs and small trees.

charate – soil remaining after a fire.

chemosynthetic – made from chemicals.

chlorenchyma – chlorophyll-containing parenchyma of plants.

chi-square – a specific statistical test employed to gauge variation between two populations.

coagulation – clotting or thickening of a substance.

colchicine – a poisonous alkaloid that inhibits mitosis, is extracted from the corms or seeds of the autumn crocus (*Colchicum autumnale*), and is used especially in the treatment of gout and to produce polyploidy in plants.

community – all populations within an ecosystem.

competition – the interaction among organisms that vie for the same resources in an ecosystem.

compost – a natural soil and humus mixture that improves soil fertility and soil structure.

confidence limits – the end points of a confidence interval.

consumer – organism that cannot synthesize its own food from inorganic materials and therefore must use the bodies of other organisms as a source of energy and body-building materials; also called a heterotroph.

contamination – a process of contaminating; a state of being contaminated.

Crassulacean Acid Metabolism (CAM) – the process in succulent plants of the desert region whereby CO_2 is fixed into an organic acid, malic acid, and is stored in cellular vacuoles until the energy from sunlight is available for photosynthesis.

crystal violet – a triphenylmethane dye found in gentian violet used in staining slides.

decarboxylation – the removal or elimination of carboxyl from a molecule.

deforestation – the removal of forest without adequate replanting.

detritus – an organism that consumes fragments of dead organisms.

diaspore – a general term for dispersal structures on trees such as fruit, seeds, etc.

diurnal – having a daily cycle.

ecosystem – the interacting system that encompasses a community and its nonliving, physical environment.

ectotherm – a cold-blooded animal.

endogenous – growing or produced by growth from deep tissue (i.e., plant roots).

energetics – the total energy relations and transformations of a physical, chemical, or biological system.

eutrophication – the enrichment of a lake or pond by nutrients; natural eutrophication occurs slowly when a lake gradually fills in and converts to a marsh, eventually disappearing.

fenestra – a small anatomical opening; an oval opening between the middle ear and the vestibule having the base of the stapes or columella attached to its membrane.

fermentation – an enzymatically controlled anaerobic breakdown of an energy-rich compounds such as sugar.

First Law of Thermodynamics – energy cannot be created or destroyed, although it may be transformed from one form to another.

flavonoid – any of a group of aromatic compounds that includes many common pigments.

fuchsin – dye that is produced by oxidation of a mixture of aniline and toluidines and yields a brilliant bluish red.

greenhouse effect – the global warming of our atmosphere produced by the buildup of carbon dioxide and other greenhouse gases that trap the sun's radiation in much the same way that glass does in a greenhouse; greenhouse gases allow the sun's energy to penetrate to the Earth's surface but do not allow as much of it to escape as heat.

grid – a system of close equidistant and parallel lines or bars.

habitat – the natural environment or place where an organism, population, or species lives.

hectare – unit of area in the metric system equal to 100 acres, or 10,000 square meters, and the equivalent of 2.471 acres in British Imperial and U.S. Customary measure.

herbaceous – angiosperm plants that have soft, flexible aerial portions which die each year.

herbivore – a consumer that eats only producers.

heterotrophic – (see consumer).

humus – black or dark brown decomposed organic material.

hydrostatic pressure – exertion of pressure by fluids.

interactive – mutually or reciprocally active.

intertidal – of, relating to, or being the part of the littoral zone above low-tide mark.

lamina – the blade of a leaf.

limnology – the scientific study of bodies of fresh water.

methylene blue – an acid/base indicator.

microaerophile – an organism that needs some oxygen to live but can survive in low oxygen conditions.

microcosm – a small version (either natural or artificial) of a large ecosystem (e.g., a terrarium).

microenvironment – a small or relatively small, usually distinctly specialized and effectively isolated habitat (as a forest canopy) or environment (as of a nerve cell).

mitochondrion – any of various round or long cellular organelles of most eukaryotes that are found outside the nucleus, produce energy for the cell through cellular respiration, and are rich in fats, proteins, and enzymes.

molar concentration – a solution that contains one mole of solute in one liter of solution.

mortality – the proportion of deaths to population.

mutagen – an agent (as mustard gas or various radiations) that tends to increase the frequency or extent of mutation.

null – amounting to nothing.

ordinate – the Cartesian coordinate obtained by measuring parallel to the y-axis.

palatability – agreeable to the palate or taste.

parameter – a quantity (as a mean or variance) that describes a statistical population.

parthenogenesis – reproduction by development of an unfertilized, usually female gamete that occurs especially among lower plants and invertebrate animals.

particulate – of or relating to minute separate particles.

pasteurize – a method of preservation by heating a liquid (such as milk) to kill or reduce the number of microorganisms.

Appendix B

petiole – a slender stem that supports the blade of a foliage leaf.

plankton – the passively floating or weakly swimming, usually minute animal and plant life of a body of water.

pollutant – any chemical or other agent that causes pollution.

pollution – the action of polluting, especially by environmental contamination with man-made waste.

producer – any of various organisms (as a green plant) that produce their own organic compounds from simple precursors (as carbon dioxide and inorganic nitrogen) and many of which are food sources for other organisms.

proteolytic enzyme – also called proteinase; any of a group of enzymes that break the long chainlike molecules of proteins into shorter fragments (peptides) and eventually into their components, amino acids.

putrefaction – the decomposition of organic matter; especially the typically anaerobic splitting of proteins by bacteria and fungi with the formation of foul-smelling, incompletely oxidized products.

pyruvic acid – a 3-carbon keto acid that in carbohydrate metabolism is an important intermediate product formed as pyruvate by glycolysis.

quadrat – typically a rectangular plot marked off for use in ecological or population studies.

rain forest – a tropical and temperate woodland with an annual rainfall of at least 100 inches (254 centimeters) and marked by lofty broad-leaved evergreen trees forming a continuous canopy.

ratio – the relationship in quantity, amount, or size between two or more things.

regression – a functional relationship between two or more correlated variables that is often empirically determined from data and is used especially to predict values of one variable when given values of the others.

scatter plot – a two-dimensional graph in rectangular coordinates consisting of points whose coordinates represent values of two variables under study.

simulation – examination of a problem often not subject to direct experimentation by means of a simulating device.

slope – the part of a continent draining to a particular ocean.

sludge – a muddy deposit.

stagnate – to become or remain stagnant.

subtidal – the zone just below the tide line.

succession – unidirectional change in the composition of an ecosystem as the available competing organisms and especially the plants respond to and modify the environment.

supratidal – the zone just above the tide line.

symbiosis – any of several living arrangements between members of two different species, including mutualism, commensalism, and parasitism.

taxonomy – the study of the general principles of scientific classification.

terminal – of or relating to an end, extremity, boundary, or terminus.

transect – a sample area (as of vegetation) usually in the form of a long, continuous strip.

transpiration – the act or process or an instance of transpiring; especially the passage of watery vapor from a living body through a membrane or pores.

transport – to transfer or convey from one place to another.

trophic level – one of the hierarchical strata of a food web characterized by organisms that are the same number of steps removed from the primary producers.

variant – manifesting variety, deviation, or disagreement.

vivarium – a terrarium used especially for small animals.

watershed – a region or area bounded peripherally by a divide and draining ultimately to a particular watercourse or body of water.

zonation – distribution of kinds of organisms in biogeographic zones.

variant – manifesting variety, deviation, or disagreement.

vivarium – a terrarium used especially for small animals.

watershed – a region or area bounded peripherally by a divide and draining ultimately to a particular watercourse or body of water.

zonation – distribution of kinds of organisms in biogeographic zones.

References

Aaronson, S. (1970). *Experimental Microbial Ecology.* New York: Academic Press.

Abrahamson, D.E. (Ed). (1989). *The Challenge of Global Warming.* Washington, DC: Island Press.

Adams, L.W. & Dove, L.E. (1989). *Wildlife Reserves and Corridors in the Urban Environment.* Columbia, MD: National Institute for Urban Wildlife.

Adey, W.H. (1992). Ecosystem encounters. *The Science Teacher, 59*(6), 22-27.

Adler, J. & Hager, M. (1988, July 11). Heat waves: Inside the greenhouse. *Newsweek.*

Air Quality Management District. (1997). *Fifty Years of Progress Toward Clean Air.* California: Diamond Bar.

Alcamo, I.E. (1987). *Fundamentals of Microbiology* (2nd ed.). Menlo Park, CA: The Benjamin Cummings Publishing Company.

Allee, W.C., Emerson, A.E., Park, O., Park, T. & Schmidt, K.P. (1949). *Principles of Animal Ecology.* Philadelphia, PA: W.B. Saunders Company.

Alsher, R.G. (1990). *Stress Responses in Plants: Adaptation and Acclimation.* New York: Wiley-Liss.

Amen, R.D. (1968). A model of seed dormancy. *Botanical Review, 34,*1-31.

American Public Health Association. (1985). *Standard Methods for Examination of Water and Wastewater.* Washington, DC: Author.

Ames, B.N., Durston, W.E., Yamasakim, E. & Lee, F.P. (1973). Carcinogens are mutagens: A simple test system combining liver homogenates for activation and bacteria for detection. *Proceedings of the National Academy of Sciences, 70,* 2281-2285.

Amos, W.H. & Amos, S.H. (1985). *The Audubon Society Nature Guides: Atlantic and Gulf Coasts.* New York: Chanticleer Press.

Atlas, R.M. & Bartha, R. (1981). *Microbial Ecology: Fundamentals and Applications.* Reading, PA: Addison Wesley.

Atwater, B.R. (1980). Germination, dormancy and morphology of the seeds of herbaceous ornamental plants. *Seed Science and Technology, 8,* 523-573.

Augspurger, C.K. (1986). Morphology and dispersal potential of wind-dispersed diaspores of neotropical trees. *American Journal of Botany, 73,* 353-363.

Augspurger, C.K. & Franson, S.E. (1987). Wind dispersal of artificial fruits varying in mass, area, and morphology. *Ecology, 68,* 27-42.

Augspurger, C.K. & Hogan, K.P. (1983). Wind dispersal of fruits with variable seed number in a tropical tree (*Lonchocarpus pentaphyllus:* Leguminosae). *American Journal of Botany, 70,* 1031-1037.

Avila, V.L. (1995). *Biology: Investigating Life on Earth* (2nd ed.). Jamal, CA: Bookmark Publishers.

Axelrod, H.R., Emmens, C.W., Burgess, W.E., Pronek, N. & Axelrod, G. (undated). *Exotic Tropical Fishes.* Neptune, NJ: T.F.H. Publications, Inc.

Barfknecht, T.R. & Naismith, R.W. (1988). Practical mutagenicity testing. In S.C. Grad (Ed.), *Product Safety Evaluation Handbook* (pp. 143-217). New York: Marcel Dekker.

Barker, J.A. (1983). The giant nematode 'Nematodius' spp. *Journal of Biological Education, 17*(3), 199-200.

Barnes, R.D. (1987). *Invertebrate Zoology,* 5th ed. New York: Holt, Rinehart and Winston.

Bell, E.A. & Tirimanna, S.L. (1965). Associations of amino acids and related compounds in the seeds of forty-seven species of *Vicia:* Their taxonomic and nutritional significance. *Biochemical Journal, 97,* 104-111.

Bennett, D.P. & Humphries, D.A. (1974). *Introduction to Field Biology.* London: Edward Arnold.

Bolin, B., Doos, B.R., Jager, J. & Warrick, R.A. (Eds.). (1986). *The Greenhouse Effect, Climatic Change, and Ecosystems.* New York: John Wiley & Sons.

Brady, N.C. (1996). *The Nature and Properties of Soils,* 11th ed. New York: Macmillan Publishing Co., Inc.

Brower, J.E. & Zar, J.H. (1984). *Field and Laboratory Methods for General Ecology* (2nd ed.). Dubuque, IA: Wm. C. Brown Co. Publishers.

Brower, J.E., Zar, J.H. & von Ende, C. (1990). *Field & Laboratory Methods for General Ecology,* 2nd ed. Dubuque, IA: Wm. C. Brown Co. Publishers.

Brown, S.A. (1964). Lignin and tannin biosyntheses. In J.B. Harborne (Ed.), *Biochemistry of Phenolic Compounds,* 359-398. London: Academic Press.

Buchanan, R.E. & Gibbons, N.E. (1974). *Bergey's Manual of Determinative Bacteriology.* Baltimore, MD: Williams and Wilkins.

Buchsbaum, R., Buchsbaum, M., Pearse, J. & Pearse, V. (1987). *Animals Without Backbones,* 3rd ed. Chicago: University of Chicago Press.

Burrows, F.M. (1973). Calculation of the primary trajectories of plumed seeds in steady winds with variable convection. *New Phytologist, 72,* 647-664.

Burrows, F.M. (1975). Wind-borne seed and fruit movement. *New Phytologist, 75,* 405-418.

Butler, M.I. & Burns, C.W. (1993). Water mite predation on planktonic Cladocera: parallel curve analysis of functional responses. *Oikos, 66,* 5-16.

Calman, W.T. (1911). *The Life of Crustacea.* London: Methuen.

Calver, M.C. & King, D.R. (1986). Controlling vertebrate pests with fluoracetate: lessons in wildlife management, bioethics and co-evolution. *Journal of Biological Education, 20(4)* 257-262.

Calver, M.C. & Porter, B.D. (1986). Unravelling the food web: dietary analysis in modern ecology. *Journal of Biological Education, 20(1)* 42-46.

Campbell, N.A. (1990). *Biology.* Redwood City, CA: The Benjamin Cummings Publishing Co.

Campbell, N., Mitchell, L. & Reece, J. (1997). *Biology: Concepts and Connections* (2nd ed.). Menlo Park, CA: Benjamin Cummings.

Cannatella, M.M. & Arnold, R.E. (1985). *Plants of the Texas Shore: A Beachcomber's Guide.* College Station, TX: Texas A&M University Press.

Capon, B. & Van AsDall, W. (1967). Heat pre-treatment as a means of increasing germination of desert annual-seeds. *Ecology, 42(2),* 305-306.

Casas, J. & Hulliger, B. (1994). Statistical analysis of functional response experiments. *Biocontrol Science and Technology, 4,* 133-145.

Cates, R.G. & Orians, G.H. (1975). Successional states and palatability of plants and generalized herbivores. *Ecology, 56,* 410-418.

Chinery, M. (1973). *A Field Guide to the Insects of Britain and Europe.* London: Collins.

Clapham, A.R., Tutin, T.G. & Warburg, E.F. (1962). *Flora of the British Isles.* Cambridge: Cambridge University Press.

Claridge, M.F. & Wilson, W.R. (1978). British insects and trees, a study of island biogeography or insect/plant co-evolution? *American Naturalist, 112,* 451-456.

Clarke, G.L. (1963). *Elements of Ecology.* New York: John Wiley and Sons.

Coker, R.E. (1954). *Streams, Lakes, Ponds.* New York: Harper & Row Publishing, Inc.

Collette, A.T. & Chiappetta, E.L. (1986). *Science Instruction in the Middle and Secondary Schools.* Columbus, OH: Merrill Publishing Co.

Cook, L.M. (1993). HUNT: a simulation of predator searching behaviour. *Journal of Biological Education, 27(4),* 287-290.

Corner, T.R. (1992). Ecology in a jar. *The Science Teacher, 59(3),* 32-35.

Cox, G.W. (1980). *Laboratory Manual for General Ecology* (4th ed.). Dubuque, IA: Wm. C. Brown Co. Publishers.

Cresswell, J.E. (1991). Capture rates and composition of insect prey of the pitcher plant *Sarracenia purpurea*. *The American Midland Naturalist, 125*(1), 1-9.

Croghan, P.C. (1958). The osmotic and ionic regulation of *Artemia salina* (L.). *Journal of Experimental Biology, 35,* 219-233.

Crutzen, P. (1993). Atmospheric Change: *An Earth System Perspective*. New York: W.H. Freeman

Cushwa, C.T., Martin, R.E. & Miller, R.L. (1968). The effects of fire on seed germination. *Journal of Range Management, 21,* 250-254.

Dolphin, W. (1992). *Biology Laboratory Manual* (3rd ed.). Dubuque, IA: Wm. C. Brown.

Drew, E.A. & Robertson, W.A.A. (1974). A simple field version of the Winkler determination of dissolved oxygen. *New Phytologist, 73,* 793-796.

Dubos, R. (1962). *The Unseen World*. New York: The Rockefeller Institute Press.

Ebenreck, S. (1989). The value of trees. In G. Moll & S. Ebenreck (Eds.), *Shading Our Cities* (pp. 49-57). Washington: Island Press Publishers.

Ebert-May, D., Rowland, P. & Tashiro, J.S. (1993). Ecology as a way of knowing. *Bulletin of the Ecological Society of America, 74*(2), 125-130.

Edmondson, W.T. (Ed.). (1959). *Freshwater Biology* (2nd ed.). New York: John Wiley & Sons.

Edwards, P.J. & Wratten, S.D. (In press). *Plant-Herbivore Interactions*. Studies in Biology Series. London: Edward Arnold.

Ehrlich, P. & Ehrlich, A. (1973). *Population, Resources, Environment.* San Francisco: Freeman and Co.

Ehrlich, P.R. & Roughgarden, J. (1987). *The Science of Ecology*. New York: Macmillan Publishing Company.

Ehrlich, P.R. & Wilson, E.O. (1991). Biodiversity studies: Science and policy. *Science, 253,* 758-762.

Emery, D. (1964). Seed propagation of native California plants. *Leaflets of the Santa Barbara Botanic Garden, 1,* 81-96.

Evans, J.D. (1976). Brine shrimp biology. *School Science Review, 57*(201), 708-712.

Fan, Y.Q. & Petitt, F.L. (1997). Functional response. Variance and regression analysis – a reply to Williams and Juliano. *Environmental Entomology, 26,* 1, 3.

Feeny, P.P. (1970). Seasonal changes in oak leaf tannins and nutrients as a cause of spring feeding by winter moth caterpillars. *Ecology, 51,* 565-581.

Feeny, P.P. (1976). Plant apparency and chemical defense. *Recent Advances in Phytochemistry, 10,* 1-40.

Finstein, M.S. (1972). *Pollution Microbiology: A Laboratory Manual*. New York: Marcel Dekker, Inc.

Fiskesjo, G. (1981). Benzo(a)pyrene and N-methyl-N-nitro-N-nitrosoguanidine in the allium test. *Hereditas, 95,* 155-162.

Fiskesjo, G. (1985). The Allium test as a standard in environmental monitoring. *Hereditas, 102,* 99-112.

Fiskesjo, G. (1988). The Allium test – an alternative in environmental studies: The relative toxicity of metal ions. *Mutation Research, 197,* 243-260.

Fitzpatrick, J.F. (1983). *How to Know the Freshwater Crustacea*. Dubuque, IA: Wm. C. Brown Co. Publishers.

Fotheringham, N. & Brunenmeister, S. (1989). *Beachcomber's Guide to Gulf Coast Marine Life* (2nd ed.). Houston: Gulf Publishing Company.

Franklin, J.F. (1973). *Natural Vegetation of Oregon and Washington*. Portland, OR: Pacific Northwest Forest and Range Experiment Station, Forest Service, U.S. Department of Agriculture.

Fretwell, S.D. (1977). The regulation of plant communities by the food chains exploiting them. *Perspectives in Biology & Medicine, 20,* 169-185.

Friday, L. & Laskey, R. (1989). *The Fragile Environment*. New York: Cambridge University Press.

Funk, H.J., Okey, J.R., Fiel, R.L., Jaus, H.N. & Sprague, C.S. (1979). *Learning Science Process Skills*. Dubuque, IA: Kendall/Hunt Publishing Co.

Gardner, G.T. & Stern, P.C. (1996). *Environmental Problems and Human Behavior*. Needham Heights, MA: Allyn & Bacon.

Gause, G.F. (1934). *The Struggle for Existence*. Baltimore: Williams & Wilkins.

Gebelein, C. (1997). *Chemistry and Our World*. Boston: Wm. C. Brown Publishers.

Gendron, R.O. & Stadden, J.E.R. (1984). Laboratory simulation of foraging behaviour: the effect of search rate on the probability of detecting prey. *The American Naturalist, 124,* 407-415.

Gibson, D.J., Middleton, B.A., Saunders, G.W., Mathis, M., Weaver, W.T., Neely, J., Rivera, J. & Oyler, M. (1999). Learning ecology by doing ecology: Long-term field experiments in succession. *The American Biology Teacher, 61*(3) 217-222.

Godwin, H. (1956). *The History of the British Flora*. Cambridge: Cambridge University Press.

Grant, W.F. (1978). Chromosome aberrations in plants as a monitoring system. *Environmental Health Perspectives, 27,* 37-43.

Grant, W.F. (1982). Chromosome aberration assays in Allium. A report of the U.S. Environmental Protection Agency Gene-Tox Program. *Mutation Research, 99,* 273-291.

Green, D.S. (1980). The terminal velocity and dispersal of spinning samaras. *American Journal of Botany, 67,* 1218-1224.

Green, J. (1961). *A Biology of Crustacea*. London: H.F. & G. Witherby.

Gregory, K.J. & Walling, D.E. (1973). *Drainage Basin Form and Process: A Geomorphological Approach*. New York: Halsted Press.

Guries, R.P. & Nordheim, E.V. (1984). Flight characteristics and dispersal potential of maple samaras. *Forest Science, 30,* 434-440.

Hamilton, W.D. & May, R.M. (1977). Dispersal in stable habitats. *Nature, 269,* 578-581.

Harper, J.L., Lovell, P.H. & Moore, K.G. (1970). The shapes and sizes of seeds. *Annual Review of Ecology and Systematics, 1,* 327-356.

Harris, L.D. & Gallagher, P.B. (1989). New initiatives for wildlife conservation: The need for movement corridors. In G. Macintosh (Ed.), *Preserving Communities & Corridors* (pp. 11-34). Washington: Defenders of Wildlife.

Hassard, T.H. (1991). *Understanding Biostatistics*. St. Louis, MO: Mosby-Year Book, Inc.

Hattori, T. (1973). *Microbial Life in the Soil*. New York: Marcel Dekker.

Hazel, J.R. (1989). Cold adaptation in ectotherms: Regulation of membrane function and cellular metabolism. *Advances in Comparative Environmental Physiology, 4,* 1-50.

Heslop-Harrison, Y. (1978). Carnivorous plants. *Scientific American, 238*(2), 104-114.

Hoese, H.D. & Moore, R.H. (1977). *Fishes of the Gulf of Mexico: Texas, Louisiana, and Adjacent Waters*. College Station, TX: Texas A&M University Press.

Holling, C.S. (1959a). Some characteristics of simple types of predation and parasitism. *Canadian Entomologist, 91,* 385-398.

Holling, C.S. (1959b). The components of predation as revealed by a study of small mammal predation on the European pine sawfly. *Canadian Entomologist, 91,* 385-398.

House, H.L. (1969). Effects of different proportions of nutrients on insects. *Entomologia Experimentalis et Applicata, 12,* 651-669.

Howe, H.F. & Smallwood, J. (1982). Ecology of seed dispersal. *Annual Review of Ecology and Systematics, 13,* 201-228.

Hynes, H.B.N. (1970). *The Ecology of Running Waters.* Toronto: University of Toronto Press.

Hynes, H.B.N. (1971). *The Biology of Polluted Waters.* Liverpool: Liverpool University Press.

Hyslop, E.J. (1980). Stomach contents analysis - A review of methods and their application. *Journal of Fish Biology, 17,* 411-429.

Ingram D.L. (1975). *Man and Animals in Hot Environments.* New York: Springer-Verlag.

Inness, W.T. (1966). *Exotic Aquarium Fishes.* Maywood, NJ: Metaframe Corp.

International Commission for Protection Against Environmental Mutagens and Carcinogens. (1983). Regulatory approaches to the control of environmental mutagens and carcinogens. *Mutation Research, 114,* 179-216.

Ivlev, V.S. (1961). *Experimental Ecology of the Feeding of Fishes.* New Haven, CT: Yale University Press.

Jager, J. (1988). Anticipating climatic change. *Environment, 30*(7), 12-33.

Janzen, D.H. (1969). Seed-eaters versus seed size, number, toxicity and dispersal. *Evolution, 23,* 1-27.

Jones, L.L.C. (1992). Strike it rich with classroom compost. *The American Biology Teacher, 54*(7), 420-424.

Juliano, S.A. (1993). Nonlinear curve fitting: predation and functional response curves. In S.M. Scheiner & J. Gurevitch (Eds.), *Design and Analysis of Ecological Experiments* (pp. 159-182). New York: Chapman and Hall.

Juniper, B.E., Robins, R.J. & Joel, D.M. (1989). *The Carnivorous Plants.* New York: Academic Press.

Kavaler, L. (1981). *A Matter of Degree: Heat, Life, and Death.* New York: Harper & Row.

Keeley, J.E. (1987). Role of fire in seed germination of woody taxa in California chaparral. *Ecology, 68*(2),434-443.

Keeley, J.E. & Keeley, S.C. (1987). Role of fire in the germination of chaparral herbs and suffrutescents. *Madrano, 34*(3), 240-249.

Keeley, J.E., Morton, B.A., Pedrosa, A. & Trotter, P. (1985). Role of alleopathy, heat and charred wood in the germination of chaparral herbs and suffrutescents. *Journal of Ecology, 73,* 445-458.

Keith, L.H. (1996). *Principles of Environmental Sampling* (2nd ed.). Washington, DC: American Chemical Society.

Kellert, S.R. & Wilson, E.O. (1993). *The Biophilia Hypothesis.* Washington: The Island Press.

Klots, E.B. (1966). *The New Fieldbook of Freshwater Life.* New York: G.P. Putnam's Son.

Knill, R. & Allen, J.A. (1995). Does polymorphism protect? An experiment with human 'predators'. *Ethology, 99,* 127-138.

Krebs, C.J. (1985). *Ecology: The Experimental Analysis of Distribution and Abundance.* New York: Harper & Row Publishers.

Kuserk, F.T., Kaplan, L.A. & Bott, T.L. (1984). In situ measures of dissolved organic carbon flux in a rural stream. *Canadian Journal of Fisheries and Aquatic Sciences, 41,* 964-973.

Larsen, D., Denoyelles Jr., RE, Stay, F. & Shiroyama, T. (1986). Comparisons of single-species microcosm and experimental pond responses to atrazine exposure. *Environmental Toxicology and Chemistry, 5(2),* 179-190.

Lawton, J.H. & Schroder, D. (1977). Effects of plant type, size of geographical range and taxonomic isolation on number of insect species associated with British plants. *Nature, 265,* 137-140.

Lechowicz, M.J. (1982). The sampling characteristics of electivity indices. *Oecologia (Berl), 52,* 22-30.

Levan, A. (1938). The effect of colchicine on root mitoses in Allium. *Hereditas, 24,* 471-486.

Levin, D.A. (1981). Dispersal versus gene flow in plants. *Annuals of the Missouri Botanical Garden, 68,* 233-253.

Levin, D.A. & Kerster, H.W. (1974). Gene flow in seed plants. *Evolutionary Biology, 7,* 139-220.

Light, R.W., Adler, P.H. & Arnold, D.E. (1983). Evaluation of gastric lavage for stomach analysis. *North American Journal of Fishery Management, 3,* 81-85.

Lind, O.T. (1979). *Handbook of Common Methods of Limnology* (3rd ed.). St. Louis, MO: C.V. Mosby Co.

Lock, M.A. & Williams, D.D. (1981). *Perspectives in Running Water Ecology.* New York: Plenum Press.

Lotka, A.J. (1932). The growth of mixed population: two species competing for a common food supply. *Journal of the Washington Academy of Sciences, 22,* 461-469.

MacArthur, R.H. (1972). *Geographical Ecology - Patterns in the Distribution of Species.* Princeton, NJ: Princeton University Press.

Mackay, R.J. & Kalff, J. (1969). Seasonal variation in standing crop and species diversity of insect communities in a small Quebec stream. *Ecology, 50,* 101-109.

Mackean, D.G. (1986). *GCSE Biology.* London: John Murray.

Magurran, A.E. (1988). *Ecological Diversity and Its Measurement.* Princeton, NJ: Princeton University Press.

Maiorana, C. (1978). What kinds of plants do herbivores really prefer? *American Naturalist, 112,* 631-635.

Manabe, S. & Wetherald, R.T. (1986). Reduction in summer soil wetness induced by an increase in atmospheric carbon dioxide. *Science, 232,* 626-632.

Maugh, T.H. (1978). Chemical carcinogens: The scientific basis for regulation. *Science, 201,* 1200-1205.

McCann, J., Choi, E. & Yamasaki, E. (1975). Detection of carcinogens as mutagens in the Salmonella/microsome test: Assay of 300 chemicals. *Proceedings of the National Academy of Sciences, 72,* 5135-5139.

McCutchen, C.W. (1977). The spinning rotation of ash and tulip tree samaras. *Science, 197,* 691-692.

Meehan, W.R. & Miller, R.A. (1978). Stomach flushing: Effectiveness and influence on survival and condition of juvenile salmonids. *Journal of the Fisheries Research Board of Canada, 35,* 1359-1363.

Monger, G. (1988). *Nuffield Coordinated Science (Biology).* London: Longman.

Moomaw, W.R. (1989). In search of the greenhouse fingerprint. *Orion, 8(1),* 4-11.

Munz, P. (1961). *California Spring Wildflowers.* Berkeley: University of California Press.

Munz, P. (1962). *California Desert Wildflowers.* Berkeley: University of California Press.

Munz, P. (1963). *California Mountain Wildflowers.* Berkeley: University of California Press.

Munz, P. (1964). *Shore Wildflowers of California, Oregon, and Washington.* Berkeley: University of California Press.

Murphy, T.M., Canington, D. & Walker, D.E. (1992). Herbivory, predation, and biological control. *The American Biology Teacher, 54*(7), 416-419.

Myers, N. (1984). *The Primary Source: Tropical Forests and our Future.* New York: W.W. Norton & Co., Inc.

Nash, M. (1987, October 19). The heat is on. *Time,* 58-67.

Needham, J.G. & Needham, P.R. (1977). *A Guide to the Study of Freshwater Biology* (5th ed.). San Francisco, CA: Holden-Day, Inc.

Neish, A.C. (1964). Major pathways of biosynthesis of phenols. In J.B. Harborne (Ed.), *Biochemistry of Phenolic Compounds,* 295-357. London: Academic Press.

Nester, E.W., Roberts, C.E., Pearsall, N.N. & McCarthy, B.J. (1978). *Microbiology* (2nd ed.). New York: Holt, Rinehart and Winston.

Nobel, P. (1988). *Environmental Biology of Agaves and Cacti.* Cambridge: Cambridge University Press.

NOVA. (1992). *Return to Mt. St. Helens; Revival of the Desert; and Other Titles.* Deerfield, IL: Coronet/MTI Film and Video.

Odum, E.P. (1963). *Ecology.* New York: Holt, Rinehart and Winston.

Odum, E.P. (1971). *Fundamentals of Ecology.* Philadelphia, PA: Saunders College Publishing/Holt, Rinehart and Winston.

Odum, E.P. (1975). *Ecology* (2nd ed.). New York: Holt, Rinehart and Winston.

Odum, H.T. & Deyers, R. (1992). *Microcosms and Mesocosms in Scientific Research.* New York: Springer-Verlag.

Ojima, D.S., Kittel, T.G.F., Rosswall, T. & Walker, B.H. (1991). Critical issues for understanding global change effects on terrestrial ecosystems. *Ecological Applications, 1*(3), 316-325.

Opler, P.A. (1974). Oaks as evolutionary islands for leaf-mining insects. *American Scientist, 62,* 67-73.

Oram, R.F., Hummer Jr., P.J. & Smoot, R.C. (1983). *Biology: Living Systems.* Columbus, OH: Merrill Publishing Co.

Owen, D.F. & Wiegert, R.G. (1976). Do consumers maximize plant "fitness." *Oikos, 27,* 488-492.

Owen, D.F. (1978). The effect of a consumer, *Phytomyza ilicis,* on seasonal leaf-fall in the holly, *Ilex aquifolium. Oikos, 31,* 268-271.

Pain, S. (1988, November 12). No escape from the global greenhouse. *New Scientist,* 38-43.

Peck, M.E. (1961). *A Manual of the Higher Plants of Oregon* (2nd ed.). Corvallis, OR: Oregon State University Press.

Pearl, R. & Reed, L.J. (1920). On the rate of growth of the population of the United States since 1790 and its mathematical representation. *Proceedings of the National Academy of Sciences, 6*(6), 275-288.

Pelczar Jr., M.J., Reid, R.D. & Chan, E.C.S. (1977). *Microbiology.* New York: McGraw-Hill.

Pennak, R.W. (1989). *Freshwater Invertebrates of the United States* (3rd ed.). New York: John Wiley & Sons.

Perring, F.H. & Walters, S.M. (1962). *Atlas of the British Flora.* London: Nelson.

Peters, R.L. & Darling, D.S. (1985). The greenhouse effect and nature reserves. *BioScience, 35*(11), 707-717.

Phillips, E.A. (1959). *Methods of Vegetation Study.* New York: Henry Holt.

Plotkin, M.J. (1993). *Tales of a Shaman's Apprentice: An Ethnobotanist Searches for New Medicines in the Amazon Rain Forest*. New York: Viking (Penguin).

Plummer, G.L. & Kethley, J.B. (1964). Foliar absorption of amino acids, peptides and other nutrients by the pitcher plant, *Sarracenia flava*. *Botanical Gazette, 125*(4), 245-260.

Power, M.E. (1990). Effects of fish in river food webs. *Science, 250*, 811-814.

Prescott, G.W. (1970). *How To Know the Freshwater Algae*. Dubuque, IA: Wm. C. Brown Co. Publishers.

Prescott, G.W. (1983). *How to Know the Freshwater Algae* (3rd. ed). Dubuque, IA: Win. C. Brown Co. Publishers.

Ramsden, E.N. & Lee, R.E. (1984). *Air*. Cheltenham, Gloustershire, England: Stanley Thornes.

Raven, P.H. & Johnson, G.B. (1991). *Understanding Biology* (2nd ed.). St. Louis, MO: Mosby-Year Book, Inc.

Raven, P.R. (1990). The politics of preserving biodiversity. *BioScience, 40*, 769-774.

Raven, P.R., Berg, L.R. & Johnson, G.B. (1993). *Environment*. Fort Worth: Harcourt Brace & Co.

Reid, G.K. (1961). *Ecology of Inland Waters and Estuaries*. New York: Van Nostrand Reinhold Company.

Reid, G.K. (1967). *Pond Life*. New York: Golden Press.

Revelle, P. & Revelle, C. (1988). *The Environment: Issues and Choices for Society*. Boston: Jones & Bartlett Publishers.

Revkin, A.C. (1988, October). Endless summer: Living with the greenhouse effect. *Discover*, 53-61.

Ricciuti, E.R. (1982). *The Beachcomber's Guide: The Seashore from Maine to Florida*. Garden City, NJ: Doubleday Publishers.

Ricklefs, R.E. (1993). *The Economy of Nature*. New York: W.H. Freeman.

Ridley, H.N. (1930). *The Dispersal of Plants Throughout the World*. Ashford, England: L. Reeve and Company.

Ringler, N.H. (1979). Prey selection by benthic feeders. In R.H. Stroud & L.H. Clepper (Eds.), *Predator-Prey Systems in Fisheries Management*. Washington, DC: Sport Fishing Institute.

Rogers, D. (1972). Random search and insect population models. *Journal of Animal Ecology, 41*, 369-383.

Sampson, R.N. (1989). *Needed: A New Vision for Our Communities*.

SATIS (Science and Technology in Society). (1987). *Making Fertilizers*. Hatfield, England: Association for Science Education.

Schmidt-Nielsen, K. (1979). *Animal Physiology* (2nd ed.). New York: Cambridge University Press.

Schnell, D.E. (1976). *Carnivorous Plants of the United States and Canada*. Winston-Salem, NC: John E. Blair.

Schram, F.R. (1986). *Crustacea*. Oxford: Oxford University Press.

Sellers, P.E. & Allen, J.A. (1991). On adopting the right attitude: a demonstration of the survival value of choosing a matching background. *Journal of Biological Education, 25*(2), 111-115.

Sharpe, D.M. & Fields, D.E. (1982). Integrating the effects of climate and seed fall velocities on seed dispersal by wind: A model and application. *Ecological Modeling, 17*, 297-310.

Sheldon, J.C. & Burrows, F.M. (1973). The dispersal effectiveness of the achene-pappus units of selected Compositae in steady winds with convection. *New Phytologist, 72*, 665-675.

Siegel, S. (1956). *Nonparametric Statistics*. New York: McGraw-Hill.

Smith, C. (1993). Foraging and flocking behavior. In J.M. Beiswenger (Ed.), *Experiments To Teach Ecology* (pp. 111-135). Washington, DC: Ecological Society of America.

Smith, R.E. (1990). *Ecology and Field Biology*. New York: Harper and Row.

Snow, N. (1993). Environmental issues: Tropical deforestation. In J.M. Beiswenger & D.P. Bagby (Eds.), *Fundamentals of Biology: Laboratory Manual* (pp. 17-21). Edina, MN: Burgess Publishing.

Southwood, T.R.E. (1961). The numbers of insects associated with various trees. *Journal of Animal Ecology, 30,* 1-8.

Southwood, T.R.E. (1973). The insect/plant relationship - An evolutionary perspective. In *Insect-Plant Relationships*. Symposia of the Royal Entomological Society 6. London: Blackwell.

Sprague, F.L. & Hansen, H.P. (1946). Forest succession in the McDonald Forest, Williamette Valley, Oregon. *Northwest Science, 20,* 89-98.

Starr, C. (1994). *Biology: Concepts and Applications* (2nd ed.). Belmont, CA: Wadsworth Publishing Company.

Steckmayer, B. (1978). The Winogradsky column. *Carolina Tips, 41*(9), 33-34.

Strauss, R.E. (1982). Reliability estimates for Ivlev's electivity index, the forage ratio, and a proposed linear index of food selection. *Transactions of the American Fisheries Society, 108,* 344-352.

Strong, D.R. (1974). Nonasymptomatic species richness models and the insects of British trees. *Proceedings of the National Academy of Science, 71,* 2766-2769.

Sykes, G. & Skinner, F.A. (1971). *Microbial Aspects of Pollution*. New York: Academic Press.

Taub, F.B. (1969). A biological model for a freshwater community: A gnotobiotic ecosystem. *Limnology and Oceanography, 14*(1), 136-142.

Taylor, L. & Kaufman, D. (unpublished). *Using Microcosms to Teach About the Environment: A Teacher's Guide*. (Contact David Kaufman at Miami University, Oxford, OH).

Taylor, M.F., Clark, W.J. & Ho, L. (1990). Nutrient availability and the algal growth potential AGP in a small microcosm. *Water Research, 24*(4), 529-532.

Taylor, R.J. (1984). *Predation*. New York: Chapman & Hall.

Taylorson, R.B. & Hendricks, S.B. (1977). Dormancy in seeds. *Annual Review of Plant Physiology, 28,* 331-354.

Tesco Stores Ltd. (1989). *Phosphates and the Water Supply*. Tesco, Cheshunt, Herts EN8 9SL.

Thilenius, J.F. (1968). The *Quercus garryana* forests of the Williamette Valley, Oregon. *Ecology, 49,* 1124-1133.

Tomkins, S.P. & Williams, P.H. (1990). Fast plants for finer science - An introduction to the biology of rapid-cycling *Brassica campestris (rapa)* L. *Journal of Biological Education, 24,* 239-250.

Towers, G.H.N. (1969). Metabolism of phenolics in higher plants and microorganisms. In J.B. Harborne (Ed.), Biochemistry of Phenolic Compounds, 249-294. London: Academic Press.

Tranter, J.A. (1982). The use of a little-known group of insects — the raisin bugs — in laboratory simulations of mimicry. *Journal of Biological Education, 16*(1), 39-41.

Turco, R. (1997). *Earth Under Siege: From Air Pollution to Global Change*. New York: Oxford University Press.

U.S. Army Corps of Engineers *Common Wetland Plants of Southeast Texas*. Galveston District: U.S. Army Corps of Engineers.

van Emden, H.F. (1972). Aphids as phytochemicals. In J.B. Harborne (Ed.), *Phytochemical Ecology*. London: Academic Press.

Vannote, R.L., Minshall, G.W., Cummins, K.W., Sedell, J.R. & Cushing, C.E. (1980). The river continuum concept. *Canadian Journal of Fisheries and Aquatic Sciences, 37,* 130-137.

Veldkamp, H. (1970). Enrichment cultures of procaryotic organisms. In J.R. Norris & D.W. Ribbons (Eds.), *Methods in Microbiology,* IIIA. New York: Academic Press.

Vernberg, F.J. & Vernberg, W.B. (Eds.). (1983). *The Biology of Crustacea: Vol. 8 – Environmental Adaptations*. New York: Academic Press.

Volterra, V. (1926). Variations and fluctuations of the numbers of individuals in animal species living together. In R.N. Chapman (Ed.), (1931), *Animal Ecology* (Appendix, pp. 409-448). New York: McGraw Hill.

Wagner, R.H. (1978). *Environment and Man*. New York: W.W. Norton & Company, Inc.

Walpole, R.E. (1983). *Elementary Statistical Concepts*. New York: Macmillan Publishing Company.

Weisburger, J.H. & Williams, G.M. (1981). Carcinogen testing: Current problems and new approaches. *Science, 214*, 401-407.

Wilkes, J.W. (1983). Students as scientists: A study of the effects of sewage plant effluent. *The American Biology Teacher, 45*(8), 415-418.

Willoughby, L.G. (1976). *Freshwater Biology*. New York: Pica Press.

Wilson, E.O. (1989). Threats to biodiversity. *Scientific American, 261*(3), 108-116.

Winogradsky, S.N. (1949). *Microbiologie du Sol. Oeuvres Completes*. Paris: Masson.

Wolfe, L.M. (1981). Feeding behavior of a plant: Differential prey capture in old and new leaves of the pitcher plant (*Sarracenia purpurea*). *The American Midland Naturalist, 106*(2), 352-359.

World Atlas of Agriculture. (1969). Novara, Italy: Instituto Geografico de Ogostini.

Wratten, S.D. & Fry, G.L.A. (1979). *Field and Laboratory Exercises in Ecology*. London: Edward Arnold.

Zimmerman, M.C. (1983). The use of the biotic index as an indication of water quality. *Proceedings, Volume V, the Association of Biology Laboratory Educators Conference,* Clemson University, June 1983.

Zoto, G.A., Dellon, D.O. & Schlichting, H.E. (1973). A rapid method for clearing diatoms for taxonomic and ecological studies. *Phycologia, 12*, 69-70.